BIOSTATISTICS: An Introductory Text

BIOSTATISTICS

An
Introductory
Text

A V R A M   G O L D S T E I N

Professor of Pharmacology, Stanford University

MACMILLAN PUBLISHING CO., INC.
New York
COLLIER MACMILLAN PUBLISHERS
London

Library of Congress catalog card number: 64–11036

MACMILLAN PUBLISHING CO., INC.
866 Third Avenue, New York, New York 10022

COLLIER MACMILLAN CANADA, LTD.

Printed in the United States of America

Printing   12 13 14 15   Year   9

To dbg

Preface

This book traces its origin to the pharmacology course at Harvard Medical School given more than ten years ago, where Douglas S. Riggs and I undertook to teach medical students some principles of biostatistics. There was a short monograph, and also a laboratory exercise in tossing pennies and drawing colored shoe-buttons out of jars. A few years later (Riggs having meanwhile taken the chair of pharmacology at Buffalo) I obtained the cooperation of William E. Reynolds (then in the Department of Preventive Medicine at Harvard, now associated with the University of California) and together we organized and taught the first required biostatistics course for Harvard medical students. At the same time (and in a few cases much earlier) regular instruction in this subject was being established at other medical schools; and in the years since, biostatistics has taken its rightful place in the medical curriculum of most institutions. Training in statistics has, of course, long been recognised as indispensable for students of biology, and of psychology and other behavioral sciences.

My teaching experience with students of medicine and the biological sciences has largely shaped the content and format of this book. Very few students in these fields will wish to learn statistics through a systematic mastery of its mathematical basis. The great majority, however, are well disposed toward the subject at the outset because they know it will provide useful tools for their life's work. The student must be shown when, where, and how the tools can best be used, and in a general way why they work. He does not have to know how the tools were fashioned, nor even the proofs that they can do what the statisticians claim for them. To use biostatistics intelligently, or to understand its use by others and the conclusions to which it leads, requires principally a grasp of the rationale underlying its applications and of the correct ways of formulating problems and hypotheses for statistical analysis. I have tried to frame the arguments, explanations, illustrations, examples, and problems in terms common to everyday laboratory or clinical experience. The book is not meant to be sufficient in itself for all possible needs. However, the examples include prototypes of a great many problems that commonly arise, and the tables will satisfy every ordinary requirement. Thus the book should continue to serve as a working manual for most procedures long after it has fulfilled its role as introductory text.

The description of procedures and the construction of the tables proceed from two premises—first, that biological experiments hardly ever yield data that are meaningful beyond three significant figures, and second, that the conventional levels of significance (0.05 and 0.01) are quite sufficient for all ordinary purposes. It has therefore been possible, especially in transcribing the various tables, to effect numerous simplifications and abbreviations.

In rounding off numbers the usual rule has been followed: If an exact half is to be dropped, round to the nearest *even* number. In the long run half of all the numbers retained are slightly too large, half slightly too small, so no systematic bias results. However, in the tables of critical values of various statistics, the following rule has been adopted: If any digits are to be dropped, round in the *conservative* direction, upward or downward depending upon the particular statistics. Thus an occasional test of significance will be very slightly more rigorous than intended.

Worthy of special mention is the inclusion of three very useful nonparametric procedures. Two of these compare favorably in efficiency with the *t*-test, and are far simpler to apply, yet there has been a surprising lag in their more widespread adoption.

Insofar as the ideas in this book originated in the teaching experiments referred to, I am very much indebted to Drs. Riggs and Reynolds. The latter was also good enough to offer constructive suggestions for improving an early draft of the present text. Dr. Rupert G. Miller, Associate Professor of Statistics at Stanford, offered much helpful criticism and advice, and I am deeply appreciative of the patience and care with which he read the manuscript. Dr. Helena C. Kraemer, Research Associate in Statistics, carried out a painstaking verification of the examples and problems, and made several useful criticisms. Many of their suggestions have been incorporated, but, of course, they share no responsibility for errors that may remain. I owe thanks also to my colleagues, Drs. Lewis Aronow and Sumner M. Kalman, for their comments on a preliminary draft, and for their generosity in temporarily releasing me from the obligations of co-authorship of another text so that I might complete this one. I am indebted to the late Professor Sir Ronald A. Fisher, F.R.S., Cambridge and to Dr. Frank Yates, F.R.S., Rothamsted, also to Messrs. Oliver & Boyd Ltd., Edinburgh, for permission to reprint Tables I, II, IV, XI, and XXVII from their book *Statistical Tables for Biological, Agricultural and Medical Research*. Finally, I wish to express my gratitude to Mrs. Ray Jeffery for secretarial assistance of the highest quality, without which the preparation of this book would have been far more difficult.

AVRAM GOLDSTEIN

Contents

Tables

BIOSTATISTICS: An Introductory Text

The Logical Basis of Statistical Inference

INTRODUCTION

A good understanding of biostatistics has become an essential ingredient in the training of students in every branch of the biological sciences and medicine. The reason is that the methods of biostatistics are indispensable tools for the design and interpretation of experiments. The wise investigator draws a statistician into consultation to make sure that his experiment is well designed to answer the question at hand, and that it will yield a maximum of useful information with a minimum expenditure of animals, patients, or time. In evaluating data he again utilizes the statistician's skill so that his conclusions will be as definitive and as general as the findings will permit, but no more so. Unfortunately, too many experiments still being carried out and published are so poorly designed that they cannot support any valid conclusions. The purpose of this book is primarily to outline the logical basis of the statistical approach to experimental problems, and the main features of those statistical methods commonly used in biological experimentation. A better working knowledge of the procedures and their rationale on the part of every student of the biological sciences and medicine can only be beneficial. Such a preliminary acquaintance should lead not only to some facility in applying biostatistical methods, but also to a better appreciation of their potential value, so that expert advice will be sought more readily when the occasion arises.

The full text is intended for the reader who has never studied statistics before and whose mathematical training may be rather scant. Emphasis is placed upon the applications of biostatistics to real experimental problems of the kinds encountered in the laboratory or clinic. The rationale of each procedure is explained intuitively, or demonstrated empirically, but no attempt is made to provide mathematical proofs. The student with some previous exposure to statistics, or with a more sophisticated mathematical background, will find much of the text too elementary, but should still profit from studying the examples and working the problems. Numerous references are provided to sources of additional explanation, to mathematical proofs, and to texts containing further illustrative examples. All the necessary tables are at the back of the book.

SOME IMPORTANT ASPECTS OF EXPERIMENTAL DESIGN

The principal application of biostatistics is in the analysis of data derived from experiments. No matter how elegant the statistical treatment, the conclusions may be false unless the experiments themselves were properly designed and carried out. It is well, therefore, to begin by considering some fundamental principles of biological experimentation. This is a subject with many ramifications, and special works devoted to it should be consulted for fuller information. Here we shall discuss briefly some of the most important requirements of proper experimental design, which bear upon the validity of data to which statistical analysis is to be applied.

The problems that mainly concern us have to do with the effects of experimental manipulations upon biological systems. Such deliberate interventions by the investigator are known as *treatments*. A result produced by a treatment is known as an *effect*.

> We may wish to find out whether or not a certain drug reduces the concentration of glucose in the circulating blood. The treatment consists in administering the drug under specified conditions of dosage, frequency, duration, and so on, to a group of subjects. The effect would be a measurable lowering of blood glucose concentration.
>
> We might want to know how the lever-pressing behavior of rats is affected by periodic food reinforcements. The treatment is the specified reinforcement schedule. The effect would be a measurable change in the rate or temporal pattern of lever presses.
>
> We may be interested in learning how exposure to heat influences the subsequent germination of tomato seeds. The treatment is exposure of the seeds to certain temperatures for specified periods of time. The effect

would be measurable as a change in the percent of seeds which germinate, or in the average time to germination, or in some qualitative feature of the germination process.

Since we wish to know what effect a treatment produces, the chief aim in planning and conducting an experiment is to ensure insofar as possible that no factor other than the treatment will contribute to the observed result. This ideal is almost never attainable, since extraneous influences are nearly always present. The practical aim is therefore to ensure that all influences except for the treatment under test will act equally upon the *treated* subjects and upon a comparable group of *control* subjects exposed to all the same conditions but not to the treatment.

Let us examine a possible experimental design for investigating the effects of a drug that might lower the blood glucose level. The group of subjects is assembled at a convenient time in the morning and initial blood samples are drawn. The drug is then given, and an hour later blood samples are drawn again. When glucose concentrations are determined they are found to be considerably lower in every postdrug sample than in the corresponding initial sample. Can it be concluded that the drug lowers blood glucose? Certainly not. In this case the fault in the experimental design is transparent—all subjects were treated and there was no control group at all. We do not know what would have happened to the blood glucose concentrations in these same subjects over the same one-hour interval if the drug had not been given.

In the above example an apparent effect (lowering of blood glucose) was found, but because the experiment was uncontrolled there was no way of deciding whether or not the treatment (drug administration) was responsible. Suppose, on the other hand, that there had been no change in blood glucose concentration. One might be tempted, in that case, to dismiss the possibility that the drug lowers blood glucose, but a little reflection will convince one that no such inference can be drawn. Had the drug not been administered, the blood glucose of all the subjects might possibly have *increased* during the same period, so that the drug effectively reduced what otherwise would have been a much higher concentration. Thus, regardless of the outcome, no valid conclusion can be drawn from an uncontrolled experiment.

Let us now consider the following improvement in the experimental design. The subjects' cooperation is obtained on two successive mornings. On the first (control) morning, blood samples are drawn initially and again one hour later, but no drug is administered. On the next morning the identical procedure is repeated, but the drug is given as soon as the initial blood samples have been secured. Suppose the chemical analyses now reveal that on the first day there was no important difference between the initial and final blood glucose levels, whereas on the second day the concentrations all fell during the hour after drug administration. Can we then conclude that the drug was responsible for lowering the blood glucose?

It might seem that proper controls are now built into the experiment, but two major faults remain, which render any conclusion uncertain. First, the very act of drug administration may have influenced the observed outcome, even if the drug itself were inert. The question must be answered, what would happen to the blood glucose levels if dummy injections, or inert pills were given, instead of the drug? The importance of this kind of simulated treatment (known as *placebo control*) will be considered at length later. The second major fault is the assumption that the only difference between the first day and the second was that drug was given on the latter but not on the former. To attribute prime importance to our own deliberate intervention is a common and understandable error, but nonetheless a serious one. Whatever treatment we may administer, other influences about which we know nothing at all may cause part or all of the observed results which we interpret as treatment effects. The simple truth is that today is not yesterday. The subjects' physical, emotional, and nutritional states may have been quite different on the two days, the room temperature and other environmental circumstances may have differed, and so on. Certainly different (and possibly relevant to blood glucose responses) are subjects' emotional reactions to the novel experience of the first day in contrast to the familiar one of the second. Even in the simplest laboratory experiments, conditions may change from one time to another without the awareness of the investigator, who may then falsely attribute to a treatment what was really caused by an unknown and extraneous circumstance.

For reasons made evident above, a good experiment whenever possible embodies the principle of *concurrent control,* i.e., the inclusion of a control group in the same experiment with the treated group or groups. Sometimes there are good reasons why an experiment cannot include concurrent controls, but however good the reasons may be, the conclusions of such experiments are bound to be clouded by some degree of uncertainty. The commonest illustration of this is the "before-after" comparison. A certain drug, for example, is generally believed to prolong the survival of children suffering from leukemia. It is certainly true that the drug-treated children of today survive many months longer than did victims of this disease before introduction of the drug. During the same period of years, however, numerous other advances in medical care have occurred. Would today's patients do as poorly without the drug as did their counterparts several years ago, or have other influences contributed to the apparent beneficial effects of today's drug treatments? This question can no longer be answered experimentally, because it would not now be ethical to withhold a drug that is believed to be effective, in order to establish a concurrent control group of patients. This peculiar difficulty in human experimentation points to the importance of conducting thoroughly conclusive experiments early in the trial period of any new drug or therapeutic procedure.

Assuming that an experiment will include a concurrent control, how shall subjects be assigned to the treatment and control groups? It might be supposed that any haphazard allocation of subjects would suffice, but experience shows that this is not so. Essential to good experimental design is as nearly complete an equivalence of control and treatment groups as can be achieved. Otherwise differences in the outcome will be supposed to arise from the treatment, which may really only reflect innate differences among the subjects themselves.

Consider a clinical trial to determine whether a new drug is superior to an inert material (a placebo) in shortening the duration of common colds. As patients with colds appear (for example in an industrial clinic), the physician-investigator at his own whim prescribes either the drug or the placebo. Subconscious bias can play a surprisingly large role in determining such assignments, so that the patients with milder symptoms may receive the drug more often and those with severe symptoms may receive the placebo more often. The outcome of such an experiment may be that the colds are over sooner in the drug-treated subjects, but the conclusion that the drug was responsible does not merit confidence, since the drug-treated group might well have had shorter colds than the placebo group even if the drug were worthless.

It should not be thought that inadvertent selection in assigning subjects to groups occurs only in human experimentation. So simple a matter as dividing 50 mice into two equal groups for control and treatment can be hazardous, because some characteristics of the mice may readily influence their allocation by the investigator to one or the other group. For example, if he removes 25 mice to another cage, they are very likely to be heavier and more sluggish (easier to catch) than the ones left behind. Groups selected in such a manner could not really be used for any experiment whatsoever. Regardless of the outcome, one would have doubts about the equivalence of the control and treated groups, and so any conclusion about the presence or absence of a treatment effect would rest upon a shaky foundation.

The only thoroughly reliable way to set up equivalent groups is to *randomize* the assignments.[1] Here the key requirement is that *no characteristic of a subject whatsoever shall play any part in his assignment to a group.* Tossing coins, rolling dice, or drawing lots are suitable procedures. The most universally applicable random device is the table of random numbers. Such tables have been generated by a system (e.g., electronically) designed so that each of the ten digits has equal probability of appearing at any position in a sequence. Table 1 is an extract of 1,000 sequential digits from a larger random series. It lends itself to a variety of uses, only one of which will be illustrated here.

Example 1-1. Randomization.

An experiment is to include 100 subjects, divided equally among four different treatment groups: placebo, drug A, drug B, and drug C. Make the assignments randomly, by means of Table 1.

The first step is to assign a number to each subject. In this case the subjects would be numbered from 01 to 100 (denoted by 00). Then enter the table at any point and begin filling one of the groups according to the sequences of numbers in the table. For example, if we start at the upper left corner of Table 1, we find there 94847 47234 476 . . . If we have decided to fill the placebo group first, we assign subjects 94, 84, 74, 72, 34, 47, and so on, to this group. If a number that has already been used appears again we simply ignore it. When 25 subjects have been placed in the placebo group we continue in the same way to assign 25 subjects to each of the next two groups. Then the remaining 25 are placed automatically in the final group. It will be observed that every subject has an equal chance of being placed in any group, and also an equal chance of being placed together with any other subject.

[1]"The logical reason for randomizing is that it is possible on the basis of a model reflecting the randomization to draw sound statistical inferences, the probability basis of the model being provided not by wishful thinking but by the actual process of randomization which is part of the experiment. . . ." H. Scheffé, *The Analysis of Variance* (New York: John Wiley & Sons, Inc., 1959), p. 106.

The first step (assigning a number to each subject) does not require that there be an actual list of subjects. The sequential numbers might refer to the order in which patients may, in the future, present themselves at a hospital clinic. In that case the assignments described above would mean that in order of their arrival at the clinic, the 94th, 84th, 74th, 72nd (and so on) patients would be placed in a placebo group.

It is a good idea to let numbers represent subjects in such a way that maximum use is made of the numbers in the table. Suppose there are only 12 subjects to be divided into groups. If we used only the digit pairs from 01 to 12, we would probably have to look through a considerable part of the table before all those particular numbers turned up, and we would have to discard a great many numbers along the way. A more efficient procedure is to use as many cycles of 12 as we can. Eight cycles of 12 will fit between 01 and 96; the digit-pairs 97, 98, 99, 00 will be discarded if they appear. Now two-digit random numbers from 13 to 96 will obviously yield random remainders on division by 12. We therefore enter the table and accept all numbers between 01 and 96. If a number is greater than 12, we divide it by 12 and use only the remainder to designate a subject, allowing a remainder of zero to denote subject 12. Thus, on the bottom line of Table 1, the sequence 24415 95858 would represent subjects 12, 5, 11, 10 (the repeated 10 represented by the final 58 being discarded).

A warning is in order about an appealingly simple but incorrect way of randomizing, in which the digits in Table 1 are permitted to stand for the groups rather than for the subjects. For example, in assigning 12 subjects to three groups, the digits 1, 2, 3 might stand for group A; 4, 5, 6 for group B; 7, 8, 9 for group C; and 0 would be discarded. Now the subjects on a list are assigned to groups according to the sequence of numbers in the table. Thus if the digits 31665 appear, we would assign the first and second subjects on the list to group A; the third, fourth, and fifth to group B. Now as some of the groups are bound to be filled with the desired number of subjects sooner than others, it will be evident that subjects toward the end of the list will have an unusually high probability of being assigned together, particularly in filling out the last vacant group. The probability that a subject at the end of the list will be in the same group as one at the beginning is therefore less than in a truly random procedure, and the probability that he will be in the same group as the subject just above him in the list is very substantially higher than it should be. These defects may have serious practical consequences in experiments where the "list" is wholly or partly determined by some characteristics of the subjects, as when animals have to be caught and then randomly distributed. For example, a group of the animals that were hardest to catch would very likely be assigned together to the group that happened to be filled last.

To avoid using the same sequence of random digits repeatedly, a procedure is desirable for entering the table at a different place each time it is employed. Any method that accomplishes this is suitable. One can simply mark each stopping place and begin there on the next occasion. Alternatively, one can number the columns and rows so that a randomly chosen number can then specify a point of entry.

Once the random assignment of subjects to groups has been completed, the remaining concern is that all groups be subjected to identical conditions during the experiment, except for the treatments under study. Again the pitfalls are many. A major one is failing to recognize, or minimizing the importance of some of the conditions associated with, but not considered an intrinsic part of, the treatment. Consider an experiment to determine whether a certain drug diminishes the fertility of mice. The control mice remain untreated and undisturbed. The treated mice are removed from their cages several times daily and injected with the drug. The criterion of effect is the number and size of litters within a given period of time. These might turn out to be substantially smaller in the treated group. Nevertheless, a conclusion that the drug reduces fertility may be quite false, because the controls were not subjected to the same conditions as the treated mice. Repeated handling or the trauma of injection may have played a major role in reducing fertility in the treated group. If the treatment group received drug injections, the control group should have had placebo injections on the same occasions.

If a treatment under study is an operative procedure, controls must be subjected to a sham operation, as nearly like the real one as possible, and including the same anesthetics (which often produce significant effects themselves). If a lesion is to be placed electrolytically in an animal's brain, an identical electrode should be similarly placed in a control animal, but without passage of the electrolytic current. Ideally, to avoid inadvertent selection of animals, the electrode would be inserted *before* it had been decided whether the particular animal was to be treated or kept as a control, and the decision whether or not to pass the electrolytic current would then be made by tossing a coin. Precautions of this kind may sometimes seem extreme, even absurd, but the careful experimenter keeps them in mind and employs them whenever he can reasonably do so.

A special technique known as *blind design* ensures against the investigator's bias (conscious or unconscious) influencing the conduct of an experiment or the evaluation of the results. The essence of this procedure is that the personnel who carry out the treatments should not know which subjects belong to which groups. Sometimes this is manifestly impossible, as when treatment and control procedures differ grossly. However, if control animals are to receive inert injections while others receive drugs, it is not very difficult to arrange for the actual injections to be coded, and then administered by someone who is "blind" with respect to the coding. It is even more important when criteria of effect are being assessed, that the investigator be able to measure, count, or otherwise evaluate results with complete objectivity. Objectivity cannot be guaranteed if he knows to which groups the subjects belong, because he usually has some emotional stake in the experiment, or he probably would not have undertaken it.

It might be thought that insistence upon "blind" technique is merely an exaggerated fussiness about abstract principles of experimental design. On the contrary, the literature of experimental psychology and of medicine is full of reports on experiments whose outcomes were determined more by an investigator's bias than by any treatment under test. One example will suffice. Shortly after the introduction of the antihistamine drugs into medicine, their effectiveness in the treatment of the common cold was investigated in several field trials. The results were very favorable to the new drugs, with the consequence that antihistamines were widely promoted as cold cures. In these experiments, however, no safeguards had been employed to prevent the examining physicians (who rated the progress of each cold) from knowing which subject had received placebo and which had received drug. "Blind" experiments, undertaken subsequently, showed consistently and conclusively that the drugs were without effect. Later, in the elegant clinical trials that established the value of streptomycin in the treatment of pulmonary tuberculosis, the "blind" technique was scrupulously observed. Even the radiologists evaluating X-ray films were not allowed to know what treatments had been given, since independent studies had revealed a pronounced influence of such prior information upon radiological interpretations. Even in laboratory experimentation, although measurements may be made with very accurate instruments, it is surprising how often accidental errors can occur in the direction of an investigator's bias!

In human (as compared with animal) experimentation the difficulties are compounded, because the subject's knowledge about the experiment and his preconceptions about the anticipated effects can also influence the outcome. Neither the subjects nor the investigator directly involved in the experiment must know how the treatments have been assigned. Medications are given serial code numbers, and the person with access to the code refrains from any contact with the actual experiment until all the data have been collected. Nevertheless, even this "double-blind" system is not foolproof. A drug may reveal itself through a side effect such as drowsiness or dry mouth, which cannot be duplicated in the placebo. If the subject becomes convinced (rightly or wrongly) that he has received a potent drug, or that he has been given a placebo, his responses may reflect this conviction to a remarkable degree. Under such circumstances, interpretations become extremely difficult.

Suppose now that subjects have been assigned randomly to a treated group and to a concurrent control group, and that proper blind precautions have been taken. The validity of the outcome in such an experimental design will then depend very largely upon the practical equivalence of the two groups. Even though the subjects were assigned randomly, the groups might still differ accidentally in important ways, especially if there are but few subjects per group. A difference in outcome might then only reflect some chance difference between subjects in the two groups, whereas it would be falsely interpreted as a treatment effect. This difficulty can be overcome by using a *balanced design.* We would perform the experiment in two parts, first using one group as the concurrent control, then reversing the roles of the two groups in what is known as a *crossover.* The effect of any intrinsic differences between the groups would thereby be minimized.

A crossover experiment for testing the effect of a drug on blood glucose in human subjects might be conducted as follows. Subjects reporting for the experiment would be assigned to group A or group B by means of the random number table. Group A would receive placebo on the first day, drug on the second; group B would receive drug on the first day, placebo on the second. Under these conditions, provided the proper blind precautions were taken, a lowering of blood glucose which occurred in both groups when drug was given and in neither group when placebo was administered could be taken seriously as evidence of a treatment effect.

If more than two groups are involved, the crossover principle becomes more elaborate. The *Latin square* may be used to ensure that each group receives every treatment in a systematic fashion. Latin squares were introduced originally for the purpose of subdividing plots of land for agricultural experiments, so that treatments could be tested even though different parts of a field had various soil conditions. In a Latin square, letters of the alphabet are placed in such a way that each letter appears once and only once in every row and in every column. Suppose we wish to test four different treatments (including a control) on the spontaneous activity of mice, in a balanced design. We assign the desired number of mice randomly to each group A, B, C, and D. We then choose a 4 × 4 Latin square, such as the one below, and assign meanings to the columns and rows, as indicated.[2]

Treatment	Day 1	Day 2	Day 3	Day 4
1	A	B	C	D
2	B	C	D	A
3	C	D	A	B
4	D	A	B	C

The square provides the specifications for carrying out the desired experiment on four successive days. Each group of mice will receive each treatment once, and all groups will be treated each day. We shall see later how easy it is to analyze the data obtained in balanced experiments. Here we could ascertain not only if the treatments differ from each other and from the control, regardless of the day of treatment, but also if the spontaneous activity of the mice differs from day to day regardless of treatment, and finally if treatment effects depend in any way upon the day of treatment.

The Latin square or equivalent balancing procedures may be useful during the course of an experiment as well as in its initial planning. The principle of maintaining similar conditions for all groups throughout an experiment requires that even unforeseen influences must be prevented from acting preferentially upon any particular group. Every investigator can recall some unfortunate experience that taught him this particular lesson. The following example is fairly typical. An experiment to ascertain whether a particular extract had antibacterial activity required the incubation of agar plates containing bacteria and extract (treatment group) and of similar plates from which the extract was omitted (control group).

[2]There are many different Latin squares of each size. One of these may be selected randomly from the collection catalogued in R. A. Fisher and F. Yates, *Statistical Tables for Biological, Agricultural and Medical Research*, 4th ed. (New York: Hafner Publishing Company Inc., 1953), Table XV and pp. 18ff.

The bacteria failed to grow on treatment plates and grew well on control plates. A follow-up experiment employed serial dilutions of the extract to estimate its antibacterial potency. Again, although control plates grew normally, no growth occurred on treatment plates, even after millionfold dilution. It finally developed, however, that no bacteria grew on "treatment" plates, even when no extract was added. A temperature gradient from right to left in a defective incubator was wholly responsible. Control plates had been regularly placed at the left, where the thermometer was located, and where the temperature was correct. Treatment plates had always been placed to the right, where the temperature was too high to support any bacterial growth. A systematic alternation in the placement of control and treatment plates would have revealed the true situation at once.

The placement of animal cages in a room might also seem unworthy of special planning. Yet light, temperature, noise, vibration are among the many conditions that can vary from place to place in an animal room. Systematic placement of cages according to a Latin square plan helps equalize extraneous influences. For the same reasons the order in which procedures are carried out with various experimental groups should be varied systematically, in order to balance out any possible influence on the outcome.

There are several variations on the balancing principle, some of which are used very frequently. One such design is the *randomized block*. Often one wishes to provide as broad a basis as possible for generalization of an experimental conclusion. For example, it may be worthwhile to examine treatment effects in several strains of animal rather than limiting the experiment to a single strain. In that case one has to choose between randomly mixing animals of different strains, and keeping each strain as a distinct group. The latter is by far the better procedure, for without losing any information about effects on all the animals taken collectively, information may be gained about strain-specific differences in the effects. Suppose one wished to test a number of chemicals for their ability to produce fetal malformations when administered to pregnant rats. The entire experiment will be replicated in several "blocks," each block consisting of animals belonging to a single strain. The assignments of the chemicals are made randomly within each block. If there were four strains (W, X, Y, Z) and five chemicals (A, B, C, D, E) under test, and 60 animals in all, then each chemical would be tested in three animals of every strain. The data would be observations on the number of malformed young in each litter, and they could be tabulated on the following grid:

	Chemicals					
Strains	A	B	C	D	E	*Total*
W						
X						
Y						
Z						
Total						

Each box of the table will contain three observations, there will be 12 observations on each chemical, and 15 observations on each strain. Such a design is efficient because it answers a number of questions in a single experiment, and it tends to improve the reliability of the results because differences between strains can be taken into account in assessing the reality of any differences between chemicals.

In a *factorial* design combinations of treatments are examined. Several *levels* of one factor are criss-crossed with several levels of another. For example, an anticonvulsant drug (factor A) might be studied at four different doses (including a zero-dose control) in animals made to convulse by three different procedures (factor B). The available animals may then be divided equally and randomly among the twelve combinations of the factors, as in the following grid:

	Factor A *Doses of Anticonvulsant Drug*				
Factor B *Convulsant Procedure*	0	*a*	*b*	*c*	*Total*
1					
2					
3					
Total					

Here each box will contain one or more animals, and the design ensures that each level of factor *A* is tested in combination with every level of factor *B*, and vice versa. Factorial designs may permit one to assess in a single experiment not only the primary effects of the levels of each factor independently, but also the joint effects of the combinations.

A *nested* (or *hierarchical*) design is one in which the factors do not criss-cross, but rather are present in various *tiers*, each contained within a higher one. An example would be a comparison of the accuracy and precision of blood-cell counting in several clinical laboratories. Suppose portions of the same blood were coded appropriately and then submitted to three laboratories, each employing a number of technicians. It might be of interest to know to what extent the counts obtained in the different laboratories agree, whether or not the results obtained by different technicians in the same laboratory differ in any systematic way, and also whether or not each single technician obtains a reproducible count in replicate trials with the same blood. Here the lowest tier contains "replicates within technicians," the next contains "technicians within laboratories," and the highest contains the three laboratories. The data might be five replicate counts by each technician, and they would fall into the following hierarchical tabulation:

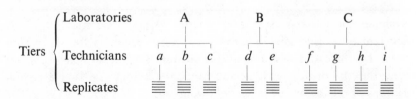

The methods of analyzing data in these and other types of experimental design will be described in Chap. 2. The designs described here are merely the simplest and most commonly encountered, but much more elaborate ones are also used. Detailed information about this subject may be found in the references beginning at page 192.

Whether or not the reader ever has to set up an experiment embodying the design principles outlined here, he will certainly be called upon to read and interpret published reports of investigations in which statistical methods were used. It cannot be emphasized too strongly that statistical procedures yield valid conclusions only for adequate experiments. One of the first steps in evaluating a report of an experiment is therefore to satisfy oneself that the principles of preliminary randomization and subsequent control were followed. Only then is it appropriate to inquire whether or not treatment had any effect.

SAMPLING DISTRIBUTIONS

Experimental observations in all fields of science are to some extent variable, but variability is especially prominent in biological experimentation. Any single experiment is necessarily of finite scope, yielding a limited *sample* of data. If the same experiment were repeated, a somewhat different set of data would generally be obtained, so we cannot attach any special importance to a particular sample. Rather do we regard each sample of data as having been drawn randomly from an infinitely large collection of similar data that happen not to have been included in the sample. This hypothetical infinitude of data, of which the sample is representative, we call a *population*.

Data that characterize a sample are known as *statistics*. An example of a statistic is the mean[3] DNA content of 100 randomly chosen unfertilized sea-urchin eggs. Another statistic is the number of mice in a group of 25 which are paralyzed by a given dose of drug. Now it is almost always the case that we are interested in populations, not in samples. This is merely another way of saying that experimental observations are useful to the extent they have general relevance. What we wish to know is the DNA content of unfertilized sea-urchin eggs in general, not the content of the eggs chosen for a particular experiment. Likewise we are interested in what a drug does to mice in general, not to a particular group of 25 mice.

Numbers that characterize a population are known as *parameters*. Parameters corresponding to the sample statistics just cited would be the mean DNA content of all unfertilized sea-urchin eggs, and the percent of all mice that the given dose of drug would paralyze. The only way we can obtain information about populations is to make observations on samples. Sample statistics are then used as *estimators* of the corresponding population parameters. That is why the procedures of randomization and control discussed earlier are so important; they ensure that the samples we deal with will be truly representative of the populations from which they were drawn and therefore that the statistics we obtain will be fair estimators of the parameters in which we are really interested.

[3]A *mean* is an ordinary arithmetical average. There are other kinds of averages, to be defined later.

Suppose that the true mean weight of all students of a given age is 165 lb. We shall weigh randomly chosen groups of students, compute the mean weight in each group, and see how well these sample means estimate the true mean. Let us begin with the smallest possible group, a sample of one ($N = 1$), namely the individual student. Each such weight is an *unbiased* estimate of the parameter, 165 lb, because it is just as likely to be high as low, and the long-term average of the estimates will approach the value of the parameter in question. But obviously the weight of an individual student is not likely, except occasionally, to be 165 or even very close to 165.

Now consider groups of ten students ($N = 10$). The mean weight in each sample is again an unbiased estimate of the population mean because in the long run the fluctuations above and below 165 will balance each other. Each sample of 10 is almost certain to contain weights above and below 165, so the mean of such a sample is likely to be closer to 165 than was the weight of a randomly selected individual student. It should therefore be evident that a statistic estimates the corresponding parameter ever more accurately as the sample size increases. At the extreme, if a sample approached the size of the population ($N \rightarrow \infty$), the sample statistic would become indistinguishable from the population parameter.

Besides sample size, the amount of variability in a population also determines how accurately a statistic will estimate the corresponding parameter. Clearly, if no student's weight differed from 165 lb by more than a pound or two, then even statistics from very small samples would be pretty good estimators. For any specified sample size, the statistic will better estimate the parameter, the smaller is the variability in the population from which the sample was drawn.

These generalizations about statistics and parameters are true, but they are not precise enough to be useful. In each instance we need to know just *how* well a statistic estimates its corresponding parameter. Suppose, for example, that we want to know the mean blood glucose concentration in young adults after an overnight fast. We could randomly select a convenient number of subjects (let us say 20), draw blood, and determine these blood glucose concentrations. The mean concentration in the sample will then be an unbiased estimate of the true blood glucose concentration of all similar people under the same conditions. The variability of the sample data will also tell us something about how variable blood glucose levels are in the population. If it should happen that all the sample values are in the range 0.90–1.10 mg/ml, then probably most of the population values are also in this range. We can imagine then that the population mean might well be something like 0.93 or 1.02, but we would be very reluctant to believe it could be 1.37. The general line of reasoning can be grasped intuitively. If the population mean were 1.37, there would have to be values above as well as below this. Under such circumstances it would be very very improbable that we should draw a random sample of 20 subjects, all of whose blood glucose concentrations were lower than 1.10. Since the truth is that we did draw such a sample, we reject the hypothesis that the population mean is as high as 1.37. If we consider, one by one, a series of such hypotheses about the population mean—that it is 1.36, 1.35, 1.34, and so on—we will eventually come into a region of acceptable hypotheses. For example, the hypothetical value 1.09 would probably be regarded as acceptable, as would other values in the range covered by the sample data. At still lower values we would again enter a region of rejected hypotheses. The process of inferring from the properties of a sample, within what range a parameter probably lies is known as estimating a *confidence interval* (or *confidence limits*) for that parameter.

Assume now that we somehow know what the mean blood glucose concentration is in a control population, and we conduct an experiment to ascertain whether or not a drug lowers this concentration. We shall obtain data from a treated group of subjects and compute the sample mean. Using these sample data we can then estimate a confidence interval for the mean of the treated population. Now if this entire interval, representing the range of probable values of the true mean after treatment, lies below the known control mean, then we can conclude that the drug has a *significant* effect in reducing the blood glucose concentration. On the other hand, if the confidence interval for the mean of the treated population includes the control mean, we would be unable to conclude that the drug had any effect, since the sample data are not inconsistent with the hypothesis that the treated sample was drawn from the control population, and that the observed sample mean is a reasonable estimate of the known control mean.

The foregoing discussion assumed *a priori* knowledge about a parameter. We rarely have such knowledge. Often we have two experimental groups, control and treated, and we want to know whether or not treatment has had an effect. This is tantamount to asking whether or not both samples could reasonably have been drawn from the same (untreated) population. Of course, we expect the sample means to differ somewhat even if both samples did come from the same population. The real question is whether the difference between the two sample means is so large that we feel compelled to reject the hypothesis that they are estimates of the same parameter. Here the required confidence interval is for a *difference* between two parameters. Suppose the mean blood glucose concentration in the control sample is 1.00 and in the treated sample 0.89. There is an apparent difference of −0.11, which is our best estimate of the true difference. The confidence interval for the true difference, however, might be (for example) −0.26 to +0.04. Since a zero difference is included in these confidence limits, we cannot assert that the drug had any effect, because we cannot be certain there was any real difference between control and treated blood glucose concentrations. Yet neither can we deny that the drug might have had some effect. The confidence interval gives the probable limits of magnitude of the effect—i.e., if there was any lowering of blood sugar, it was probably no greater than 0.26 mg/ml, and there might even have been a small rise of blood sugar, no greater than 0.04 mg/ml, which the sample accidentally failed to detect. On the other hand, if the confidence interval had not included zero, we could have asserted the efficacy of the drug and stated the probable quantitative limits of its effectiveness.

In discussing the meaning of confidence limits and the rationale for deciding whether or not observed effects are to be taken seriously, we made use of rather vague words like "probably" and "reasonably." We said, for example, that if a population mean lay outside a certain interval, it was not "probable" that we would have observed a particular sample mean. To get at a precise definition of such terms we need concrete information about the probability of drawing various sample statistics by chance from populations with specified parameters.

The *probability* of an event is the long-term frequency of occurrence of that event, relative to all alternative events. It is expressed as a decimal fraction between zero (the event never occurs) and unity (the event always occurs and no alternative event ever occurs). Sometimes a probability is known *a priori*, as in penny-tossing, where we know that in the long run heads and tails will each fall with relative frequency 0.5, and this is therefore the probability that any particular toss will produce heads. Sometimes a probability can only be estimated empirically by observing the relative frequency toward which the results of a great many trials converge.

A *sampling distribution* is a graph showing the probabilities of obtaining all possible statistics in samples drawn randomly from a specified population. Figure 1-1 is a histogram depicting the expected sampling distribution for throws of two dice, computed *a priori* on the assumption that each face has equal opportunity to be uppermost. The eleven discrete possible outcomes are given on the horizontal axis, the probability of obtaining each is shown on the vertical axis. Figure 1-2 shows an expected sampling distribution of mean weights in samples of 10 students from a hypothetical population whose true mean is 165 lb. In order to plot this sampling

Figure I–I   Sampling distribution for throws of two dice.

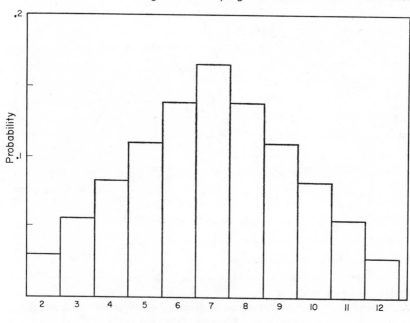

Sum Of The Numbers On Both Dice

distribution an assumption also had to be made about the variability in the population. In contrast to Fig. 1-1, this sampling distribution is a continuous curve, since here sample means are not limited to discrete integer values but may assume any intermediate values as well. In the next chapter the origins of such sampling distributions as are depicted in these figures will be considered more closely. For the present we may observe that a sampling distribution shows how likely it is that a randomly drawn sample statistic will deviate to any given extent from the parameter it estimates. Thus, if we have a particular sample statistic in hand, the sampling distribution will tell us the exact probability of its having been obtained randomly from a hypothetical population with a given parameter. That probability, as we shall see, then becomes a basis for judgment as to whether or not the sample was actually drawn from the hypothetical population.

Figure 1–2 Sampling distribution for mean weights in samples of 10 from a hypothetical population with mean 165lb.

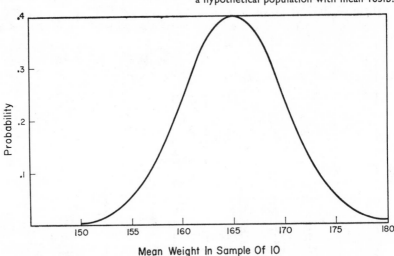

Mean Weight In Sample Of 10

Example 1-2. Probability of an outcome.

From the sampling distribution shown in Fig. 1-1, estimate the probability of throwing 4 or less with two dice.

The total area under the histogram represents the sum of the probabilities for all possible outcomes, i.e., unity. The probability desired here is the fractional area to the left of 5. Since the bars of the histogram are of equal width, the desired area is proportional to the heights, $0.03 + 0.06 + 0.08 = 0.17$.

Example 1-3. Probability of obtaining an extreme statistic.

Estimate from Fig. 1-2 the probability of drawing, from the hypothetical population, a random sample of 10 with mean weight outside the limits 160–170 lb.

Here it can be seen that about two-thirds of the area lies within the stated interval, about one-third outside. So the required probability is about 0.34. Since the curve is symmetrical, there is probability 0.17 of obtaining a sample mean less than 160, and 0.17 for obtaining one greater than 170. If we actually weighed many such samples, about two-thirds of the means would, in the long run, be between 160 and 170. It would certainly occasion no surprise, however, if a sample were selected randomly and its mean turned out to be 171, inasmuch as 17 of every 100 sample means will exceed 170.

Example I-4. Deviation corresponding to a given probability.

You would certainly be surprised if you chose a single random sample and then found that its mean deviated from the population mean by more than did 95 out of 100 similarly selected sample statistics. Approximately how low or high would the sample mean have to be in order to occasion such surprise, assuming the sampling distribution of Fig. 1-2?

Here we wish to know the interval of mean weights that includes 95% of the total area under the curve. The correct answer is 155–175, so a sample mean outside this range would indeed surprise us. The answer could have been found by actually measuring the area but it is more readily obtained from a special table of areas that will be described in the next chapter.

STATISTICAL HYPOTHESES AND DECISION RULES

Imagine that you are shown a penny, heads up, and are asked to decide, without examining it, whether it is an ordinary penny or a two-headed one. You are permitted to see the outcome of as many tosses as you like. What is the best way to proceed? Naturally, if it is an ordinary penny it will fall tails sooner or later, so the simple answer is to keep tossing it as long as possible. If tails appears, the problem is solved. If tails does not appear, however, you will have to decide sooner or later that the penny is two-headed. No matter when you make this decision, you may be wrong; the very next toss might conceivably have fallen tails. But obviously, the longer you wait the more certain you will be of making the right decision.

The problem would be more interesting, and somewhat more realistic as an analogy to experimental situations, if there were some cost attached to each toss, and some penalty for a wrong decision. Your course of action would then certainly be determined by these new contingencies. If the cost of continued tossing was low, and the penalty was high for wrongly concluding the penny was two-headed, you would wait to see a long succession of heads before arriving at any conclusion. If, on the other hand, the cost of tossing was high and the penalty for a wrong decision was low, you would terminate the series early, perhaps after a very few tosses.

In this case, since *a priori* probabilities for the behavior of a true penny are known, it is easy for us to arrive at decision rules. The first step is to formulate a hypothesis which is to be accepted or rejected on the basis of sample data. Here the hypothesis to be tested is that the penny has two different faces, heads and tails; the alternative is that the penny is two-headed. The next step is to decide how often, in the long run, we are willing to reject the hypothesis wrongly—i.e., what probability we are willing to accept for calling the penny two-headed when it is not. This probability is known as the *level of significance* at which the hypothesis will be rejected; it is designated by the letter P.[4] As we have noted already, both cost and penalty will influence the choice of the level of significance. Suppose we are willing to be wrong as often as five times in every hundred trials, but no more often ($P \leq 0.05$).[5] Then we can reject the hypothesis if and only if a sample outcome is observed, which would have been expected with probability 0.05 or less, were the hypothesis in fact true.

Let us consider the probability that the first tails will appear at any specified toss of a true penny. Obviously this is $1/2$ for the 1st toss. For the first tails to appear at the 2nd toss, heads is required at the 1st (probability $1/2$) and then tails at the 2nd (probability $1/2$), giving a combined probability $(1/2)/(1/2)$ for both required events. Similarly the probabilities of the first tails appearing at the 3rd, 4th, 5th, and higher tosses are found to be $(1/2)^3$, $(1/2)^4$, $(1/2)^5$, etc. These probabilities are plotted as a histogram in Fig. 1-3.

Now the probability that the first tails will not appear sooner than the 5th toss is given by unity less the sum of the probabilities for its appearance on the 1st, 2nd, 3rd, and 4th tosses; or (which is the same thing) by the sum of the probabilities for its appearance on the 5th, 6th, and all higher tosses; or (which is also the same thing) by the area contained in the histograms at, and to the right of, the 5th toss, relative to the total area of all the histograms. This probability is readily found to be

$$1 - [(1/2) + (1/2)^2 + (1/2)^3 + (1/2)^4] = 0.0625$$

which exceeds our desired level of significance. The shaded area, on the other hand, including the 6th and higher tosses, represents a total probability 0.03125, well below the desired level. Thus, since the probability of getting four heads in a row and then tails on the 5th toss exceeds 0.05, we would not consider that outcome incompatible with the hypothesis of a true penny; whereas getting five heads in a row would happen rarely enough with a true penny to make us reject the hypothesis. The decision

---

[4]Rejecting the hypothesis when it is true is referred to as a *Type I error*. The probability (designated by the Greek letter α) of committing a Type I error is obviously the same as the level of significance (P). The two symbols will be used interchangeably.

[5]$<$ means "less than"; $>$ means "greater than"; $\leq$ means "equal to or less than."

rule must therefore be: Accept the hypothesis if any tail appears, but reject it if no tail appears within five tosses. For two-headed pennies this rule will be free of error, but the honesty of ordinary pennies will be impugned wrongly about 3 times in every 100 trials.

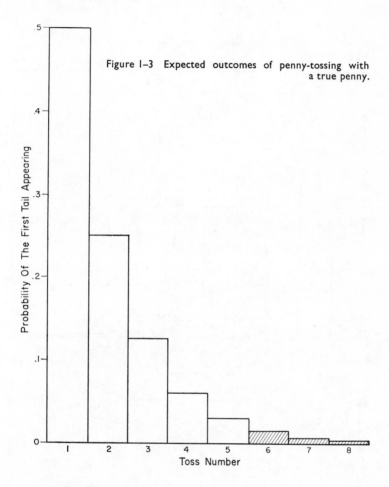

Figure I-3 Expected outcomes of penny-tossing with a true penny.

Now suppose you are given a jar of beads and you must decide whether or not half of them are red, on the basis of a single random sample of 10. Your hypothesis will state that there are actually 50% red beads in the population. Now it is known that the proportion of red beads in repeated samples from such a population would fluctuate above and below 50%, over a wide range if the samples were small, over a narrow range if they were large. The exact sampling distribution for proportions to be expected in samples of a given size drawn from a population containing a given proportion can be calculated, or can be found in an appropriate table. The sampling distribution for $N = 10$ in a population with true proportion

Figure I–4 Expected outcomes of sampling from populations with 50% A and 30% A.

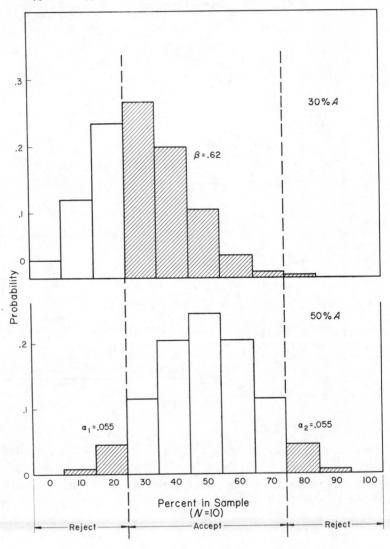

50% A[6] is shown at the bottom of Fig. 1-4. Evidently the probability is 0.055 for drawing a sample of 10 containing fewer than 3 red, and the same for drawing a sample containing more than 7 red. The probability of drawing a sample containing fewer than 3 *or* more than 7 red is the sum of both "tails" of the probability distribution, or 0.11. If we had happened to choose a level of significance slightly larger than this (e.g., $P < 0.15$), the decision rule would be: If the sample of 10 beads contains between 3 and 7 red, accept the hypothesis; otherwise reject it.[7]

The model sampling distribution depicted at the bottom of Fig. 1-4 could equally well pertain to a biological experiment. Suppose a certain disease has a known mortality of 50%, i.e., in the long run half of all its victims will die. If groups of 10 patients are selected randomly and given no treatment, the sample mortalities will then occur as indicated by the histogram. Only once in about 1,000 samples will all 10 patients survive or all 10 die; this probability is so small it cannot even be shown in the figure. We should expect 9 or more to survive in about 11 samples out of every 1,000; this is the sum of the probabilities for 10 surviving and for 9 surviving. The probability of observing fewer than 3 deaths out of 10 patients is 0.055, and this is the case already considered in connection with the bead model.

We may now examine the decision process in an experiment to ascertain the value of a new drug in treating the disease. Let us suppose it is practicable to treat 10 patients, and that we will adopt the level of significance $P < 0.10$. The hypothesis is that the population mortality is still 50% (i.e., that the drug is ineffective);[8] the alternative which we are testing, that it is lower than 50%. The decision rule must then be: If 3 or more patients die, accept the hypothesis; otherwise reject it and accept the alternative that the drug has reduced the mortality. In this case, although we were willing to accept a Type I error as large as 0.10, the discrete outcomes in the sampling distribution result in an actual Type I error not much greater than 0.05. Only about 5 times in 100, in the long run, would we conclude that the drug is effective when it is really worthless. On the other hand,

---

[6] A designates any relevant classification, such as "red."

[7] With small samples the proportions can only assume a limited number of discrete values, so the chosen level of significance may not be met exactly. Here, for example, P was chosen to be <0.15, but the decision rule will result in a Type I error of only 0.11. However, if the rule had permitted between 4 and 6 red, the Type I error would have been 0.34, which is greater than the acceptable level.

[8] This is an example of a *null hypothesis*, namely, that any difference between a sample statistic and a parameter (or between sample statistics) is attributable to sampling variations due to chance.

there is a very good chance of accepting the hypothesis when it is really false, i.e., of concluding the drug is worthless when it actually has some definite effect. This kind of false conclusion is known as a *Type II error* and its probability is denoted by the Greek letter β. The relationship between the two types of error is summarized in the following table:

		Hypothesis Is Actually	
		True	*False*
	Accepted	No error	Type II error (β)
Hypothesis Is			
	Rejected	Type I error (α or P)	No error

Whereas the probability (α) of a Type I error is chosen by the investigator, the probability (β) of a Type II error is then determined in a rather complex way by three main factors. The first is the relevant parameter of the alternative population; β will change with each alternative parameter that may be specified. The upper part of Fig. 1-4 shows a particular alternative parameter (30% instead of 50% mortality) and its sampling distribution for $N = 10$. The decision rule previously adopted is diagrammed as a vertical broken line just to the left of sample mortality 30%. Now if we treat a group of 10 patients and 3 or more die, we will have to accept the hypothesis that the untreated 50% mortality was not changed by treatment. Yet we see here that the acceptance area to the right of the vertical line, which includes 95% of the control population, also includes a large fraction of the sampling distribution for the alternative population with a true 30% mortality. What this means is that if treatment actually did reduce the mortality to 30%, we would nevertheless falsely conclude, 62 times out of 100 (the cumulative probability to the right of the vertical line in the upper histogram), that the 50% mortality was unchanged. In other words, for this particular case, with $N = 10$, when we choose $\alpha = 0.05$, we will necessarily have $\beta = 0.62$. The basic generalization here is that the Type II error is largely determined by the extent to which the two alternative sampling distributions overlap. The more widely separated are the two alternative parameters, the smaller will β be, for any chosen value of α.

The second factor upon which β depends is the sample size. As the sample size increases, β decreases, because both sampling distributions become narrower, and therefore overlap less. Figure 1-5 presents hypothetical sampling distributions ($N = 16$) for blood glucose concentrations in samples from a control population with mean 1.00 mg/ml (bottom) and in samples from a treated population whose true mean has been reduced to 0.90 mg/ml (top). Here, when α is chosen to be 0.05, $\beta = 0.36$. Figure 1-6 shows the effect of increasing sample size to 100. Both sampling distributions are strikingly narrowed, so that the area of overlap between them is greatly reduced, even though each population mean is the same as before. The result is that for $\alpha = 0.05$, β now becomes vanishingly small. In summary, regardless of sample size, a treatment effect would be asserted once in 20 experiments when there was none. With samples of 16, a real reduction from 1.00 to 0.90 (or an effect of lesser magnitude) would be missed more often than once in every three experiments. With samples of 100, however, an effect of this magnitude would almost certainly be detected.

The third factor that determines β is the value chosen for α. It should be apparent from Figs. 1-4, 1-5, and 1-6 that for any given pair of alternative sampling distributions, the greater is α the smaller will be β. Thus by moving the vertical line (decision rule) to the right, we can accept a higher level of significance and simultaneously reduce β. We would, consequently, have a better chance to discover treatment effects of low intensity, but only at the price of concluding more often that treatment was effective when it really was not.

Naturally, every investigator would like to employ decision rules which will only rarely be in error, so that it might seem one should always work with extremely small values of both α and β. Unfortunately, this is not feasible. We could readily choose a level of significance $P < 0.001$, so that we would rarely reject a true hypothesis, but this would make β very large for all likely alternative hypotheses. We would then rarely find out anything useful, for even impressive treatment effects would be attributed to the vagaries of chance sampling. True enough, we could make P very small and nevertheless decrease β by greatly increasing the sample size, but this would make experiments more difficult, more costly, and sometimes entirely impractical. For these reasons it has become customary in biological work to adopt $P < 0.05$ as a reasonable compromise level of significance. Once in 20 times we will follow up a false lead, but this is thought to be tolerable by most investigators. When a hypothesis is

Figure 1-5   Sampling distributions from two populations with the same variability but different means.   (N = 16.)

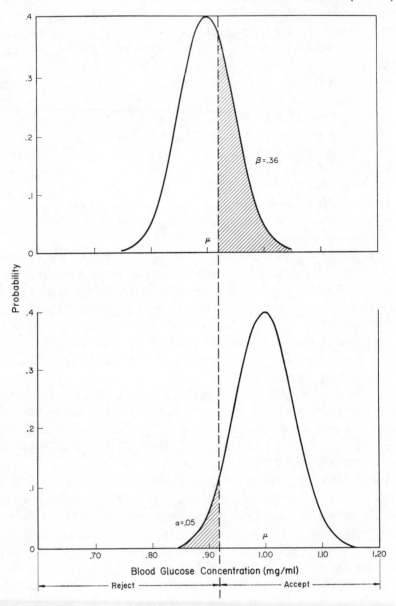

Figure I–6 Sampling distributions from same two populations as in Figure
I–5. (N = 100.)

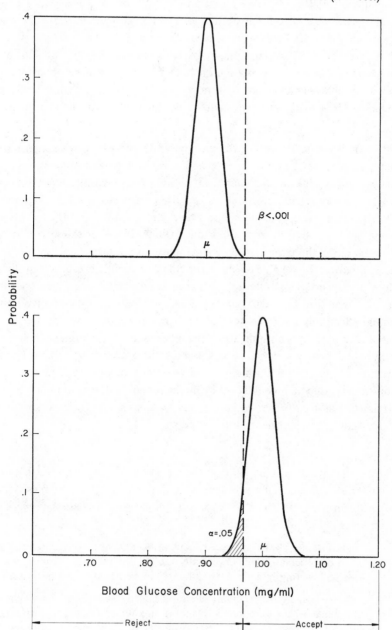

rejected at this level, it is conventional to describe the conclusion as "significant at the 5% level." One might say, for example, that a drug under test "was effective in reducing the mortality ($P < 0.05$)," or that "mortality in the treated group was significantly ($P < 0.05$) less than 50%." The level $P < 0.01$ is used as a more decisive criterion, and conclusions are then spoken of as "highly significant." These conventions are arbitrary but they are sanctioned by custom. If one wishes to set other levels of significance in particular experiments, they should always be stated explicitly.

There is an important difference between *statistical significance* (as expressed in the P value) and *practical significance*. If an outcome is not statistically significant, we cannot attribute it to a treatment under study, but under some circumstances further investigation may be warranted. On the other hand, an outcome can be highly significant in the statistical sense, and yet be of no real importance whatsoever. For example, a drug developed for the treatment of obesity may, in an adequate clinical trial, actually lower the weights of obese patients to a slightly greater extent than does a placebo. This difference between drug and placebo may well be highly significant ($P < 0.01$) and thus not attributable to chance, yet the actual effect may be so small as to be of no consequence in therapy. The P value in itself tells nothing about the magnitude of a treatment effect but only whether or not it is real. If it is real, there are other statistical procedures, as we shall see, which permit one to estimate its true magnitude. But then a value judgment has to be made, to which statistical methods are irrelevant, as to whether or not a real treatment effect of the specified magnitude is of any practical importance.

The chapters that follow take up the various statistical methods that are appropriate for analyzing problems of different kinds. The simplest kind of problem concerns the estimation or comparison of *single parameters*. Two sorts of data occur:

> *Quantitative data* deal with the intensity, magnitude, or degree of an effect or observation. Examples are weights of students, extent of blood glucose lowering by a drug, duration of the germination period of seeds.

> *Enumeration data* deal with the numbers or proportions of individuals or events in various categories. Examples are numbers of patients who succumb to a disease, percent of animals affected by a treatment, proportion of various outcomes in dice-throwing, number of cells in a counting chamber.

A more complicated kind of problem concerns the association (also known as *correlation*) of *two parameters* in the same system. Examples are the simultaneous increase of height and weight in growing children, the diminishing proportion of live bacteria with time in the presence of a disinfectant. A correlation of especial importance is that between the amount or intensity of a treatment and the magnitude or intensity of effect produced, the so-called *dose-response relationship.* Correlation problems may contain data of the quantitative or enumeration types, or a combination of both.

Problems

CHAPTER 1 (ANSWERS ON P. 196)

The problems are meant to be prototypic of those encountered in real experiments, but the data are almost wholly invented. The reference at the end of each problem indicates where relevant explanation and worked examples are to be found in the text.

PI-I.

Streptomycin was the first antibiotic to be developed against pulmonary tuber-culosis. It became widely available about 1946. Well-controlled clinical trials showed it to be highly effective compared with placebo medication. Since 1946 tuberculosis morbidity and mortality rates in the United States have declined progressively. Criticize the conclusion that streptomycin is responsible. (Cf. p. 4).

PI-2.

It was stated in the text that "so simple a matter as dividing 50 mice into two equal groups for control and treatment can be hazardous, because some characteristics of the mice may readily influence their allocation ..." Suppose an experiment is to test the effect of a tranquilizing drug on spontaneous activity of the mice, measured automatically by the jiggling of delicately suspended cages. Suppose the treatment and control groups are set up by arbitrarily drawing 25 mice out of the cage containing 50 mice, and (*a*) letting the removed mice receive drug and the remaining mice receive placebo, or (b) the reverse assignment. Consider how the outcome of the experiment might be affected in each case (a and b), if (1) the drug is an effective tranquilizer, or (2) the drug is inert. (Cf. p. 5.)

PI-3.

Describe a suitable procedure for assigning 50 mice equally to control and treatment groups by means of the table of random digits (Table 1). (Cf. p. 6.)

PI-4.

For an experiment on perception a class of students was divided into three equal groups by means of an alphabetical class list. Those whose last names began with A–J were untreated controls, K–P received decaffeinated coffee, and Q–Z received real coffee. The experimental procedure consisted of writing down rapidly flashed words as they were recognized. The three groups were found not to differ significantly in their performance of this task. Is there any feature of the experimental design that might conceivably cast doubt upon the finding? (Cf. p. 6.)

PI-5.

In a trial of insect attractants, five compounds are to be tested. Each can be placed in a trap so that flies which are attracted can be counted. It is reasonable to place the attractants far enough apart so their influences will not overlap; this is accomplished by choosing five locations in a large field. Show a Latin square design for a balanced experiment. (Cf. p. 11.)

PI-6.

Measurements of the systolic blood pressure of many healthy young adults have shown that readings in the range 110–120 are exceedingly common. Suppose that an expanded range 100–130 was found to include 98% of all subjects, the remaining 2% being equally distributed above and below this range. We wish to screen army recruits, and not admit those with high blood pressure. An acceptable level of significance is 0.01. State the hypothesis to be tested and the decision rule to be applied. (Cf. p. 25.)

PI-7.

An intriguing old problem in probabilities provides an interesting exercise in framing decision rules. There are three cards. One has an O on both sides, another an X on both sides, the third an O on one side and an X on the other. You mix the cards in a hat and draw one. You are allowed to look at one side. You must then decide what is on the other side. Many people feel intuitively that no matter what symbol you see, there is an equal probability of *O* or *X* on the other side. This is not so. If you are not already familiar with the problem, work out why it is not so. Then consider this hypothesis: *The other side is X.* What are the appropriate decision rules for accepting or rejecting, and what are the probabilities (α and β) for Type I and Type II error? (Cf. p. 24.)

PI-8.

There is a question whether or not a single alcoholic drink adversely affects one's ability to drive a motor vehicle. In a crossover design, two groups of drivers were tested on two occasions, with and without the alcoholic drink. An objectively determined driving score was computed for each individual on the two occasions, and a series of score differences, treated minus control, were thus generated. Each individual had a single-score difference representing his control score minus his alcohol score. Some of these differences were very close to zero, none were negative, some were positive and of considerable magnitude. State the null hypothesis and explain on what grounds it will be accepted or rejected. (Cf. p. 25.)

PI-9.

When we compare a treated and control group we may (*a*) accept or reject a null hypothesis, or (*b*) estimate a confidence interval for a difference. What are the relative merits of these two approaches? (Cf. p. 17.)

PI-10.

Two vaccines were shown to give significant protection against a disease, vaccine A at $P < 0.05$ (but > 0.01), vaccine B at $P < 0.01$. Does this mean that B is more effective than A? (Cf. p. 29.)

PI-11.

A long-term experiment was conducted to evaluate a new tranquilizer on disturbed patients in a psychiatric hospital. The new drug was compared with placebo and with an established tranquilizer in a three-way crossover, with balanced orders of administration. Drugs were assigned to patients according to a list prepared previously with a table of random numbers. The medications were contained in identical capsules, in jars labeled *A*, *B*, or *C*. The standard comparison drug was *A*, *B* was the placebo, *C* was the new drug. The meaning of the labels *A*, *B*, *C* was known only to an individual who had no direct contact with any phase of the experiment, and who kept the code in a locked safe. The experiment was conducted with double-blind precautions throughout. Criticize the experimental design. (Cf. p. 10.)

CHAPTER **2**

Quantitative Data

THE NORMAL DISTRIBUTION

All measurements are to some extent uncertain because of unavoidable error in the measurement process. An acid-base titration, for example, will yield a slightly different result each time it is performed, even when all the steps are carried out with utmost care. There is, of course, one and only one correct value, which we attempt to estimate by a single titration or by the mean of a number of titrations. Numerous small uncontrollable influences may cause a given titration result to be a little above or a little below the true value. If we repeat the titration a number of times we find that most outcomes tend to cluster about a central value while a few deviate more or less from it. A frequency distribution of the results forms a somewhat irregular histogram with the density of measurements greatest in the center and diminishing to the right and left. This is shown in Fig. 2-1 for 10, 30, 100, and 300 random single observations. It is seen that as more data accumulate, the irregularities in the histogram tend to smooth out. The distribution approaches more and more closely to the shape of a mathematically defined bell-shaped curve known as the Gaussian curve of error, or simply the *normal distribution*. This theoretical curve toward which the finite measurements converge (Fig. 2-2) will be recognized from Chap. 1 as simply the frequency distribution of the population of data from which samples are drawn.

A normal distribution curve is specified completely by two parameters.[1]

[1]The mathematical equation of the curve is

$$f(x) = \frac{1}{\sqrt{2\pi}\,\sigma}\, e^{-\frac{(x-\mu)^2}{2\sigma^2}}$$

also known as the "density function" because the height of the curve at any distance $(x - \mu)$ from μ reflects the density of the observations at that point. The equation will not be derived.

34

The *mean* (μ) locates the center of the distribution on the axis of measurements (x-axis). It is the expected value of a measurement, x; in other words, it is the long-run arithmetical average of all x-values. It is also the center of gravity of the distribution, the fulcrum upon which the entire

Figure 2–I Hypothetical results for titrations of 5.00 ml of $N/10$ HCl with $N/10$ NaOH. Shown are the first 10, first 30, first 100, and first 300 titrations.*

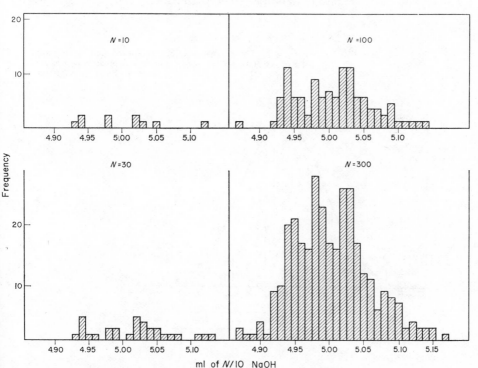

*Data obtained from the random normal deviates in *A Million Random Digits with 100,000 Normal Deviates*, (New York: The Free Press of Glencoe, 1955).

population would balance if each measurement had unit weight. In the population of titration data in Fig. 2-2, the mean is seen to be 5.00 ml of alkali.

The *variance* (σ^2) describes the amount of variability (dispersion) of the data, which in turn determines the breadth of the distribution curve. It is the expected value of the squared deviation of a measurement from the mean, $(x - \mu)^2$; in other words, it is the long-run arithmetical average of all such squared deviations.

The square root of the variance is known as the *standard deviation* (σ). It is the distance measured along the x-axis, from the center (μ) to the point of inflection of the curve, which is its steepest point. Since it has the same units as the mean and represents an actual distance on a graph, the standard deviation is readily visualized. For the distribution shown in Fig. 2-2, the standard deviation is 0.05 ml of alkali.

Figure 2–2   The normal distribution approached by titrating 5.00 ml of N/10 HCl innumerable times. Measurements are expressed to the nearest 0.01ml.

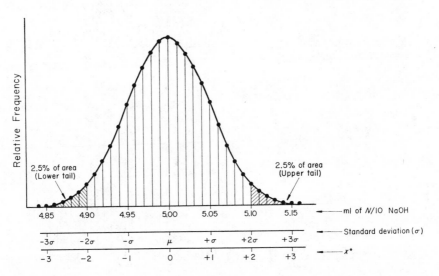

Now if data are very variable, the population will contain a high proportion of values that deviate considerably from the mean, the variance and standard deviation will be large, and the distribution curve will be broad. The converse will be true if the data are very homogeneous. The breadth of the curve, however, is not determined by the absolute magnitude of σ but by its magnitude relative to the mean. We express this relative variability as the *coefficient of variation* (C.V.), which is simply σ as a percent of μ. In Fig. 2-2, for example, C.V. $= 100(0.05)/5.00 = 1.0\%$. The C.V. is especially useful for comparing variability in different populations whose means may differ widely, or whose data may be measured in entirely different units.

It would obviously be useful if we could make all normal curves comparable, regardless of the units of measurement or their absolute values. This is readily done by expressing deviations from the mean in terms of σ. The ratio $\dfrac{(x - \mu)}{\sigma}$ is assigned the symbol x^*. In Fig. 2-2, three scales of measurement are shown. Along the x-axis are actual units of the titration, ml of $N/10$ NaOH. Beneath this is a σ scale, and at the bottom a x^* scale. Since any normal curve is specified completely by its μ and σ, it follows that all normal curves will be identical after the transformation to zero mean and unit variance, represented by the bottom scale.

General questions about normal distributions may now be answered with reference to the properties of the single standardized curve of the frequency distribution of x^*. For example, what fraction of all the measurements will be found within any specified distance (in x^* units) from the mean? The answer is found in a standard table which gives the area under the normal curve between μ $(x^* = 0)$ and any value of $\pm x^*$, as a fraction of the total area (i.e., of the total number of observations). Such information is found in Table 4, and may be verified by inspection of Fig. 2-2. For example, the entry at $P = 0.50$ is 0.674. This means that half the total area lies outside the range $(\mu - 0.674\sigma)$ to $(\mu + 0.674\sigma)$, so half the area lies within about two-thirds of a standard deviation on either side of μ. To discover how much of the area lies in the range $\pm\sigma$, we locate $x^* = 1.00$ in the body of the table, and see that the corresponding area is approximately 0.31, so 31% of the total area lies outside $\pm\sigma$ and 69% must lie within that distance of μ. Likewise, about 5% of all the observations are seen to lie outside the limits $\pm 1.96\sigma$, 2.5% in the upper tail of the curve, 2.5% in the lower, as shown by the shaded areas in Fig. 2-2. Finally, only 1% of all the measurements lie outside $\pm 2.58\sigma$, and only 3 per thousand (not shown in the table) outside $\pm 3\sigma$.

Biological measurements of many kinds have frequency distributions that fit the normal curve reasonably well. The innate complexity of biological systems usually causes a degree of variability much larger than can be accounted for by measurement errors alone. Sometimes, however, a very carefully performed experiment with a homogeneous group of subjects (e.g., animals of an inbred strain) yields a remarkably low coefficient of variation. Such an example is presented in Fig. 2-3. The histogram depicts data from an experiment to determine what blood alcohol concentration is lethal to rats. Progressively larger amounts of alcohol were injected into each rat and the blood alcohol level was determined as soon as respiratory failure occurred. Although some irregularities are still evident despite the large number of measurements, the fit

Figure 2–3   Blood alcohol concentrations at respiratory failure in 236 fasted rats. (Data of Haggard et al.*) Observations are represented by the histogram. The smooth curve is a fitted normal frequency distribution with $\mu = 9.30, \sigma = 0.15$ mg/ml.

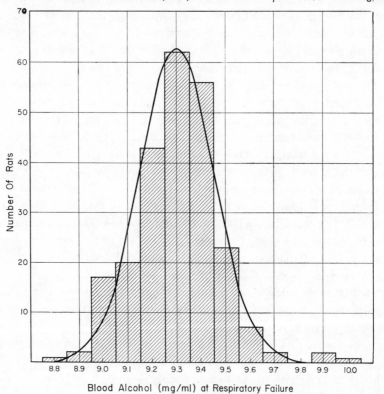

Blood Alcohol (mg/ml) at Respiratory Failure

*H. W. Haggard et al., *J. Pharmacol. Exptl. Therap.* **69** 252 (1940).

to a normal curve ($\mu = 9.3$, $\sigma = 0.15$ mg/ml) is remarkably good. The homogeneity of the data is indicated by C.V. $= 100(0.15)/9.3 = 1.6\%$.

Let us examine the applicability of Table 4 to these experimental data. As shown above, the table predicts that 69% of the measurements should lie within the interval $\pm\sigma$ on both sides of the mean. Since in this case $\sigma = 0.15$ mg/ml, the corresponding interval would be 9.30 ± 0.15, or 9.15 to 9.45 mg/ml, and there are actually 161 out of 236 measurements (68%) in this region. About 12 measurements (5%) are expected to lie outside the broader range 9.0 to 9.6 mg/ml ($\pm 1.96\sigma$) and we find that 8 actually do. The fitted normal curve may be regarded as a sampling distribution for $N = 1$, and Table 4 gives the probability of obtaining a random observation which equals or exceeds a specified deviation.

Now suppose we test a new drug reputed to be an antidote to alcohol, by pretreating a single randomly chosen rat, and then performing the usual alcohol infusion. Suppose the lethal blood concentration is found to be 9.7 mg/ml in this rat. So high a value would occur by chance in this population with a frequency lower than 5%. This may, of course, have been just such a chance event. But it is also possible that the pretreatment altered the toxicity of the alcohol. We would reject the former (null) hypothesis and accept the latter, asserting at the 95% confidence level ($P < 0.05$), that the drug is an effective antidote. In this way areas under the normal curve provide a basis for accepting or rejecting statistical hypotheses.

VARIANCE OF A SAMPLE MEAN

We have already seen in a qualitative way in Chap. 1 how sample means estimate a population mean more reliably as the sample size increases. We may now introduce a quantitative statement of this principle, known as the "central limit theorem." Let us designate a sample mean[2] by $\bar{x} = \Sigma x/N$. Samples containing N measurements are drawn repeatedly from a population of measurements, and each $\bar{x}$ is recorded on a graph. Eventually the graph will portray a fairly smooth population of $\bar{x}$-values. The theorem states that this $\bar{x}$ population will be normally distributed[3];

---

[2] Σ means "the sum of all such terms," so Σx means "the sum of all individual x-values." Other averages than the mean are sometimes of interest. The *median* of a population frequency distribution is the x-value that bisects the area of the curve, so that the probabilities of x assuming a higher or a lower value are both $1/2$. This parameter is estimated by the sample median, which is the middle point in a ranked array of observations. The *mode* (there may be more than one) of a population frequency distribution is an x-value at which the density (i.e., height) of the distribution passes through a maximum. A sample mode is an interval on the scale of measurements in which a maximum number of observations occurs. In a normal distribution the mean, median, and mode are identical.

[3] The $\bar{x}$ population tends to be normally distributed even when the population of measurements from which the samples were drawn is not normally distributed. This is a very useful property since the exact shape of population distributions is not often known.

its mean will be μ (the mean of the population of individual measurements); and its variance, $\sigma_{\bar{x}}^2$, will be smaller than σ to an extent that depends directly upon sample size, so that $\sigma_{\bar{x}}^2 = \sigma^2/N$.

A model population was prepared, consisting of several thousand disks. Upon each was inscribed a number, representing a measurement value. The frequencies of the various numbers were so chosen that the

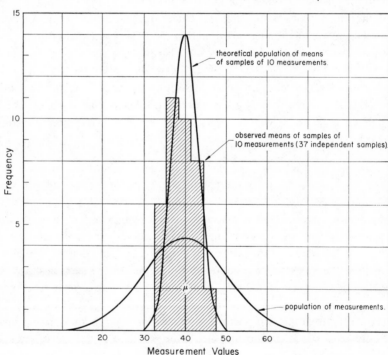

Figure 2–4   Means of samples of 10 measurements drawn from a model population with $\mu = 40$, $\sigma = 10$.

population mean was 40 and its standard deviation was 10. The disks were mixed well and a sample of 10 disks was drawn out, the numbers recorded, and the disks replaced. This process was repeated 37 times. Figure 2-4 shows the normally distributed population of measurements and also a histogram of the means of the 37 samples. Knowing that $\sigma^2 = 100$ in our model population, we may predict that the means of random samples of 10 disks should form a distribution whose variance is $\sigma_{\bar{x}}^2 = 100/10 = 10$,

$\sigma_{\bar{x}} = 3.2$. This theoretical $\bar{x}$ population with $\mu = 40$, $\sigma_{\bar{x}} = 3.2$ is shown as the smooth narrow curve, quite well approximated by the random observations. Thus, if the mean and variance of a population of measurements are known, the sampling distribution for means of samples of all sizes can be specified. This then permits hypotheses about the population to be tested by the properties of samples, as described in Chap. 1.

To avoid confusion with the variance of individual measurements (σ^2), the variance of sample means ($\sigma_{\bar{x}}^2$) is called the *variance of the mean*. The standard deviation of sample means is called the *standard error of the mean*, or simply the *standard error*.

All the foregoing is based on the optimistic assumption that we know the variance in the population from which the samples are drawn, whereas it is nearly always the case that the only information we have about the population comes from a sample. This complicates matters. Suppose, in the case of the disks, we knew nothing whatsoever about the population and we drew a single sample of 10. This sample might be any of the 37 whose means are shown, or any of the infinitude of similar samples that might be drawn. How, from our single sample, can we estimate μ with a known degree of precision? Our estimate of μ is obviously $\bar{x}$, the mean of our particular sample. But we know that while it is unbiased and may well be an excellent estimate, it may also be a very poor one. If only we knew $\sigma_{\bar{x}}^2$ (and thus $\sigma_{\bar{x}}$) we could find in a table of areas of the normal curve how often any given deviation ($\bar{x} - \mu$) would be exceeded, and thus conclude how far from μ our randomly chosen $\bar{x}$ might reasonably be. We could in turn readily calculate $\sigma_{\bar{x}}^2 = \sigma^2/N$ if only we knew the population variance, σ^2. Our first problem is therefore to estimate σ^2 from the scatter of measurements within our sample, a reasonable procedure since the sample measurements must reflect the variability of the population from which they were drawn.

The unbiased estimate of σ^2 from sample data is designated s^2. It is given by[4]

$$s^2 = \frac{\sum (x - \bar{x})^2}{(N - 1)}$$

[4] It might be supposed that the mean squared deviation from the sample mean, $\Sigma(x - \bar{x})^2/N$, would be an unbiased estimate of σ^2 but this is not so. That the denominator should be smaller than N is evident from the following argument. Most $\bar{x}$ will deviate from μ. Consequently, the mean squared deviation of x from $\bar{x}$ will necessarily be smaller than from μ. Therefore $\Sigma (x - \bar{x})^2/N$ would tend to underestimate σ^2 and a smaller denominator will be required to make the estimate unbiased. Proof that the replacement of N by $(N-1)$ exactly corrects the bias will not be given here, but may be found in textbooks of statistical theory.

We take the deviation of each x from the sample mean and square these individually. The squared deviations are then added, to yield $\sum (x - \bar{x})^2$, known as the *sum of squares* (SS). This is divided by $(N - 1)$ to give s^2; $s_{\bar{x}}^2$ can then be obtained as s^2/N, the square root of which is $s_{\bar{x}}$.

Example 2-1. Long method of computing variance.

Calculate the sample mean and variance estimates from the data given below. These were the actual results for one of the disk samples of Fig. 2-4, ranked here for convenience in the computations. The table of squares (Table 2) will be useful in this and subsequent problems.

Deviations

x	$(x - \bar{x})$	$(x - \bar{x})^2$
52	$+13.7$	187.69
48	$+ 9.7$	94.09
46	$+ 7.7$	59.29
41	$+ 2.7$	7.29
40	$+ 1.7$	2.89
37	$- 1.3$	1.69
37	$- 1.3$	1.69
32	$- 6.3$	39.69
26	-12.3	151.29
24	-14.3	204.49
$\sum x = 383$	$\sum (x - \bar{x}) = 0$	SS $= 750.10$

$$\bar{x} = \frac{\sum x}{N} = 38.3$$

$$s^2 = \frac{\text{SS}}{N - 1} = \frac{750.10}{9} = 83.3$$

$$s_{\bar{x}}^2 = \frac{s^2}{N} = \frac{83.3}{10} = 8.33$$

$$s_{\bar{x}} = \sqrt{8.33} = 2.9$$

In the example, summing the column of deviations serves as a useful check even though it is not actually required. It is always wise to keep more significant figures than are needed until the very end of the computation, especially (as in the shortcut methods to follow) when there is a subtractive step. Then $s_{\bar{x}}$ should be expressed to the same smallest unit as $\bar{x}$.

In this case, since the original data were in whole numbers, the mean is expressed to one decimal place, as is also the standard error.

SHORTCUT METHOD OF COMPUTING THE SUM OF SQUARES. We may describe symbolically the procedure we followed to obtain SS, as follows:

$$SS = (x_1 - \bar{x})^2 + (x_2 - \bar{x})^2 + \cdots + (x_N - \bar{x})^2 = \sum (x - \bar{x})^2$$

Expanding each term, we have

$$SS = (x_1^2 - 2\bar{x}x_1 + \bar{x}^2) + (x_2^2 - 2\bar{x}x_2 + \bar{x}^2) + \cdots$$
$$= \sum x^2 - 2\bar{x} \sum x + N\bar{x}^2$$

and substituting $\bar{x} = \sum x/N$,

$$SS = \sum x^2 - 2\frac{(\sum x)^2}{N} + \frac{(\sum x)^2}{N}$$
$$= \sum x^2 - \frac{(\sum x)^2}{N}$$

Thus, SS can be obtained simply by squaring the x-values themselves, summing them, and subtracting another term which is simply the sum of all the x-values, squared and divided by N. The total of all the x-values, $\sum x$, is also symbolized by T.

Then for any sample of measurement data,

$$\bar{x} = \frac{T}{N}$$

$$SS = \sum x^2 - \frac{T^2}{N}$$

A particular advantage of this shortcut is that both required terms, $T(=\sum x)$ and $\sum x^2$, can be computed directly on calculating machines, but even for manual computation it is much simpler than the long method.

Example 2-2. Shortcut computation of the sum of squares.

Calculate $\bar{x}$ and SS from the same data as in Example 2-1, using the shortcut method.

x	x^2
52	2704
48	2304
46	2116
41	1681
40	1600
37	1369
37	1369
32	1024
26	676
24	576

$$T = 383 \qquad\qquad \sum x^2 = 15{,}419$$

$$T^2 = 146{,}689$$

$$\frac{T^2}{N} = 14{,}668.9 \longrightarrow 14{,}668.9$$

$$\boxed{\bar{x} = \frac{T}{N} = 38.3} \qquad\qquad \boxed{SS = 750.1}$$

SHORTCUT BY CODING. Although not especially useful in the present examples, it is often very helpful to be able to reduce the data to simpler numbers before beginning the statistical computations. This is known as *coding* the data. If a fixed quantity is added to, or subtracted from every x-value, the mean will obviously be increased or decreased by that same quantity. However, the variance estimate will remain unchanged, since the whole distribution of x-values has merely been shifted along the x-axis without any change in its shape. On the other hand, if every x-value is multiplied or divided by a fixed quantity, the mean will be increased or decreased by that same factor, and the sum of squares (or variance estimate) by the square of the factor. These coding rules are summarized below.

If every x is coded by	the coded $\bar{x}$ must be	and the coded SS must be
adding k	decreased by k	left unchanged
subtracting k	increased by k	left unchanged
multiplying by k	divided by k	divided by k^2
dividing by k	multiplied by k	multiplied by k^2

Example 2-3.   Coding.

Calculate $\bar{x}$ and SS from the following data by coding. The subscript c will designate coded values.

x	$\times 10$	$-1,250 = x_c$	x_c^2
126.4	1,264	14	196
124.9	1,249	-1	1
121.3	1,213	-37	1,369
125.1	1,251	1	1
		$T_c = -23$	$\sum x_c^2 = \overline{1,567}$

$$\frac{T_c^2}{N} = \frac{529}{4} = 132.25 \longrightarrow 132.25$$

$$\text{SS}_c = 1,434.75$$

$$\bar{x}_c = \frac{T_c}{N} = -5.75$$

Then

$$\bar{x} = \frac{\bar{x}_c + 1,250}{10} = 124.42$$

$$\text{SS} = \frac{\text{SS}_c}{(10)^2} = 14.35$$

The reader may wish to compute without coding to confirm the result.

CONFIDENCE INTERVAL FOR μ FROM SAMPLE DATA

The meaning of a confidence interval was presented in Chap. 1. If we knew σ, we could calculate accurate confidence limits of μ, as follows. From p. 37,

$$x^* = \frac{(x - \mu)}{\sigma}$$

In a population of sample means, the individual measurements are $\bar{x}$ rather than x, but the mean is still μ. We may therefore write

$$x^* = \frac{(\bar{x} - \mu)}{\sigma_{\bar{x}}}$$

and rearranging,

$$\mu = \bar{x} \pm x^*(\sigma_{\bar{x}})$$

The confidence interval for μ then depends upon the value of $\pm x^*$ (Table 4) for a desired area of the normal curve. Thus, for 95% confidence limits $x^* = \pm 1.96$, for 99% confidence limits $x^* = \pm 2.58$.

In the experiment of Fig. 2-3, N is so large and the normal curve is fitted so well that we may accept 0.15 mg/ml as a fairly accurate estimate of σ. Then the mean of the entire sample has a standard error,

$$s_{\bar{x}} = \frac{0.15}{\sqrt{236}} = 0.0097$$

Then the 99% confidence interval for the true lethal blood alcohol concentration in rats is given by

$$\mu = 9.30 \pm 2.58(0.0097) = 9.27 \text{ to } 9.33 \text{ mg/ml}$$

There is a probability of only 1% that the true mean lies outside these limits.

Although the procedure described above is correct for large samples, it will not yield a wide enough confidence interval if a sample contains fewer than about 30 items. The reason is that a single small sample is unlikely to include any representatives of the few very large deviations which contribute significantly to the population variance. Thus in most small samples, s^2 will underestimate σ^2, although in a few samples it will greatly overestimate σ^2.

We have seen that the standardized variable $x^* = \dfrac{(\bar{x} - \mu)}{\sigma_{\bar{x}}}$ is normally distributed. An analogous variable $t = \dfrac{(\bar{x} - \mu)}{s_{\bar{x}}}$, in which a sample estimate is substituted for σ, is not normally distributed. Its sampling distribution is broader for very small samples but approaches the normal distribution as N becomes greater than about 30. A tabulation of the critical areas of this distribution is shown in Table 5. *Degrees of Freedom* (DF) are given rather than sample size. This refers to the number of items of data that are free to vary independently. In a set of quantitative data, for a specified value of the mean, only $(N - 1)$ items are free to vary; the value of the Nth item is then absolutely determined by the values assumed by the others and by the mean. Thus, for single-parameter quantitative data DF is always one less than the sample size.

Table 5 shows that for large enough samples (DF > 30), 5% of all t values (just as 5% of all x^*) lie outside the interval ± 1.96. For smaller samples however, the range required to include 95% of all *t*-values becomes larger; with samples of 4 (3 DF), for example, the range is ± 3.18.

The *t*-distribution may also be rewritten to denote a confidence interval,

$$\mu = \bar{x} \pm t(s_{\bar{x}})$$

and since *t* for large samples is equivalent to *x**, this expression is applicable to any sample size.

As shown above, the critical values of *t* become larger as sample sizes become smaller. If we compute a confidence interval for μ from a small and a large sample belonging to the same population, we will see two effects. First, the small sample will yield a higher value of $s_{\bar{x}}$ (because of the smaller *N* in $s_{\bar{x}} = s/\sqrt{N}$), reflecting the greater scatter of small-sample means about μ. Second, $s_{\bar{x}}$ from the small sample will tend to underestimate $\sigma_{\bar{x}}$, and this will be compensated by a larger tabulated value of *t*. Both effects result in a wider confidence range based on a small sample than on a larger one. The wider range is less useful, because it locates μ less exactly, but it is just as valid as a narrow range based on a larger sample. In giving a 95% confidence interval we are asserting that μ lies between certain values. There is probability $\alpha = 0.05$ that the statement is wrong, i.e., that μ lies outside the upper or lower limit, and this chance of being wrong is the same, regardless of the sample size on which the confidence interval is computed.

Example 2-4. Confidence interval for the true mean.

Compute the 95% and 99% confidence intervals of μ from the sample data of Example 2-1, where $\bar{x} = 38.3$ and $s_{\bar{x}} = 2.9$.

Here $\mu = 38.3 \pm t(2.9)$. Entering Table 5 at 9 DF, we find $t = 2.26$ at $P = 0.05$ and $t = 3.25$ at $P = 0.01$. Then $\mu = 38.3 \pm (2.26)(2.9)$, so 31.7 to 44.9 is the correct 95% confidence interval of μ, and 28.9 to 47.7 is found to be the 99% confidence interval.

A 95% confidence interval was computed, as in Example 2-4, from the data of each of the 37 disk samples whose means were shown in Fig. 2-4. The true value of μ, of which all 37 $\bar{x}$-values were estimates, was known to be 40. The lowest limit of the 37 confidence ranges was 24, the highest was 53. The narrowest range was ± 5, the widest was ± 11. Only one out of the 37 confidence intervals failed to include μ; in the long run, of course, this figure would be 5 out of 100.

COMPUTATION BY CLASS INTERVALS.   If the number of measurements in a sample is fairly large it is inconvenient to deal with each value individually. Instead, we group data into convenient equal intervals and assign the midpoint of each interval to all the data grouped there. If the intervals are kept reasonably small, this simplification alters the result very little.

Example 2-5. Computation by class intervals.

Measurements of heart rate were made on 113 students and the data were grouped into intervals of 5 beats per minute. Calculate the 99% confidence interval for the mean heart rate of students represented by the random sample of 113 presented below. Also find the coefficient of variation for the heart rates and compare with that for lethal alcohol concentrations in rats (p. 38).

Class Interval	Frequency f	x_c	fx_c	x_c^2	fx_c^2
55–59	2	−4	− 8	16	32
60–64	4	−3	−12	9	36
65–69	11	−2	−22	4	44
70–74	23	−1	−23	1	23
75–79	20	0	0	0	0
80–84	21	1	+21	1	21
85–89	13	2	+26	4	52
90–94	7	3	+21	9	63
95–99	5	4	+20	16	80
100–104	1	5	+ 5	25	25
105–109	1	6	+ 6	36	36
110–114	1	7	+ 7	49	49
115–119	4	8	+32	64	256
	113		−65		$\sum x_c^2 = 717$
			+138		
			$T_c = 73$		

$$\frac{T_c}{N} = \frac{73}{113} = 0.646 \qquad\qquad T_c^2 = 5,329$$

$$\bar{x} = 5(0.646) + 77 = 80.23 \qquad \frac{T_c^2}{N} = \frac{5,329}{113} = 47.16 \longrightarrow 47.16$$

$$SS_c = 669.84$$
$$\times 25$$
$$SS = 16,746$$

$$s^2 = \frac{16{,}746}{112} = 149.5$$

$$s_{\bar{x}}^2 = \frac{149.5}{113} = 1.323$$

$$s_{\bar{x}} = \sqrt{1.323} = 1.15$$

Here we list the number of measurements in each class interval under the column headed f. We set the midpoint of the interval 75–79 equal to zero, i.e., we code by subtracting 77 from all the data. We further assign each equal interval a unit value, i.e., we code by dividing by 5. At the end we multiply $\bar{x}_c$ by 5 and then add 77 to obtain $\bar{x}$; and we multiply SS_c by $(5)^2$ to obtain SS. The remaining steps follow routinely.

Consulting Table 5 for DF $= \infty$ at $P = 0.01$, we find $t = 2.58$. Then, $\mu = 80.2 \pm (2.58)(1.15) = 80.2 \pm 3.0$ and the desired 99% confidence interval is 77.2 to 83.2 beats per minute.

For the coefficient of variation,

$$s^2 = 149.5$$

$$s = 12.2$$

$$\text{C.V.} = \frac{100s}{\bar{x}} = 1{,}220/80.2 = 15.2\%$$

Thus, the heterogeneity of data here is much greater than in the rats, where we found C.V. $= 1.6\%$.

TOLERANCE LIMITS FOR INDIVIDUAL OBSERVATIONS

Occasionally one is not interested in knowing the true value of a population mean, but rather in estimating the lowest or highest likely value of a future observation from a population. Of course, if μ and σ were known, the areas of the normal curve would provide the required estimates. However, when only $\bar{x}$ and s are available, in a sample of N observations, there are two kinds of uncertainty: the exact value of μ is unknown, and σ may actually be greater or smaller than s. Fortunately, these combined uncertainties have been taken into account in extensive tabulations[5] of a factor that can be used to compute limits within which a given percent of the population distribution from which the sample was drawn may be asserted to lie. Unlike a confidence interval, which predicts

[5] For example, Tables 8.2 and 8.3, pp. 224ff. in A. H. Bowker and G. J. Lieberman, *Engineering Statistics*, (Englewood Cliffs, N.J.: Prentice-Hall Inc., 1959).

a minimum and maximum value of a parameter, these limits have to do with the values of individual observations. They are called "tolerance limits" because of their use in industry, where a manufacturer wishes, on the basis of a sample of measurements, to predict a tolerance which will not be exceeded by more than a certain small percent of his future production.

Table 6 gives factors for *one-sided tolerance limits*, which are more generally useful than an interval with an upper and a lower bound. Here the assertion to be made is of the form, "At least 95% (99%) of observations from this population will be smaller than ——(greater than ——)." Such an assertion may be made at any chosen level of confidence; Table 6 permits a choice of $P = 0.05$ or $P = 0.01$. Thus, if the assertion, "At least 99% of observations will be smaller than ——" is made at $P = 0.05$, this means that once in 20 trials in the long run the assertion will be wrong, and fewer than 99% of observations will be smaller than ——.

Example 2-6.   One-sided tolerance limits.

Find the lower tolerance limit for 99% of the population represented by the sample in Example 2-3, with 0.95 probability of being correct.

Here the sample observations were 126.4, 124.9, 121.3, 125.1

$$\bar{x} = 124.4$$

$$SS = 14.35$$

$$s^2 = 14.35/3 = 4.78$$

$$s = 2.19$$

From Table 6, at $N = 4$, $P = 0.05$, 99% column, $K = 7.04$. Then, the lower limit is $\bar{x} - K(s) = 124.4 - 7.04(2.19) = 109.0$. It can be asserted that at least 99% of future observations will exceed 109.0, and the statement will be correct 95 times out of 100 in the long run.

METHODS OF REPORTING QUANTITATIVE DATA

An important rule in presenting statistical data is to give the reader all the information he needs to reconstruct the essentials of the measurements

and to perform all tests of hypotheses for himself. There are three acceptable ways of meeting this requirement.

(1) Present all the raw data, if there are few enough to make this
practical.

(2) If the main interest of the data lies in the variability of individual
measurements, report the sample mean and the estimate of standard
deviation (or coefficient of variation), and also give the sample size. For
example, the performance of a class on an examination might be reported
as $\bar{x} = 70.2$ ($s = 3.4$, $N = 125$), whence it would be apparent that the
examination spread the class very poorly indeed. The student heart rates
of Example 2-5 might be reported as $\bar{x} = 80.2$ ($s = 12.2$, $N = 113$) or
$\bar{x} = 80.2$ (C.V. $= 15.2\%$, $N = 113$), provided the main interest was in the
homogeneity or heterogeneity of the data.

(3) Usually, however, a sample statistic will be used to draw inferences
about a corresponding parameter. In that case an appropriate estimate of
variability is the standard error of the mean, for it indicates how other
samples from the same population would differ from the one under consideration. Thus, if the point of the observations on heart rates was to gain
an idea of the true mean heart rate of students under specified conditions,
the result should be reported as follows: $\bar{x} = 80.2 \pm 1.2$ ($N = 113$). The
number which follows the $\pm$ sign is understood to be $s_{\bar{x}}$ unless otherwise
stated, but some investigators avoid all possibility of misunderstanding by
specifying (S.E.) after the datum, to indicate "standard error."

An even better approach is to give the mean and its confidence limits at a
stated level of significance, and also the sample size. Such a statement
conveys the maximum information about the true value of the mean. In the
experiment of Fig. 2-3, for example (p. 38), the mean lethal blood
alcohol concentration could be stated as $9.27 < \mu < 9.33$ mg/ml ($P = 0.05$),
or $\mu = 9.30$ mg/ml (95 % confidence interval $= 9.27$ to 9.33).

COMPARISON OF SAMPLE MEANS BY THE t-TEST

Consider two sample means, $\bar{x}$ and $\bar{x}'$, drawn from a population of
sample means such as that depicted in Fig. 2-4. They will probably differ
by some amount $(\bar{x} - \bar{x}')$. As pointed out in Chap. 1 for pairs of measurements drawn repeatedly from a population, so also here the sampling
distribution of $(\bar{x} - \bar{x}')$ will be normal, with $\mu = 0$;[6] its variance will be

---

[6]When $\bar{x} < \bar{x}'$, the difference between the sample means has a negative sign.

equal to the sum of the individual variances,

$$\sigma_{(\bar{x} - \bar{x}')}{}^2 = \sigma_{\bar{x}}{}^2 + \sigma_{\bar{x}'}{}^2$$

Since the two samples are drawn from the same population of measurements with variance σ^2, it follows that if the sample sizes are equal, then

$$\sigma_{\bar{x}}{}^2 = \sigma_{\bar{x}'}{}^2 = \frac{\sigma^2}{N}$$

and

$$\sigma^2{}_{(\bar{x} - \bar{x}')} = \frac{2\sigma^2}{N}$$

If the sample sizes are unequal, then

$$\sigma^2{}_{(\bar{x} - \bar{x}')} = \frac{\sigma^2}{N} + \frac{\sigma^2}{N'} = \sigma^2 \left(\frac{1}{N} + \frac{1}{N'} \right)$$

Now we do not actually know whether or not the two sample means come from the same population. That is just what we wish to find out. We begin with the *null hypothesis*, that both samples were indeed drawn from a single population. The hypothesis will be rejected if the sample variance estimates or the sample means differ from each other more than is reasonable to expect from random sampling variations. The variance estimates are compared by means of the variance ratio, or F-test.[7] F is defined as the ratio of two variances. Obviously, if both are drawn from the same population their expected ratio is unity. Sample variance ratios much greater or smaller than unity may indicate a real difference in the two corresponding parameters. Table 7 presents the critical values that are exceeded by chance with $P = 0.05$ and $P = 0.01$ when both variances are drawn from the same population. The ratio to be tested is constructed by placing the greater variance estimate in the numerator.

Assuming we find no reason to reject the idea of equal variances,[8] we then proceed to the main comparison of the sample means. Do the samples probably come from a single population in which the true difference between means is zero, or from two populations with the same variance but different means? We shall answer the question by comparing

[7]Named in honor of R. A. Fisher, who introduced the method.

[8]In the case of heterogeneous variances special methods are required. See, for example, Anderson and Bancroft, *Statistical Theory in Research* (New York: McGraw-Hill Book Company, Inc., 1952), pp. 80–83.

the magnitude of the observed difference $(\bar{x} - \bar{x}')$ with an estimate of its standard error[9] $s_{(\bar{x}-\bar{x}')}$ and referring to the t-distribution,

$$t = \frac{(\bar{x} - \bar{x}')}{s_{(\bar{x}-\bar{x}')}}$$

We enter Table 5 with the degrees of freedom contributed by both samples $(N - 1 + N' - 1)$ to see if the observed value might reasonably have occurred by chance. If the observed t exceeds the tabulated critical value at $P = 0.05$ we reject the null hypothesis and conclude that the samples were not drawn from the same population, i.e., that they differ from each other significantly.

Example 2-7.   Comparison of two sample means by t-test.

A drug was given to 30 subjects one-half hour before bedtime, while 33 other subjects received a placebo. The next morning subjects estimated (to the nearest 5 min) how long it had taken them to fall asleep. Ascertain, for the data given below, whether the drug caused a quicker onset of sleep than did the placebo.

x (minutes)	x_c	x_c^2	f	fx_c	fx_c^2	f'	$f'x_c$	$f'x_c^2$
15	−5	25	2	−10	50	0	0	0
25	−3	9	3	−9	27	4	−12	36
30	−2	4	3	−6	12	3	−6	12
35	−1	1	5	−5	5	6	−6	6
40	0	0	6	0	0	7	0	0
45	1	1	4	4	4	6	6	6
50	2	4	3	6	12	1	2	4
55	3	9	0	0	0	1	3	9
60	4	16	4	16	64	1	4	16
65	5	25	1	5	25	0	0	0
75	7	49	1	7	49	0	0	0
100	12	144	1	12	144	1	12	144

Coding: $x_c = \dfrac{x - 40}{5}$

[9]The method of obtaining this, through the use of a pooled variance estimate, is shown in Example 2-7.

$$N = 33 \qquad T_c = 20 \quad \sum x_c^2 = 392 \quad \big| \quad N' = 30 \quad T'_c = 3 \quad \sum x'^2_c = 233$$

$$T_c^2 = 400 \qquad\qquad\qquad T'^2_c = 9$$

$$\frac{T_c^2}{N} = \frac{400}{33} = 12.12 \longrightarrow 12.12 \qquad \frac{T'^2_c}{N'} = \frac{9}{30} = 0.3 \longrightarrow 0.3$$

$$\begin{array}{r} 379.88 \\ \times 25 \\ \hline \text{SS} = 9{,}497 \end{array} \qquad\qquad \begin{array}{r} 232.7 \\ \times 25 \\ \hline \text{SS}' = 5{,}817 \end{array}$$

$$\frac{T_c}{N} = \frac{20}{33} = 0.606 \qquad\qquad \frac{T'_c}{N'} = \frac{3}{30} = 0.10$$

$$\begin{array}{r} \times 5 \\ \hline 3.03 \\ +40 \\ \hline \bar{x} = 43.03 \end{array} \qquad\qquad \begin{array}{r} \times 5 \\ \hline 0.5 \\ +40 \\ \hline \bar{x}' = 40.5 \end{array}$$

$$\bar{x} - \bar{x}' = 2.5$$

The drug group did fall asleep 2.5 min sooner, on the average, than the placebo group. But is this difference greater than could be attributed to chance?

Testing the two variance estimates, we have $9{,}497/32 = 297$ and $5{,}818/29 = 201$ so $F = 297/201 = 1.5$ with $\mathrm{DF} = 32$ and $\mathrm{DF}' = 29$. Table 7 indicates that at $P = 0.05$ and these DF, DF' any ratio smaller than about 1.8 is compatible with the null hypothesis of equal variances.

Since we have now accepted that both sample variances are estimators of the same σ^2, the best estimate of that σ^2 will be based on all the available information, namely, the pooled SS of both samples.

$$\begin{aligned}
\text{Pooled } s^2 &= \frac{\text{SS} + \text{SS}'}{(N-1) + (N'-1)} \\[2mm]
&= \frac{9{,}497 + 5{,}818}{32 + 29} \\[2mm]
&= 251.07
\end{aligned}$$

Then, since each sample is a different size, we compute an estimate of the variance of the difference between means by

$$s^2_{(\bar{x} - \bar{x}')} = s^2 \left(\frac{1}{N} + \frac{1}{N'} \right)$$

$$= 251.07 \left(\frac{1}{33} + \frac{1}{30} \right)$$

$$= 15.98$$

$$s_{(\bar{x} - \bar{x}')} = \sqrt{15.98} = 4.0$$

$$t = \frac{(\bar{x} - \bar{x}')}{s_{(\bar{x} - \bar{x}')}} = \frac{2.5}{4.0} = 0.6$$

For 61 DF we enter Table 5 at ∞ and find that for a significant difference at $P = 0.05$, t must exceed 1.96. Since our calculated t is smaller than this, we can not conclude that the time to fall asleep was really different in the two groups, and therefore we can not assert that the drug differed from placebo.

In the above example we asked whether a given difference between two sample means was too great to be attributed to chance, but we considered only the absolute magnitude of the difference without regard to sign. This would have been reasonable enough if we had no idea in what direction a drug might act. However, the actual question here was whether the drug *reduced* the time required to fall asleep, or whether the observed *reduction* was due to chance. In this circumstance the proper criterion against which to measure the apparent drug effect is the probability that *decreases* as great or greater than observed would occur by chance. The table of the t-distribution gives probabilities for extreme values in both tails. If we wish to consider only values of t falling in the 5% area at one extreme of the curve (i.e., only positive or only negative t values) we must find the critical value for both tails at $P = 0.10$ rather than $P = 0.05$. Likewise, if $P = 0.01$ is desired we should enter a table of t at $P = 0.02$. This procedure is known as a *one-tail* t-test. Table 5 gives one-tail critical values directly. Since the hypothesis about a treatment effect usually specifies its direction (i.e., increase or decrease of μ), the one-tail test is more often appropriate than the two-tail test. To avoid ambiguity one should always state whether a null hypothesis is accepted or rejected on the basis of a one-tail or a two-tail test. Obviously, if an outcome is significant by the ordinary two-tail test, it will also be significant (at an even lower P value) by the one-tail test. But t values of marginal significance in the two-tail test may prove significant when judged by the one-tail criterion. In Example 2-7, however, even by the one-tail test no drug effect is demonstrable since the critical value of t which must be exceeded is 1.64.

THE TWO-SAMPLE RANK TEST:
A SIMPLE ALTERNATIVE TO THE *t*-TEST

The two-sample rank test, originated by Wilcoxon, and developed by Mann and Whitney,[10] is one of several nonparametric procedures developed in recent years which have become increasingly popular in the

[10]This test is sometimes called the Mann-Whitney U-test.

analysis of biological data. Nonparametric methods make no assumptions about the normality of a population distribution, and do not require that the measurements be very precise, provided only that they may be arranged meaningfully in a rank order.

Consider two samples of measurements, $x_1, x_2, \ldots, x_N$ and $x'_1, x'_2, \ldots, x'_{N'}$. Arrange all data from both samples in order of increasing magnitude, beginning with the largest negative value (if there is one) and ending with the largest positive one. For each x, count the number of x' which precede it in the rank order, and add all the resulting numbers together. This sum is called U. Now if the two samples of data had been drawn from the same population, we should expect a random mixing of x and x' in the rank order, and the value of U computed from x' preceding x should be about equal to that computed from x preceding x'. If the two samples of data had been drawn from different populations, widely separated, we might obtain a rank order in which all x' preceded every x and no x preceded any x'. In this case, depending upon which set of data were designated x and which x', U would be equal to NN' or to zero. If we designate the two values of U that may be computed in any case as U and U', then the relationship between them is necessarily

$$U' = NN' - U$$

The test is concerned with the *smaller* of these two possible values, U or U'. The random sampling distribution of the smaller U has been worked out, for various sample sizes. Table 15 presents critical values for a one-tail test at the 5% and 1% levels of significance. Here (in contrast to the t-distribution) a computed U must be *smaller* than the critical value, in order to be significant, since it is small values of U that occur only rarely by chance.

Example 2-8. Comparison of two sample means by the two-sample rank test.

Determine by means of the two-sample rank test whether or not a drug has lowered the blood glucose of diabetic rats. The blood glucose levels were (in mg/ml), in controls 2.15, 1.92, 1.78, 2.04, 2.22, and in drug-treated rats 2.02, 1.71, 2.04, 1.50, 1.83, 1.69.

Arranging in rank order, and retaining underscoring to distinguish the drug-treated data, we have

1.50, 1.69, 1.71, 1.78, 1.83, 1.92, 2.02, 2.04–2.04, 2.15, 2.22

The first three values in the drug-treated group contribute nothing to U because they are not preceded by any control data. The value 1.83 is preceded by 1 control observation. The value 2.02 is preceded by 2 control observations. The value 2.04 is preceded by 2.5 control observations, the tie being treated as though each value half-preceded and half-followed the other. U is then $1 + 2 + 2.5 = 5.5$. If the same calculations are made with respect to the control group, we find $U' = 3 + 4 + 5.5 + 6 + 6 = 24.5$ and the correctness of the relationship $U = NN' - U'$ can be confirmed. The smaller value, 5.5, is compared with the critical values in Table 15. There, for $N = 5$, $N' = 6$ we find that U must be smaller than 5 for significance at the 5% level, so we cannot quite assert that the drug was effective.

The reader may find it an interesting exercise to analyze the data of Eample 2-8 by the much more laborious t-test. He will find that $t = 1.90$ which at 9 DF in the one-tail test just barely exceeds the critical value 1.83 for $P = 0.05$. Whereas in this particular case the two-sample rank test just missed detecting a significant drug effect, the t-test just barely detected it. In general, the efficiencies of the two tests are very nearly the same, and the two-sample rank test is a great deal simpler to use. For this reason it is being adopted ever more widely as an alternative to the t-test.

An easier way to carry out the two-sample rank test, expecially for larger samples, which nevertheless yields exactly the same value for U, is the following. After arranging the rank order, assign numbers sequentially to the rank positions, starting with the lowest rank. In case of ties, assign the average rank position to all the tied values and then give the next value the same rank number it would have if there were no ties. Choose either sample and add up all its rank numbers. Compute U from the formula

$$U = NN' + \frac{N(N + 1)}{2} - R$$

where R is the sum of rank numbers for the sample of size N. Then compute $U' = NN' - U$ and enter Table 15 with U or U', whichever is smaller.

Example 2-9. Shortcut formula in the two-sample rank test.

Compute U by the shortcut formula for the data of Example 2-8.

The rank order is

d,	d,	d,	c,	d,	c,	d,	dc,	c,	c,
1	2	3	4	5	6	7	8.5	10	11

Choosing the d group,

$$R = 1 + 2 + 3 + 5 + 7 + 8.5 = 26.5$$

$$U = (6)(5) + \frac{6(6+1)}{2} - 26.5 = 24.5$$

$$U' = (6)(5) - 24.5 = 5.5, \text{ as obtained before}$$

When the larger of the two samples exceeds 20, Table 15 cannot be used. However, an approximation to the normal distribution can then be applied. One can compute x^* by the equation given below, and consult Table 4 to establish the significance level. The absolute value of x^* will be the same, regardless of whether U or U' is used:

$$x^* = \frac{\left| U - \dfrac{NN'}{2} \right|}{\sqrt{\dfrac{NN'(N + N' + 1)}{12}}}$$

Example 2-10. **Further application of the two-sample rank test.**

Analyze the data of Example 2-7 by the two-sample rank test.

Since x-values are already ranked, we have only to assign the appropriate rank numbers to the placebo and drug frequencies, taking account of the numerous ties. The array becomes

2p,	3p4d	3p3d,	5p6d,	6p7d,	4p6d,
1.5,	6,	12.5,	21,	33,	44.5,

3p1d,	1d,	4p1d,	1p,	1p,	1p1d
51.5,	54,	57,	60,	61,	62.5

The sum of p ranks is then

$$2(1.5) + 3(6) + 3(12.5) + \cdots + 1(62.5) = 1,105.5$$

$$U = (33)(30) + \frac{33(34)}{2} - 1,105.5 = 445.5$$

$$x^* = \frac{\left| 445.5 - \frac{(33)(30)}{2} \right|}{\sqrt{\frac{(33)(30)(33 + 30 + 1)}{12}}}$$

$$= \frac{49.5}{72.7}$$

$$= 0.7$$

and the drug cannot be said to differ from the placebo, in agreement with the result of the t-test on the same data.[11]

PAIRED OBSERVATIONS. ANALYSIS BY t-TEST

Often two samples of data are obtained on the same subjects, as in crossover experiments where each subject serves as his own control. For example, two drugs might be administered on different occasions to a number of cats. Each cat will then provide a measurement of response to drug A and to drug B. The variability due to differences between cats is thereby eliminated, and one considers only the *difference* in response to the two drugs on the part of each cat. If the drugs had identical effects, the

[11]Strictly speaking, the presence of ties necessitates a correction to the denominator of the x^*-statistic. In practice, however, ties have only a slight effect, even when (as in Example 2-10) most of the observations are involved in ties. Moreover, if no correction is made for ties, the outcome is more conservative, in the sense that the value of x^* will be slightly too small. In the event an outcome were on the margin of significance and one wished to find the exact value of x^*, the correction could be applied. If T is the number of items in a tied group, then $(T^3 - T)$ is found for each such group and $\Sigma (T^3 - T)$ is the correction term. The equation for x^* is then

$$x^* = \frac{\left| U - \frac{NN'}{2} \right|}{\sqrt{\left(\frac{NN'}{(N + N')(N + N' - 1)} \right) \left(\frac{(N + N')^3 - (N + N') - \Sigma (T^3 - T)}{12} \right)}}$$

For Example 2-10, the correction term $\Sigma (T^3 - T)$ will be composed of $(2^3 - 2) + (7^3 - 7) + (6^3 - 6) + (11^3 - 11) + \cdots$. It will be observed that when there are no ties, the correction term is zero, and the equation above reduces to that already given.

sample of differences would represent a population of differences with $\mu = 0$. The question, then, is whether or not the observed sample of differences might reasonably have been drawn from such a population (null hypothesis). If each response difference is designated d, we have a number of d values equal to the number of cats (N), and $(N-1)$ degrees of freedom. A mean difference, $\bar{d}$, is calculated, and its standard error, $s_{\bar{d}}$, from which $t = \bar{d}/s_{\bar{d}}$. Table 5 then tells us whether $\bar{d}$ differs significantly from zero, i.e., whether the drugs differ from each other.

Example 2-11. Comparison of paired observations by t-test.

Two drugs were tested in 8 cats for their ability to slow the heart, with the results shown below. Ascertain, by means of the t-test, whether or not drug A is more effective than drug B.

	Heart Rate Change		d	d^2
Cat	Drug A	Drug B	$(A - B)$	
1	-22	-14	-8	64
2	-14	-12	-2	4
3	-36	-22	-14	196
4	-28	-30	$+2$	4
5	-8	$+10$	-18	324
6	-22	0	-22	484
7	-8	-8	0	0
8	$+2$	$+24$	-22	484
			$T = -84$	$\sum d^2 = 1{,}560$

$$T^2 = 7{,}056$$

$$\frac{T^2}{N} = 882.0 \longrightarrow 882.0$$

$$\text{SS} = 678.0$$

$$\bar{d} = \frac{T}{N} = -10.5$$

$$s^2 = \frac{678.0}{7} = 96.9$$

$$s_{\bar{d}}^2 = \frac{96.9}{8} = 12.1$$

$$t = \frac{\bar{d}}{s_{\bar{d}}} = \frac{-10.5}{3.48} = -3.02 \qquad s_{\bar{d}} = \sqrt{12.1} = 3.48$$

Since the question was whether drug A is more effective than drug B, the one-tail test is appropriate and we find in Table 5 that 3.00 is the critical value for $P = 0.01$ with 7 DF. We may therefore assert at the 1 % level of significance that drug A is more effective than drug B.

The greater efficiency usually achieved by pairing data may be illustrated by working Example 2-11 as though the data were not paired. There will then be 16 measurements, and 14 degrees of freedom instead of 7, so that the critical value of t which has to be exceeded for $P = 0.01$ will be somewhat smaller (2.62 instead of 3.00). Offsetting this advantage, however, is the greater variability, which leads to a much higher $s_{(\bar{x}-\bar{x}')}$ and thus to a lower computed value of t. It will be found that $t = 1.39$, which is not even significant at the 5 % level.

PAIRED OBSERVATIONS.
ANALYSIS BY THE SIGN TEST

A very simple nonparametric alternative to the t-test for paired observations is the sign test. A sample of differences between paired measurements should contain approximately the same number of positive and negative values if it was drawn from a population of differences with $\mu = 0$. By simply counting the number of positive and negative signs and referring to Table 10 one can discover at once whether or not the null hypothesis may be rejected. In this procedure pairs with zero difference are excluded and the sample size is reduced accordingly. Table 10 is based on the *binomial distribution*, which will be considered in Chap. 3.

Example 2-12. Sign test for paired data.

Analyze the data of Example 2-11 by the sign test.

We count in the column of differences 6 negative signs and 1 positive. Cat 7 is excluded. Table 10 shows that for $N = 7$, in the one-tail test, the null hypothesis may be rejected only if there are no signs of one kind (in this case, only if all 7 signs are negative). Therefore, the sign test does not permit us to assert that drug A is more effective than drug B.

Obviously, the sign test is less efficient than the *t*-test, or the two-sample rank test, for it makes use of very little of the available information about the measurements. It is especially useful when no assumptions can be made about the form of the underlying distribution, and it is really a test about medians and not means. If the sign test is applied and it fails to reveal a significant difference between the two samples of paired data, it is appropriate to proceed with a more efficient test, although it will have to be recognized that the sequential application of two different tests may somewhat increase the significance level.[12] If, on the other hand, the sign test permits rejection of the null hypothesis at the desired level of significance, there is ordinarily no need to go further.[13]

PAIRED OBSERVATIONS.
ANALYSIS BY THE SIGNED-RANKS TEST

This nonparametric procedure, introduced by Wilcoxon, is an improvement over the simple sign test in that it makes use of the relative magnitudes of the observed differences. All the differences are ranked in order of absolute magnitude without respect to sign, and a rank number is assigned to each, from 1 to N in order of increasing magnitude. Zero differences are dropped from the analysis as in the sign test. If more than one difference has the same value, an average rank number is assigned, as in the two-sample rank test. The original + and − signs are retained in the rank order. Now if the differences were drawn from a population with $\mu = 0$, we should expect the sums of the positive and negative ranks to be about the same, since large negative and positive differences as well as small ones would occur with about equal frequency. The sums of positive and negative ranks are computed separately and the *smaller sum* (designated T) is compared with critical values in Table 16. If T is smaller than the critical value, the null hypothesis may be rejected.

[12]If, for example, each test by itself would falsely reject a null hypothesis 5 times in 100, then the procedure recommended here might yield a Type I error slightly larger than this.

[13]Applicable here is the aphorism known as "The Principle of the Blunt Ax," for which we are indebted to Prof. L. E. Moses: "If the ax chopped down the tree, it was sharp enough."

For $N > 25$, the following equation may be used to compute x^*, which may then be compared with its critical values in Table 4:

$$x^* = \frac{T - \dfrac{N(N + 1)}{4}}{\sqrt{\dfrac{N(N + 1)(2N + 1)}{24}}}$$

Example 2-13. **Signed-ranks test for paired observations.**

Analyze the data of Example 2-11 by the signed-ranks test.

Arrange the differences in rank order, excluding cat 7. Assign rank numbers, giving tied observations the average of their rank positions.

-2	$2,$	$-8,$	$-14,$	$-18,$	-22	-22
1.5		3	4	5	6.5	

$$\sum + \text{ranks} = 1.5 = T$$

$$\sum - \text{ranks} = 26.5$$

Table 16 shows that 1.5 is smaller than the critical value 3.7 at $P = 0.05$ in the one-tail test, so we may conclude at the 5% level of significance (but not at the 1% level) that drug A was more effective than drug B.

ANALYSIS OF VARIANCE

We have thus far discussed only the common methods whereby two sample means can be compared. Often, however, we wish to compare more than two sample means, or to study a number of pertinent variables in the same experiment. The method of treating such data is known as *analysis of variance*. It is based upon the principle already introduced (p. 41) that if various samples of the same or different sizes are drawn from a single population, and a variance estimate computed from each, all these will be estimates of the same variance, σ^2. The sampling distribution of the variance ratio (F) is given in Table 7 as critical values for various sizes (actually, DF) of the two samples on which it is based. If F exceeds the critical value at a desired level of significance, we may reject the null hypothesis of equal variances and conclude that the samples were drawn from different populations.[14]

Consider first the elementary case of a comparison of two sample means. There is a general mean ($\bar{\bar{x}}$) of the observations in both samples. If the samples belonged to the same population and there was no variability whatsoever, every single observation in both samples would have the value $\bar{\bar{x}}$, so the variance would be zero. If the two samples differed and there was no variability in the measurements, then every observation in the first sample would have the value $\bar{x}$ and every observation in the second sample would have the value $\bar{x}'$. In that case there would be a variance about $\bar{\bar{x}}$, due to the several x and x' values, but no variance of the observations in each sample about their own sample mean. In real cases, where there is also random variability of the observations, there will be two variance components, that due to deviation of sample means from $\bar{\bar{x}}$, and that due to deviations of observations from their sample means. The deviation of any single measurement from $\bar{\bar{x}}$ may be regarded as the sum of two deviations, that of the sample mean from $\bar{\bar{x}}$, and that of the observation itself from its sample mean.

The total variance in any system may be partitioned in the same way. To obtain the variance arising *within samples* (error) we compute SS for the measurements in each sample about the sample mean, add these SS together, and divide by the total DF within samples (which is the sum of DF in each sample individually). For the variance arising *between samples* what we do, in effect, is to replace each measurement by its sample mean, thus eliminating the variation within samples. We then compute SS for all these equalized measurements from the overall mean, and divide by the DF between samples (i.e., one less than the number of samples). We may then construct an F-ratio from these two variance estimates and discover from Table 6 if the between-samples variance estimate is so much greater than the within-samples estimate, that the two could not reasonably be estimates of the same σ^2.

Example 2-14. Analysis of variance: One-way classification, two-sample comparison.

Male and female rats were given the same dose of a hypnotic drug. The number of minutes that each rat slept is recorded below. Ascertain, by analysis of variance, whether or not females slept longer than males. Note that since coding by addition or subtraction does not affect variances, it is not necessary

[14]Naturally, the null hypothesis is also rejected for F values that are too much smaller than unity. Table 7 will suffice for the usual case where the greater variance estimate is in the numerator.

to decode in an analysis of variance. Here we shall code by subtracting 20 from each observation.

Males		Females	
x	x_c	x'	x'_c
13	-7	20	0
16	-4	17	-3
19	-1	22	2
14	-6	24	4
16	-4	19	-1
	$T = -22$		$T' = 2$

$$\bar{x} = \frac{-22}{5} = -4.4 \qquad\qquad \bar{x}' = \frac{2}{5} = 0.4$$

$$T = -22 + 2 = -20$$

$$\bar{\bar{x}} = \frac{-20}{10} = -2$$

Deviations of observations from the general mean (total SS):

Males			Females		
x_c	$x_c - \bar{\bar{x}}$	$(x_c - \bar{\bar{x}})^2$	x'_c	$x'_c - \bar{\bar{x}}$	$(x'_c - \bar{\bar{x}}')^2$
-7	-5	25	0	$+2$	4
-4	-2	4	-3	-1	1
-1	$+1$	1	2	$+4$	16
-6	-4	16	4	$+6$	36
-4	-2	4	-1	$+1$	1
	-12	50		$+12$	58

$\sum (x_c - \bar{\bar{x}}) = 0$ This is a check on the computation.
$\sum (x_c - \bar{\bar{x}})^2 = $ total SS $= 50 + 58 = 108$

Deviations of observations from their sample means (error SS):

Males, $\bar{x} = -4.4$			Females, $\bar{x}' = 0.4$		
x_c	$x_c - \bar{x}$	$(x_c - \bar{x})^2$	x'_c	$x'_c - \bar{x}'$	$(x'_c - \bar{x}')^2$
-7	-2.6	6.76	0	-0.4	0.16
-4	$+0.4$	0.16	-3	-3.4	11.56
-1	$+3.4$	11.56	2	$+1.6$	2.56
-6	-1.6	2.56	4	$+3.6$	12.96
-4	$+0.4$	0.16	-1	-1.4	1.96
	0	21.20		0	29.20

Within samples (error) SS $= 21.2 + 29.2 = 50.4$

Deviations of sample means from the general mean (between samples SS):

		$\bar{x} - \bar{\bar{x}}$	$(\bar{x} - \bar{\bar{x}})^2$	$N(\bar{x} - \bar{\bar{x}})^2$
Males	$-4.4 - (-2) =$	-2.4	5.76	28.8
Females	$0.4 - (-2) =$	$+2.4$	5.76	28.8
		0		57.6

The squared deviation of each sample mean from the general mean had to be multiplied by the number of observations in the sample, to make it comparable with the other SS computed above.

Between-sexes SS $= 57.6$

Degrees of freedom are computed as follows:

Between 2 sexes . . .	1 DF
(Within males	4 DF)
(Within females . . .	4 DF)
Within sexes . . .	8 DF
Total for 10 observations . .	9 DF

Next we summarize the analysis in a table:

ANALYSIS OF VARIANCE

Source	SS	DF	Variance estimate[15]
Between sexes	57.6	1	57.6
Within sexes (error)	50.4	8	6.3
Total	108.0	9	

Then $F = 57.6/6.3 = 9.1$ with 1, 8 DF. Table 7 shows that this value exceeds the critical ratio 5.32 at $P = 0.05$, so we conclude that the apparent difference between the sleeping times of males and females is real and that females sleep longer at the same dose of this drug.

The above example was worked in such a way as to display each step, but shortcuts give all the required quantities directly. What we really need are three items that can be represented algebraically thus:

$$\text{Total SS} \qquad \sum (x - \bar{\bar{x}})^2$$

$$\text{Between-samples SS} \quad \sum N_m(\bar{x}_m - \bar{\bar{x}})^2$$

$$\text{Within-samples SS} \quad \sum (x_m - \bar{x}_m)^2$$

[15]SS/DF, also called "mean square" and abbreviated MS. We shall use the terms interchangeably.

where $x = $ any item

$x_m = $ an item in a particular sample

$\bar{\bar{x}} = $ the overall mean

$\bar{x}_m = $ the mean of a particular sample

$N_m = $ the number of items in a particular sample

Thus $\sum (x - \bar{\bar{x}})^2$ means "square the difference between each item and the overall mean, and sum all these squares together."

$\sum N_m(\bar{x}_m - \bar{\bar{x}})^2$ means "deal with each sample separately; square the difference between the sample mean and the overall mean, and take this squared difference as many times as there are items in the sample; and do the same for each sample, and add all these together."

$\sum (x_m - \bar{x}_m)^2$ means "square the difference between each item and the mean of its own sample, and sum all these squares together."

In the developing the shortcut, we shall use the following additional symbols:

$T = \sum x$, the grand total

$T_m = \sum x_m$, the total for a particular sample

$N = $ total number of items

Then for the total SS:

$$\sum (x - \bar{\bar{x}})^2 = \sum x^2 - \frac{T^2}{N} \quad \text{as shown on p. 43.}$$

For the between-samples SS:

$$\sum N_m(\bar{x}_m - \bar{\bar{x}})^2 = \sum N_m \bar{x}_m{}^2 - 2 \sum N_m \bar{x}_m \bar{\bar{x}} + \sum N_m \bar{\bar{x}}^2$$

$$= \frac{\sum x_m{}^2}{N_m} - 2\bar{\bar{x}} \sum x_m + \bar{\bar{x}} \sum x_m$$

$$= \sum \frac{T_m{}^2}{N_m} - \bar{\bar{x}} \sum x$$

$$= \sum \frac{T_m{}^2}{N_m} - \frac{T^2}{N}$$

For the within-samples SS:

$$\sum (x_m - \bar{x}_m)^2 = \sum {x_m}^2 - 2 \sum x_m \bar{x}_m + \sum N_m {\bar{x}_m}^2$$
$$= \sum {x_m}^2 - 2 \sum x_m \bar{x}_m + \sum x_m \bar{x}_m$$
$$= \sum {x_m}^2 - \sum x_m \frac{x_m}{N_m}$$
$$= \sum {x_m}^2 - \sum \frac{{T_m}^2}{N_m}$$

In practice, the within-samples SS is usually not calculated, but taken as the difference between the total SS and the between-samples SS. Note how, algebraically, the components of variation add up to the total SS.

Between-samples

$$\sum \frac{{T_m}^2}{N_m} - \frac{T^2}{N}$$

Within-samples

$$\sum x^2 - \sum \frac{{T_m}^2}{N_m}$$

Total

$$\sum x^2 - \frac{T^2}{N}$$

It should be clear from the foregoing that the only terms required for an analysis of variance are

$$\sum x^2 \qquad \sum \frac{{T_m}^2}{N_m} \qquad \frac{T^2}{N}$$

Means do not have to be calculated; they are implicit in the procedures. In more complicated analyses, when samples are grouped according to more than a single criterion, one has to calculate a different between-samples SS for each grouping of samples, but otherwise the procedure is the same.

Example 2-14 may now be worked by the direct method. A convenient and systematic procedure is first to prepare a preliminary table of total squares.[16] Here we have,

---

[16]This is the step-by-step method suggested by J. C. R. Li. As one becomes more familiar with the calculations, some of the preliminary steps can be omitted.

Grand total $\quad T^2 = (-20)^2 = 400$

Samples $\quad \sum T_m{}^2 = (-22)^2 + (2)^2 = 488$

Observations
$$\sum x^2 = (-7)^2 + (-4)^2 + \cdots + (-1)^2 = 148$$

PRELIMINARY CALCULATIONS

Type of Total	Total of Squares	Number of Items Squared	Number of Observations per Squared Item	Total of Squares per Observation	
Grand	400	1	10	40.0	$\left(\dfrac{T^2}{N}\right)$
Samples	488	2	5	97.6	$\left(\sum \dfrac{T_m{}^2}{N_m}\right)$
Observations	148	10	1	148.0	$\left(\sum x^2\right)$

From the preliminary table, we then compose the SS, as explained:

ANALYSIS OF VARIANCE

Source	SS	DF	Variance Estimate
Sexes (samples)	$97.6 - 40.0 = 57.6$	1	57.6
Error	$148 \quad - 97.6 = 50.4$	8	6.3
Total	$148 \quad - 40.0 = 108.0$	9	$F = 9.14$

The F-test in a two-sample comparison is really identical to a t-test. Indeed, F with 1, $(N-1)$ DF is numerically identical to t^2 with $(N-1)$ DF. Thus, if Example 2-14 is worked as a t-test, one finds $t = 3.02$, which is the square root of 9.14. Of course, examples of this type can also be worked by the nonparametric two-sample rank test. The usefulness of the analysis of variance becomes evident in more complex experimental designs, as illustrated by the following examples.

Example 2-15.   Analysis of Variance: One-way classification, many-sample comparison.

The progress of wound-healing was compared when five different postoperative regimens were employed after abdominal surgery. The 30 patients in the study were randomly assigned. The numbers below are coded data on duration of the wound-healing period.

Postoperative Regimen

	A	B	C	D	E	
	3	4	2	6	8	
	5	7	3	3	2	
	5	6	4	5	4	
	2	6	3	5	5	
	4	9	3	2	6	
	5	7	5	4	6	$\sum x^2 = 739$
$T_m =$	24	39	20	25	31	$T = 139$
$(T_m)^2 =$	576	1,521	400	625	961	$T^2 = 19,321$

PRELIMINARY CALCULATIONS

Type of Total	Total of Squares	Number of Items Squared	Number of Observations per Squared Item	Total of Squares per Observation
Grand	19,321	1	30	644.0
Regimens	4,083	5	6	680.5
Observations	739	30	1	739

ANALYSIS OF VARIANCE

Source	SS	DF	Variance Estimate (Mean Square)
Regimens	$680.5 - 644 = 36.5$	4	9.13
Error	$739 - 680.5 = 58.5$	25	2.34
Total	$739 - 644 = 95$	29	

$F = 9.13/2.34 = 3.90$ (4, 25 DF) and this exceeds the critical value 2.76 for $P = 0.05$, so we conclude that the regimens do indeed differ. The analysis of variance itself, however, does not permit us to decide which pairs of regimens differ significantly from each other and which do not.

For making simultaneous comparisons between several different means, as we wished to do in Example 2-15, the *studentized range test* is used.[17] Consulting Table 8, for the number of samples being compared and the within-samples degrees of freedom (i.e., the number of samples times one less than the number of items per sample) we obtain a preliminary factor k^*, which is then multiplied by a standard error term to obtain a minimum significant range (k), against which the actual ranges between means may be compared. The procedure is very similar to that for obtaining a confidence interval (p. 45).

$$k = k^* \sqrt{\frac{V_e}{N_m}}$$

where k^* is taken from Table 8, V_e is the error-variance estimate from the analysis of variance, N_m is the number of observations per sample. All samples should be of equal size.

Example 2-16. Studentized range test.

Apply the test to the data of Example 2-15 to ascertain which regimens differ from each other at the 5% significance level.

Here we consult Table 8 with 5 means and 25 DF [i.e., $(N_m - 1)$DF per sample] and interpolate $k^* = 4.16$. From Example 2-15, $V_e = 2.34$. Then, since each sample contains 6 observations,

$$k = 4.16 \sqrt{\frac{2.34}{6}} = 2.60$$

the smallest significant range at the 5% level of significance.
Now we find each mean as $T_m/6$ and arrange them in order of magnitude:

C	A	D	E	B
3.33	4.00	4.17	5.16	6.50

It is then apparent that of all the contrasts between pairs of means, only B and C differ by an amount as great as k. We may therefore conclude that regimen C is superior to B, but we cannot assert that it is superior to A, D, or E, or that there are any other real differences.

[17]"Studentized" refers to the tabulation of a statistical distribution based on a variance estimate, s, derived from a sample, when σ is unknown. Such procedures were introduced by W. S. Gosset, under the pseudonym "Student." The t-test, which is also based on a small-sample variance estimate, is often called "Student's t-test."
Although we shall illustrate the studentized range test in Example 2-16 upon the same data as was analyzed by the F-test in Example 2-15, it should be understood that the two tests are alternatives, not ordinarily applied sequentially to the same data.

In this particular example the studentized range test allowed us to conclude that the extreme samples differed significantly. It may happen that even though analysis of variance permits the conclusion that a set of means did not come from the same population, the studentized range test nevertheless does not reveal any particular pair of means that can be said to differ. This is no more surprising than any case in which a particular test may not be efficient enough to detect a real difference of given magnitude. In the following example, on the other hand, the studentized range test makes possible several discriminations among the sample means.

Example 2-17. Analysis of variance: One way classification; many-sample analysis of variance and studentized range test.

Four different media were compared to see if they differed in supporting the growth of mouse fibroblast cells in tissue culture. Five bottles were used with each medium, the same number of cells were implanted into all 20 bottles, and the total cell protein in each bottle was determined after 7 days. The results were as follows (μg of protein nitrogen):

Medium

A	B	C	D	E
100	101	107	100	119
100	104	103	96	122
99	98	105	99	114
101	105	105	100	120
100	102	106	99	121

The data are first coded by subtracting 100:

	A	B	C	D	E	
	0	1	7	0	19	
	0	4	3	-4	22	
	-1	-2	5	-1	14	
	1	5	5	0	20	
	0	2	6	-1	21	
T_m	0	10	26	-6	96	$T = 126$
$\bar{x} = \dfrac{T_m}{N_m}$	0	2.0	5.2	-1.2	19.2	$T^2 = 15{,}876$
$(T_m)^2$	0	100	676	36	9,216	

PRELIMINARY CALCULATIONS

Type of Total	Total of Squares	Number of Items Squared	Number of Observations per Squared Item	Total of Squares per Observation
Grand	15,876	1	25	635.0
Media	10,028	5	5	2,005.6
Observations	2,096	25	1	2,096

ANALYSIS OF VARIANCE

Source	SS	DF	Variance Estimate (Mean Square)
Media	2,005.6 − 635.0 = 1,370.6	4	342.6
Error	2,096 − 2,005.6 = 90.4	20	4.52
Total	2,096 − 635.0 = 1,461.0	24	—

$F = 342.6/4.52 = 75.8$ (4, 20 DF), which greatly exceeds the tabulated value 4.43 at $P = 0.01$, so the media differ very significantly.

Studentized range test: From Table 8, at $P = 0.01$, for 5 samples and 20 DF, $k^* = 5.29$. Then

$$k = 5.29 \sqrt{\frac{4.52}{5}} = 5.03$$

the smallest significant range at the 1% level of significance.

D	A	B	C	E
−1.2	0	2.0	5.2	19.2

We see that medium E is superior to all the others, since it exceeds even its closest neighbor by more than k. C is superior to A and D but not necessarily to B. No other comparisons are significant.

Example 2-18. Analysis of Variance: Randomized block design, 4 treatments × 5 replications.

Each observation is the weight of a mouse at 3 months after weaning.

Diet

Litter	A	B	C	D
1	20	18	18	21
2	19	17	20	23
3	20	20	17	20
4	22	21	16	23
5	19	19	16	22

Code by subtracting 20:

Litter	A	B	C	D	$T_{litters}$	$T^2_{litters}$
			Diet			
1	0	−2	−2	+1	−3	9
2	−1	−3	0	+3	−1	1
3	0	0	−3	0	−3	9
4	+2	+1	−4	+3	+2	4
5	−1	−1	−4	+2	−4	16
T_{diets}	0	−5	−13	+9	−9 = T	
T^2_{diets}	0	25	169	81		$T^2 = 81$

PRELIMINARY CALCULATIONS

Type of Total	Total of Squares	Number of Items Squared	Number of Observations per Squared Item	Total of Squares per Observation
Grand	81.0	1	20	4.05
Diets	275	4	5	55.0
Replications (litters)	39.0	5	4	9.75
Observations	89.0	20	1	89.0

ANALYSIS OF VARIANCE

Source	SS	DF	MS	F
Treatments (diets)	55.0 − 4.05 = 50.95	3	17.0	7.20**
Replication (litters)	9.75 − 4.05 = 5.70	4	1.42	<1 N.S.
Error	89.0 − 55.0 − 9.75 + 4.05 = 28.30	12	2.36	—
Total	89.0 − 4.05 = 84.95	19	—	

The error SS is obtained just as readily by subtraction of all the others from the total SS. Litters clearly do not differ from one another (since F is less than unity), but diets do, since 7.20 (3, 12 DF) exceeds the tabulated value 5.95 at the 1% significance level.[18] Diet D seems to be best and diet C poorest. The studentized range test gives us more information about this. From Table 8, for 4 means and 12 DF at $P = 0.01$, $k^* = 5.50$. Then

$$k = 5.50 \sqrt{\frac{2.36}{5}} = 3.8$$

[18]A common convention, introduced in this analysis of variance table, is to indicate "not significant" by N.S., $P < 0.05$ by *, and $P < 0.01$ by **.

The mean dietary effects were

C	B	A	D
−2.6	−1	0	1.8

whence it follows that only C and D may be asserted to differ from each other at the 1 % level of significance.

Example 2-19. Analysis of Variance: Factorial 2 × 3 design, single observations.

Two chemically similar drugs and a placebo were tested for their ability to deplete the adrenal glands of ascorbic acid in control rats and in rats anesthetized with ether. Six rats were randomly assigned to the several treatments. Figures are coded data on adrenal ascorbic acid content. The totals are designated by the generally useful subscripts c and r, denoting "columns" and "rows."

	Placebo	A	B	T_r	T_r^2
		Drug			
Control	4	−1	−20	−17	289
Anesthesia	−3	−10	−30	−43	1,849
T_c	+1	−11	−50	−60 = T	
T_c^2	1	121	2,500	$T^2 = 3,600$	

PRELIMINARY CALCULATIONS

Type of Total	Total of Squares	Number of Items Squared	Number of Observations per Squared Item	Total of Squares per Observation
Grand	3,600	1	6	600
Columns (drugs)	2,622	3	2	1,311
Rows (anesthesia)	2,138	2	3	712.7
Observations	1,426	6	1	1,426

ANALYSIS OF VARIANCE

Source	SS	DF	Variance Estimate	F
Drugs	1,311 − 600 = 711	2	355.5	309**
Anesthesia	712.7 − 600 = 112.7	1	112.7	98.0*
Error	2.3	2	1.15	—
Total	1,426 − 600 = 826	5	—	

Conclusion: The adrenal ascorbic acid content is significantly lowered by at least one of the drugs, as compared with placebo. Ether anesthesia also lowers the adrenal ascorbic acid content significantly as compared with unanesthetized animals.

In factorial experiments, when observations on each combination are replicated, a new source of variance may be segregated, which is known as an *interaction*. This means that an observation may be greater (or smaller) than expected from the factors operating independently. Thus, in the previous example it might be that drug B is especially potent in releasing adrenal ascorbic acid in the presence of ether anesthesia whereas drug A is equally active in control and anesthetized animals. Interactions cannot be tested for readily when there is only a single observation per combination of factors because then there is no independent estimate of the error variance. When observations are replicated, however, it is possible to make separate estimates of the interaction and error variances. This is illustrated in the following example.

Example 2-20. Analysis of variance: 2 × 2 factorial experiment, 5 observations per combination.

Ten male and ten female rats were divided randomly into subgroups to which two different hypnotic drugs were administered. Sleeping times were then measured, with the following results, in minutes. The data are coded by subtracting 20.

	Males			Females		
	x	x_c	x_c^2	x'	x'_c	$x'_c{}^2$
	15	-5	25	29	$+9$	81
	18	-2	4	49	$+29$	841
Drug A	26	$+6$	36	33	$+13$	169
	14	-6	36	37	$+17$	289
	19	-1	1	27	$+7$	49
		-8	102		$+75$	1,429
	14	-6	36	14	-6	36
	12	-8	64	18	-2	4
Drug B	18	-2	4	25	$+5$	25
	20	-0	0	20	0	0
	16	-4	16	26	$+6$	36
		-20	120		$+3$	101

$$T = -8 + 75 - 20 + 3 = +50, \ T^2 = 2{,}500$$

$$T_c^2 = (-8 - 20)^2 + (75 + 3)^2 = 6{,}868$$

$$T_r^2 = (-8 + 75)^2 + (-20 + 3)^2 = 4{,}778$$

$$T^2_{\text{combinations}} = (-8)^2 + (-20)^2 + (75)^2 + (3)^2 = 6{,}098$$

$$\sum x^2 = 102 + 120 + 1{,}429 + 101 = 1{,}752$$

PRELIMINARY CALCULATIONS

Type of Total	Total of Squares	Number of Items Squared	Number of Observations per Squared Item	Total of Squares per Observation
Grand	2,500	1	20	125
Sexes	6,868	2	10	686.8
Drugs	4,778	2	10	477.8
Combinations	6,098	4	5	1,219.6
Observations	1,752	20	1	1,752

ANALYSIS OF VARIANCE

Source	SS	DF	MS
Sexes	686.8 − 125 = 561.8	1	561.8
Drugs	477.8 − 125 = 352.8	1	352.8
Sexes × drugs (interaction)	(1,219.6 − 125) − 561.8 − 352.8 = 180.0	1	180.0
Error	1,752 − 1,219.6 = 532.4	16	33.3
Total	1,752 − 125 = 1,627	19	

The interaction SS may be obtained more readily by subtraction of all the other SS from the total SS. The method given above, however, shows exactly what it is composed of. It is the amount by which SS due to all the combinations exceeds the sum of SS due to sexes and SS due to drugs. In other words, if an observation at a particular combination of factors is just what we would expect from the two factors acting independently, there is no interaction; but if the observation is greater or less than expected, we will be able to obtain an interaction SS and variance estimate. It is also evident here that the error SS is simply the amount by which the total SS exceeds that due to all the combinations; it may also be referred to as SS "within combinations," or simply as the "residual" (or "unexplained") variance.

The several F-ratios may now be tested for significance as follows:

$$\frac{\text{Sexes}}{\text{Error}} = \frac{562}{33.3} = 16.9 \ (1, \ 16 \ \text{DF}) \qquad P < 0.01$$

$$\frac{\text{Drugs}}{\text{Error}} = \frac{353}{33.3} = 10.6 \ (1, \ 16 \ \text{DF}) \qquad P < 0.01$$

$$\frac{\text{Interaction}}{\text{Error}} = \frac{180}{33.3} = 5.41 \ (1, \ 16 \ \text{DF}) \qquad P < 0.05$$

Referring back to the original data we may now interpret the results as follows. Females sleep longer than males, and drug A has a longer duration of hypnotic action than drug B. Moreover, drug A causes especially long sleep in females or especially brief sleep in males; or drug B causes especially long sleep in males or especially brief sleep in females.

Example 2-20 is typical of a great many problems encountered in biological experimentation. Each main effect as well as the interaction is tested against the error variance. It is sometimes stated that if the interaction is found to be nonsignificant, then the interaction SS should be pooled with the error SS to form a new pooled error variance estimate; such a procedure, however, is not advocated by most authorities except in special situations.

Analysis of variance in factorial experiments deals with three rather different situations (known as *models*). The procedures are the same, with one important exception noted below, but the interpretations are somewhat different. In the *fixed-effect model* the conclusions to be drawn apply to the particular levels of the factors in the experiment. Example 2-20 was a fixed-effect model because we were interested in the two drugs, A and B, which were actually tested, and in the two sexes, male and female, which were included in the experiment. In the *random-effect model*, on the contrary, the factors included are themselves only random samples. For example, if five litters are included in a factorial design, one is certainly not interested in those particular litters, which are only representative of all litters that might have been chosen. One wishes, from the outcome of the experiment, to draw conclusions about differences from litter to litter in general. If four diets are also compared (as in Example 2-18), we would most likely be interested in the particular diets tested; then diets would be fixed factors, litters would be random factors, and we would have a *mixed model*. However, it is possible we might only be interested in the general question whether variation in diet could have an effect; then the diets chosen could be regarded as random factors, conclusions would not refer to any particular diets tested, and we would have a pure random-effect model.

It is, of course, always important to draw appropriate conclusions from an experiment, and the kind of model represented by the experimental design employed determines the sorts of conclusion that are warranted. As far as the procedures are concerned, there is only one that differs according to the model employed. If there are replicated observations at each combination of factors, so that an interaction variance estimate is obtained, then the following rule applies:

For the fixed-effect model, test the main effects as well as the interaction against the error variance estimate, as illustrated in Example 2-20.

For the random-effect or mixed models, test the interaction against the error variance but then test all main effects (including the fixed effects in a mixed model) against the interaction variance, as illustrated in the following example.

Example 2-21. Analysis of variance: Randomized block design, 4 treatments × 5 replications, duplicate observation. Mixed model.

Each figure is the weight of a mouse at 3 months after weaning.

		Diet		
Litter	A	B	C	D
1	20	19	23	18
	20	20	22	16
2	18	18	20	15
	20	19	21	17
3	19	20	20	18
	19	18	22	19
4	22	20	25	21
	24	22	26	21
5	19	20	22	18
	20	18	20	18

Code by subtracting 20.

	A	B	C	D	T_r	T_r^2
1	$\left.\begin{array}{c}0\\0\end{array}\right]0$	$\left.\begin{array}{c}-1\\0\end{array}\right]-1$	$\left.\begin{array}{c}3\\2\end{array}\right]5$	$\left.\begin{array}{c}-2\\-4\end{array}\right]-6$	-2	4
2	$\left.\begin{array}{c}-2\\0\end{array}\right]-2$	$\left.\begin{array}{c}-2\\-1\end{array}\right]-3$	$\left.\begin{array}{c}0\\1\end{array}\right]1$	$\left.\begin{array}{c}-5\\-3\end{array}\right]-8$	-12	144
3	$\left.\begin{array}{c}-1\\-1\end{array}\right]-2$	$\left.\begin{array}{c}0\\-2\end{array}\right]-2$	$\left.\begin{array}{c}0\\2\end{array}\right]2$	$\left.\begin{array}{c}-2\\-1\end{array}\right]-3$	-5	25
4	$\left.\begin{array}{c}2\\4\end{array}\right]6$	$\left.\begin{array}{c}0\\2\end{array}\right]2$	$\left.\begin{array}{c}5\\6\end{array}\right]11$	$\left.\begin{array}{c}1\\1\end{array}\right]2$	21	441
5	$\left.\begin{array}{c}-1\\0\end{array}\right]-1$	$\left.\begin{array}{c}0\\-2\end{array}\right]-2$	$\left.\begin{array}{c}2\\0\end{array}\right]2$	$\left.\begin{array}{c}-2\\-2\end{array}\right]4$	3	9
T_c	1	-6	21	-11	$T=5$	
T_c^2	1	36	441	121	$T^2=25$	

PRELIMINARY CALCULATIONS

Type of Total	Total of Squares	Number of Items Squared	Number of Observations per Squared Item	Total of Squares per Observation
Grand	25	1	40	0.625
Diets	599	4	10	59.9
Litters	623	5	8	77.9
Combinations	351	20	2	175.5
Observations	197	40	1	197

ANALYSIS OF VARIANCE

Source	SS	DF	Variance Estimate
Diets	$59.9 - 0.6 = 59.3$	3	19.8
Litters	$77.9 - 0.6 = 77.3$	4	19.4
Diets × litters	$175.5 - 77.9 - 59.9 + 0.6 = 38.3$	$3 \times 4 = 12$	3.19
Error	$197 - 175.5 = 21.5$	20	1.08
Total	$197 - 0.6 = 196.4$	39	

$$F \text{ (interaction)} = \frac{3.19}{1.08} = 2.95 \ (12, 20 \ DF) \qquad P < 0.05$$

$$F \text{ (diets)} \quad = \frac{19.8}{3.19} = 6.21 \ (3, 12 \ DF) \qquad P < 0.01$$

$$F \text{ (litters)} \quad = \frac{19.4}{3.19} = 6.08 \ (4, 12 \ DF) \qquad P < 0.01$$

The interaction is tested, as usual, with the error variance estimate in the denominator, but both main effects are tested with the interaction variance estimate in the denominator. In this example all the *F*-ratios are significant, so we conclude: (1) The four diets differ significantly. (2) Litter-mates tend to weigh more nearly the same than do unrelated mice; and litters, in general, differ from one another in average weight. (3) Litters, in general, may be expected to differ from one another in their responses to the four diets tested here.

The analysis of variance for *nested designs* (hierarchical classification) is similar in principle to that for factorial designs but differs in some details. Suppose we wish to compare the reliability of a certain laboratory procedure in the hands of different technicians in several laboratories. We shall want each technician to repeat the assay several times on the same material. The variance of all the data will be attributable to differences between laboratories, differences between technicians (irrespective of laboratories), and random errors of determination. We speak of the replicated observations as the lowest *tier*. These observations are said to be contained (nested) within the next tier, technicians. And the observations grouped according to technician are in turn contained within the highest tier, laboratories. The nested design is essentially a set of parallel one-way classifications contained within one another. The example given below shows a columns-and-rows presentation of the data and then gives the appropriate method of forming the analysis of variance.

Example 2-22. Analysis of variance: Nested (hierarchical) design.

The activity of a certain enzyme in the blood plasma is an indicator of the severity of tissue damage in certain kinds of heart disease. In order to test the general reliability of the enzyme activity determinations, a single plasma sample was subdivided into many portions, which were given code numbers and distributed to two technicians in each of four laboratories for routine assay along with their regular work. Each technician received three samples of the standard plasma. The coded results were as follows:

Laboratories	A		B		C		D	
Technicians	a	b	c	d	e	f	g	h
	-2	-1	3	0	-2	-3	4	3
Observations	-4	0	2	2	-2	-2	5	5
	-4	-1	1	1	0	1	4	2
$T_{technicians}$	-10	-2	6	3	-4	-4	13	10
$T^2_{technicians}$	100	4	36	9	16	16	169	100
$T_{laboratories}$	-12		9		-8		23	
$T^2_{laboratories}$	144		81		64		529	

$$T^2_{observations} = 174$$
$$T = 12$$
$$T^2 = 144$$

Preliminary calculations follow the familiar pattern except that there are no row totals or squares to compute.

PRELIMINARY CALCULATIONS

Type of Total	Total of Squares	Number of Items Squared	Number of Observations per Squared Item	Total of Squares per Observation
Grand	144	1	24	6.00
Laboratories	818	4	6	136.33
Technicians	450	8	3	150
Observations	174	24	1	174

In forming sums of squares from any table of preliminary calculations it is helpful to keep in mind the possible contributing causes of variation in each case. Here, in the nested design, the SS for the largest units (between laboratories) is computed as usual; it is simply the total of squares per observation obtained from the laboratory totals, corrected by subtraction of the grand total of squares per observation. The differences between technicians, however, may be caused in part by intrinsic differences among the technicians themselves, but also in part by differences between the laboratories in which they work. Suppose, for example, that both technicians in any given laboratory performed their work identically, but differently from the technicians of another laboratory. Then the total of squares per observation, computed from the technician totals, would be appreciably large, but it would be the same as the total of squares per observation computed from the laboratory totals. To remove the effect of laboratory differences from the apparent technician differences, we subtract the respective totals of squares per observation, as shown below. The resulting SS is then designated "technicians within laboratories," to show that laboratory-to-laboratory differences have been removed. The same principle applies to the error term (error within technicians), which is obtained as the difference between the total of squares for observations and that for technicians.

ANALYSIS OF VARIANCE

Source	SS	DF	MS
Laboratories	$136.33 - 6.00 = 130.33$	3	43.4
Technicians within laboratories	$150. - 136.33 = 13.67$	4	3.42
Error within laboratories	$174. \quad - 150. = 24.0$	16	1.50
Total	$174. \quad - \quad 6. = 168.$	23	—

In a hierarchical classification the appropriate F-ratio is the variance estimate of successive tiers. Thus,

$$F\left(\frac{\text{laboratories}}{\text{technicians within laboratories}}\right) = \frac{43.4}{3.42} = 12.7 \ (3, 4 \ \text{DF}); \qquad P < 0.05$$

$$F\left(\frac{\text{technicians within laboratories}}{\text{error within technicians}}\right) = \frac{3.42}{1.50} = 2.28 \ (4, 16 \ \text{DF}); \qquad \text{N.S.}$$

The conclusion of the experiment is therefore that laboratories differ significantly but that technicians do not, a result that suggests definite lines of further investigation to ascertain the causes of the variation among laboratories.

Provided that an experimental design is perfectly balanced, any differentiating classification or factor may be the basis for segregating a special SS, even when that classification or factor cuts across the systematic pattern of an experimental design. This is illustrated in the following example of a nested design with an additional classification.

Example 2-23. Analysis of variance: nested design with additional elements.

Suppose that in Example 2-22 one technician in each laboratory was experienced (a, c, e, g), whereas the other (b, d, f, h) was a novice. We might then ask whether experience had anything to do with the reliability of the enzyme assays. The additional basis of classification provides another SS, as follows.

	Experienced	Novice
T	5	7
T^2	25	49

So the total of squares for the new classification is 74, from 2 items squared, and 12 observations per squared item, making 6.17 the total of squares per observation. Then SS attributable to this source is $6.17 - 6.00 = 0.17$. Since a portion of the between-technicians SS has now been accounted for, as well as one degree of freedom (one less than the number of categories in the new classification), appropriate revisions have to be made in the analysis of variance.

ANALYSIS OF VARIANCE

Source	SS	DF	MS
Laboratories	130.33	3	43.4
Technicians within laboratories	13.50	3	4.50
——— Experience	0.17	1	0.17
Error within technicians	24.0	16	1.50
Total	168.00	23	—

$$F \left(\frac{\text{Laboratories}}{\text{technicians within laboratories}} \right) = \frac{43.4}{4.50} = 9.64 \ (3, 3 \ DF); \qquad P < 0.05$$

$$F \left(\frac{\text{technicians within laboratories}}{\text{error within technicians}} \right) = \frac{4.50}{1.50} = 3.00 \ (3, 16 \ DF); \ \text{N.S.}$$

$$F \left(\frac{\text{experience}}{\text{error within technicians}} \right) = \frac{0.17}{1.50}; \quad \text{N.S.}$$

It so happens that in the present case the segregation of technician experience as a cause of variability contributed no new information; it was known already that variation between technicians, regardless of experience, was not a significant factor in this problem. The example, however, illustrates the general procedure for the further partition of any SS according to its several possible sources.

It may have been noted that in the examples of analysis of variance presented so far, the number of observations per group was always the same, i.e., the experimental design was well balanced. The advantages of equal sample sizes are so considerable that experiments should always be planned accordingly. In the case of one-way classification, however, unequal numbers can be handled without serious consequences, as illustrated below.

Example 2-24. Analysis of variance: One-way classification, unequal sample sizes.

Effects of the same dose of whole-body x-irradiation were tested on animals of three inbred strains of mouse. Coded data represent decrease in circulating leukocytes for each mouse.

	Strain		
A	B	C	
5	8	2	
4	6	0	
7	4	5	
2	4		
6			
T_m	24	22	7	$T = 53$
T_m^2	576	484	49	$T^2 = 2{,}809$
$\dfrac{T_m^2}{N_m}$	$\dfrac{576}{5} = 115.2$	$\dfrac{484}{4} = 121.0$	$\dfrac{49}{3} = 16.33$	

PRELIMINARY CALCULATIONS

Type of Total	Total of Squares	Number of Items Squared	Number of Observations per Squared Item	Total of Squares per Observation
Grand	2,809	1	12	234.1
Strain	—	—	—	115.2 + 121.0 + 16.33 = 252.5
Observations	291	12	1	291.0

ANALYSIS OF VARIANCE

Source	SS	DF	Variance estimate	F	
Strains	252.5 − 234.1 = 18.4	2	9.20	2.15	N.S.
Error	291.0 − 252.5 = 38.5	9	4.28		
Total	291.0 − 234.1 = 56.9	11	—		

Thus, we cannot conclude that the strains differ in response to X-irradiation.

Note that the only special feature in handling unequal sample sizes is that the total of squares per observation is separately calculated as T_m^2/N_m for each sample, and these are then added together.

It sometimes happens that an experiment is balanced at the outset but that parts of it are lost by accident. An animal may die of causes unrelated to the experimental procedures. A patient may have to be removed from the experiment because of an adverse reaction to a treatment. A volunteer subject may withdraw. Whatever the reason, the result is that one or more observations are missing. If the design is a one-way classification, then the inequality of sample sizes does not affect the analysis. In two-way (or more complex) classifications the exact analysis is greatly complicated by a missing observation. It is possible, however, to replace the missing observation by a synthetic one and then to proceed with the usual analysis. The synthetic observation is chosen to make no contribution to the error variance, according to the following formula:

$$\text{Replacement observation} = \frac{CT_c + RT_r - T}{(C - 1)(R - 1)}$$

where C and R are the numbers of columns and rows, respectively, T_c and T_r are the column and row totals for the particular column and row containing the missing observation, and T is the grand total. The replacement observation thus calculated is not, of course, a bona fide observation and therefore it is not counted in computing the various DF. Moreover, the F-ratio eventually obtained will be slightly larger than it should be, so one should be wary of marginally significant results obtained by this approximate method.

Example 2-25. Analysis of variance: Two-way classification, missing observation.

Consider the coded data of Example 2-18 and suppose the animal of litter 4 which was treated with diet C was accidentally lost. Then the data would be:

		Diet			
Litter	A	B	C	D	T_r
1	0	−2	−2	+1	−3
2	−1	−3	0	+3	−1
3	0	0	−3	0	−3
4	+2	+1		+3	+6
5	−1	−1	−4	+2	−4
T_c	0	−5	−9	+9	−5

To replace the missing observation, we note

$C = 4$ columns
$R = 5$ rows
$T_c = -9$
$T_r = +6$
$T = -5$

$$\text{Replacement} = \frac{4(-9) + 5(+6) - (-5)}{(4 - 1)(5 - 1)} = -0.1 \cong 0$$

The remainder of the calculation of the analysis of variance is left as an exercise. The result leads to the same interpretations as before. Because of the missing observation there is one less DF in the error-variance estimate and in the total.

ANALYSIS OF VARIANCE

Source	SS	DF	Variance Estimate	F	
Diets	36.2	3	12.1	6.95	**
Litters	16.5	4	4.13	2.37	N.S.
Error	19.1	11	1.74		
Total	71.8	18	—		

Problems

CHAPTER 2 (ANSWERS ON P. 200)

Unless otherwise directed, adopt the 5% level of significance or the 95% confidence interval. The problems are meant to be prototypic of those commonly encountered in real experiments, but the data are almost wholly invented. The reference at the end of each problem indicates where relevant explanation and worked examples are to be found in the text.

P2-1.

An experiment was conducted with 10 subjects to see if a stimulant drug improves typing speed. Each subject participated on two occasions, receiving placebo once and drug once. The order of administration, which was randomized, is not shown here. Data are words typed correctly in a fixed period of time.

Subject	Placebo	Drug
A	320	334
B	300	326
C	256	275
D	326	300
E	284	280
F	306	300
G	275	292
H	297	268
I	310	315
J	320	330

Was the drug effective in increasing the typing speed? What is the smallest and greatest improvement or decrement that could be attributed to the drug? (Cf. pp. 62, 59, 45.)

P2-2.

The mean heart rate observed in a sample of 20 rats was 282, with a coefficient of variation of 15%. During anesthesia the mean heart rate in the same group of animals fell to 240, and the coefficient of variation remained the same. Was the decrease in heart rate during anesthesia significant? What are the 95% confidence limits for the change in heart rate during anesthesia? (Cf. pp. 51, 45.)

P2-3.

Brain concentration of a hypnotic drug was determined chemically 5 min after administration of the drug intravenously in rabbits. The data (μg/g) in 6 animals were: 40.2, 38.7, 41.6, 40.5, 43.2, 39.4. Calculate the mean and its standard error and the 99% confidence interval for the true mean concentration. What is the coefficient of variation for these data? (Cf. p. 43, 45.)

P2-4.

Five subjects were given caffeine (at two doses) or placebo on each of 3 days, and asked to check on a self-rating form various descriptive statements about mood and attitude. Data are arbitrary scores, always listed in the same order for the 5 subjects.

	Placebo	Caffeine, 150 mg	Caffeine, 300 mg
Alertness	0,0,1,1,0	1,2,4,2,1	2,4,4,3,3
Nervousness	1,2,1,0,0	1,0,2,2,1	2,0,1,2,2
Relaxation	3,2,2,3,2	1,2,1,3,2	1,0,0,3,1

What conclusions can be drawn? (Cf. p. 70.)

P2-5.

An experiment was conducted to see whether humming-birds had a color preference. Yellow, red, and green feeder bottles containing sugar-water were placed at various locations according to a 3×3 Latin square plan. The weekly weight loss of each bottle was taken as a measure of attractiveness to the birds, it having been ascertained that the contents were not being depleted in any other way. The results (weight loss in grams) were as follows:

Yellow	40	Red	62	Green	15
Red	70	Green	21	Yellow	38
Green	29	Yellow	51	Red	58

Is there a color preference? Are there any significant position effects? (Cf. p. 73.)

P2-6.

In a particular infection caused by a known strain of pathogenic bacterium, the highest fever (°F) in each of 15 randomly chosen patients was: 101.2, 100.6, 100.6, 101.8, 101.0, 101.2, 100.4, 102.2, 100.8, 101.6, 101.0, 100.8, 102.0, 101.6, 101.6. In a new patient in whom the diagnosis had not yet been confirmed, what temperature would have to be exceeded in order to raise a serious doubt that the same infectious process was at work? (Cf. p. 49.)

P2-7.

A mink farm conducted an experiment to see if vitamin supplementation of the animals' diets would improve the quality of the pelts. Fifteen control animals (C) were compared with 12 given the supplemented diet (X). Eventually the pelts were compared, with blind precautions, by an expert judge, who ranked all 27 pelts in order of quality. His ranking, from best to poorest, was as follows, tied groups being indicated by brackets: X,X,(CX),(CC),X,(XX),C,C,X,C, (CXX),C,(CCXX),C,X,C,C,C,C. Does vitamin supplementation, under these conditions, improve pelt quality? (Cf. p. 56.)

P2-8.

An investigation was carried out on the effects of temperature and of controlled light intensity on the growth of certain algae. Eighteen vessels were inoculated with the same initial number of cells and assigned randomly in duplicate to various combinations of temperature and light intensity. After a week the contents were centrifuged, dried, and weighed. The following weights (mg) were obtained:

	Temperatures					
Light Intensity	10°		20°		30°	
I	150	160	250	230	200	200
II	170	150	260	280	190	150
III	200	210	270	280	110	140

What conclusions can be drawn? (Cf. p. 76.)

P2-9.

In a comparison of five varieties of beans a 5×5 Latin square was used to equalize soil conditions, sunlight, and other variables in the experimental field. At harvest the yield weights (hundreds of pounds) were as follows:

		Variety		
A	B	C	D	E
5.6	5.9	4.2	7.2	5.0
5.2	6.7	4.1	7.5	5.7
5.8	6.4	4.8	6.1	4.8
6.0	5.8	5.3	6.8	5.3
5.3	6.1	5.3	5.9	5.6

Do the yields really differ, and if so, which differs from which? (Cf. p. 70.)

P2-10.

Some students maintain that music helps them study. A 2×3 factorial experiment was performed to test this assertion. Nine male and nine female students were randomly subdivided into three groups and assigned to a quiet room, a room where folk songs were being played, or a room where chamber music was being played. The same material for study was assigned to all the students, and they were tested on it two hours later. No music was played during the testing. The following scores were obtained.

		Conditions of Study	
	Quiet	Folk Songs	Chamber Music
Men	150	160	250
	120	140	260
	200	140	220

	Conditions of Study		
	Quiet	*Folk Songs*	*Chamber Music*
Women	250	100	150
	140	90	130
	150	150	190

What does the experiment show, if anything, about the effects of music upon the particular kind of learning that was examined here? (Cf. p. 76.)

P2-11.

The capacity to metabolize certain compounds is genetically controlled. On the basis of some suggestive preliminary evidence a study was undertaken on a limited scale to find out whether individual differences in the rate of disposition of a certain drug were familial, and also whether racial origin played any role. Siblings belonging to three white and three Negro families served as subjects. Each subject received the drug on three different occasions intravenously, and each time the drug concentration in the blood was determined one hour later. Data are final drug concentrations. It may be assumed that the initial concentrations were substantially the same in all subjects.

White Families	*Subject*	*Sex*	*Observations*
A	1	M	10, 15, 10
	2	M	20, 25, 15
	3	M	15, 15, 20
	4	F	20, 25, 20
B	1	F	45, 50, 50
	2	M	25, 30, 35
	3	F	40, 40, 30
C	1	F	80, 70, 65
	2	M	30, 25, 20

Negro Families	*Subject*	*Sex*	*Observations*
D	1	F	140, 100, 110
	2	F	160, 120, 150
	3	M	80, 90, 100
E	1	M	10, 20, 15
	2	M	80, 80, 55
	3	M	30, 45, 30
	4	F	100, 80, 85
	5	M	25, 25, 35

Negro Families	Subject	Sex	Observations		
F	1	F	60,	80,	75
	2	F	60,	55,	70
	3	M	30,	40,	55

What conclusions can be drawn? (Cf. pp. 83, 85.)

P2-12.

Two new types of detergent antiseptic (B and C) for surgical scrubbing were to be compared with a standard type (A). All three were known to be equally effective in killing bacteria but it was claimed that the new types would be less irritating to the surgeon's hands. A randomized block design was set up so that three surgeons at each of three hospitals could make judgments on the irritating properties of A, B, and C. Each surgeon used the detergents, one at a time on successive days, in random order, and used each one twice. Blind precautions were taken. Surgeons assigned scores from 0 (no irritation) to 10 (very irritating). The data are tabulated below.

		Type of Detergent Antiseptic		
Hospital	Surgeon	A	B	C
I	a	4, 3	6, 5	2, 3
	b	2, 2	4, 3	2, 1
	c	1, 4	2, 3	1, 2
II	d	3, 2	5, 4	2, 4
	e	2, 1	3, 3	2, 3
	f	1, 1	2, 3	1, 2
III	g	4, 5	6, 7	3, 3
	h	4, 4	7, 5	2, 3
	i	4, 6	6, 7	4, 5

Analyze and interpret the results. (Cf. p. 73.)

Enumeration Data

BINOMIAL DISTRIBUTION, PROPORTIONS
AND PERCENTS

If a population consists of items or subjects belonging to two mutually exclusive categories, it is said to be a *binomial population*. Whatever the two categories may actually be (e.g., dead-alive, pigmented-nonpigmented, success-failure) we may describe them symbolically as *A* and *not-A*. Let us designate each *A* by 1, and each *not-A* by 0. Then in this population, μ, the mean value, is simply the *proportion* of *A*, and $(1 - \mu)$ is the proportion of *not-A*. We shall assign a new symbol, π, to the proportion of *A* in a binomial population, but it is well to remember that π is really equivalent to μ. Similarly, each sample mean is the sum of the 1's and 0's in the sample, divided by *N*, in other words, the *proportion* of *A* in the sample.

In populations of quantitative data, the composition of samples depended upon both parameters, μ and σ^2, which could vary independently. In a binomial population, on the other hand, since the only observations are 1 and 0, the variance must depend only upon the relative frequencies of these two numbers. In other words, there is really only a single parameter, π, which also determines σ^2. It can be shown[1] that

$$\sigma^2 = \pi(1 - \pi)$$

Now random samples of size *N* may be drawn from a binomial population. The proportion of *A* in a sample will be designated by *p*, which is

[1]For example, if a very large but finite sample is considered to be practically equivalent

an estimate of π. The sampling distribution of p is approximately normal, with variance

$$\sigma_p{}^2 = \frac{\sigma^2}{N} = \frac{\pi(1-\pi)}{N}$$

Two examples of theoretical sampling distributions of p were presented in Fig. 1-4, for populations with $\pi = 0.5$ and $\pi = 0.3$.

The sampling distribution of p is no longer approximately normal at extreme values of π, unless N is very large. As π assumes values closer to 0 or to 1, N must become ever larger to maintain a reasonably normal sampling distribution. A rough rule is that the products, $N\pi$ and $N(1-\pi)$ (which are the expected *numbers* of A and *not-A* in a sample) must both be at least 5, or the normal approximation is probably not correct enough to use. Thus, for example, if $\pi = 0.1$, N must be at least 50.

For small samples, the exact sampling distribution is readily computed on the basis of the probabilities of all the possible outcomes. Consider samples of 2, drawn from a binomial population. There are 3 kinds of sample:—AA, A0, and 00. There is only one way to obtain AA; namely, if the first item in the sample is A, and the second is also A. The probability of these independent events is π for each, so the joint probability that the first item will be A, and also that the second item will be A is π^2. The outcome A0 may be obtained in two ways, since the first item may be A and the second 0, or the other way about. The probability of A0 (or 0A) is the product $\pi(1-\pi)$, the respective probabilities of drawing A and 0; and since there are two ways to obtain this outcome, the actual probability of obtaining it is $2\pi(1-\pi)$. Finally, there is one way to obtain 00, whose probability is given by $(1-\pi)^2$. The sum of the probabilities for all possible outcomes is therefore

$$\pi^2 + 2\pi(1-\pi) + (1-\pi)^2 = 1$$

---

to a population, we can calculate σ^2 as follows:

$$SS = \Sigma\, x^2 - \frac{T^2}{N}, \text{ as shown on p. 43.}$$

But since all observations are 0's and 1's, $x^2 = x$ and $\Sigma\, x^2 = T$, so

$$SS = T - \frac{T^2}{N} = T\left(1 - \frac{T}{N}\right)$$

$$\sigma^2 = \frac{SS}{N} = \frac{T}{N}\left(1 - \frac{T}{N}\right) = \mu(1-\mu) = \pi(1-\pi)$$

and this will be recognized as the algebraic expansion of

$$[\pi + (1 - \pi)]^2 = 1$$

It will be found that for any N, the probabilities of the various outcomes are given by the $(N + 1)$ terms of the *binomial expansion*,

$$1 = [\pi + (1 - \pi)]^N = \pi^N + \frac{N}{1} \pi^{N-1}(1 - \pi) + \frac{N(N - 1)}{1 \cdot 2} \pi^{N-2}(1 - \pi)^2$$

$$+ \frac{N(N - 1)(N - 2)}{1 \cdot 2 \cdot 3} \pi^{N-3}(1 - \pi)^3 + \cdots + (1 - \pi)^N$$

The meanings of the various terms may be illustrated with reference to penny-tossing. Here π, the probability of heads, and $(1 - \pi)$, the probability of not-heads, are both equal to $1/2$. The exponents of π and $(1 - \pi)$ in each term denote the kind of outcome (e.g., $\pi^2(1 - \pi)^2$ signifies 2 heads, 2 tails), while the coefficient of each term is the number of ways that kind of outcome can occur. When the proper probabilities are substituted for π and $(1 - \pi)$, each term in the expression will be the probability of that particular kind of outcome.

Example 3-1.   Exact binomial probabilities.

What is the probability of observing 3 or more heads in a toss of 4 pennies?

$$\pi = (1 - \pi) = \frac{1}{2}$$

$$N = 4$$

$$\left(\frac{1}{2} + \frac{1}{2}\right)^4 = \left(\frac{1}{2}\right)^4 + \frac{4}{1}\left(\frac{1}{2}\right)^3\left(\frac{1}{2}\right) + \frac{4 \cdot 3}{1 \cdot 2}\left(\frac{1}{2}\right)^2\left(\frac{1}{2}\right)^2$$

$$+ \frac{4 \cdot 3 \cdot 2}{1 \cdot 2 \cdot 3}\left(\frac{1}{2}\right)\left(\frac{1}{2}\right)^3 + \frac{4 \cdot 3 \cdot 2 \cdot 1}{1 \cdot 2 \cdot 3 \cdot 4}\left(\frac{1}{2}\right)^4$$

$$= \frac{1}{16} + \frac{4}{16} + \frac{6}{16} + \frac{4}{16} + \frac{1}{16}$$

for the respective probabilities of 4, 3, 2, 1, and 0 heads. Then $1/16 + 4/16 = 5/16$ $= 0.31$ is the desired probability.

Figure 3-1 shows the theoretical sampling distribution for tosses of 4 and of 16 pennies. Since $\pi = 0.5 = (1 - \pi)$, the distributions are perfectly symmetrical, regardless of sample size. When N is small, however, there is

Figure 3–1 Theoretical outcomes of tossing 4 or 16 pennies innumerable times, calculated from the binomial expansion. Broken lines represent samples of 4 pennies, solid lines 16 pennies.

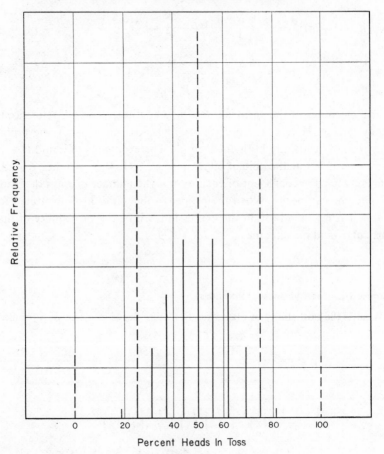

an obvious discontinuity arising from the fact that the possible values of p are discrete and widely separated. As N becomes large, the sampling distribution of p approaches a smooth normal curve, and this is true even at extreme values of π, if N becomes large enough.

The convergence of the sampling distribution of p to a normal curve suggests a way of rationalizing the empirical finding that many biological measurements are normally distributed. One may suppose that a quantitative observation in a biological system is the resultant of a very large number of unit determinants, both genetic and environmental in origin. Each determinant may tend to raise or lower the quantitative property by a small amount. Then a normal distribution of quantitative measurements would be expected from the chance association of unit determinants in each individual organism.

The computation of exact probabilities of all outcomes by the binomial expansion is obviously impractical except for very small samples, and tabulations of the individual terms for samples of moderate size are available.[2] However, the first and last terms of the binomial expansion $[\pi^N, (1 - \pi)^N]$ are often useful and are easily computed; they give the probabilities of the most favorable and least favorable outcomes. One can then estimate the minimum sample size that would be required to demonstrate a treatment effect, if the treatment were completely effective. For example, in a disease with 50% mortality, if we had a reliably curative drug and wished to assert its efficacy at the 5% significance level, we should have to observe an outcome that would occur with probability <0.05 by chance sampling. Then we would require $(0.5)^N < 0.05$, whence $N \geq 5$. To show the same effect at $P < 0.01$ would require $(0.5)^N < 0.01$, $N \geq 7$. It would be foolish to attempt an experiment in such a disease with less than five patients, since even the most favorable outcome would be inconclusive.

Example 3-2. Minimum sample size for demonstrating an extreme outcome.

In a disease with known mortality 10%, what is the minimum number of patients required to demonstrate the efficacy of a completely curative drug?

$$\pi(\text{survival}) = 0.9$$

$$(1 - \pi)(\text{death}) = 0.1$$

$$(0.9)^N < 0.05$$

$$N \geq 29$$

---

[2]For example, E. S. Pearson and H. O. Hartley, *Biometrika Tables for Statisticians*, Vol. 1 (London: Cambridge University Press, 1954), Table 37.

Unless such calculations are made, one is very apt to underestimate the number of patients or experimental subjects required to establish the efficacy of a treatment. On the other hand, in a disease with very high mortality, the virtue of a curative drug might be demonstrated with very few patients, and in the extreme case a drug may practically prove itself by curing a single patient suffering from a hitherto incurable disease.

The factors that determine the minimum sample size may be summarized as follows: (1) The more effective is the treatment, the smaller will be the sample required to demonstrate efficacy. (2) The more likely is a favorable spontaneous outcome, the larger will be the sample required to show an improvement over that outcome. (3) The lower is the level of significance at which one wishes to assert efficacy, the more subjects will be required to demonstrate it.

If we wish to find the confidence interval of a true proportion, π, from a small-sample p, we cannot assume a normal sampling distribution, so the familiar equations of the type $\mu = \bar{x} \pm x^*(s_{\bar{x}})$ are out of the question. It would be necessary to solve the binomial expansion for the particular sample N and various hypothetical values of π, to determine with what probability the observed p occurs. Fortunately tables, charts, and nomograms are available which incorporate the results of such calculations. Table 11 should nearly always suffice; more extensive tabulations are also available.[3]

Example 3-3.   Confidence interval of π from a very small sample.

A tranquilizing drug caused anemia in two of the first 10 patients in whom it was tried. Assume that the 10 patients were representative of all who might be given the drug. Suppose that a true toxicity of this kind is tolerable only if it does not affect more than 10% of treated patients. Should the drug be withdrawn or tested further?

For $p = 0.2$, $N = 10$, Table 11 gives 0.02–0.56 as the 95% confidence interval of π. It is therefore uncertain whether or not the true toxicity exceeds the tolerable limit.

What would be required to demonstrate that the true toxicity is less than 10%? Since we wish 0.10 to be the upper confidence limit, we enter Table 11 at this value of π. We may then examine what outcome would have to be observed in samples of various sizes, by reading the value of p at each intersection with a

[3]R. A. Fisher and F. Yates, *Statistical Tables for Biological, Agricultural and Medical Research*, 4th ed. (New York: Hafner Publishing Company, Inc., 1953), Table VIII₁. Further graphic aids will be found in D. Mainland, *Elementary Medical Statistics* (Philadelphia: W. B. Saunders Company, 1952).

sample curve. Thus at $N = 40$, p would have to be less than 0.01; that is to say, no single case of anemia should be seen among 40 patients. For $N = 60$, p would have to be less than about 0.02; in other words only one instance of toxicity would be tolerable. At $N = 100$, $p = 0.04$, so if there were fewer than four cases of anemia among 100 patients given this drug, we could be fairly certain that the true toxicity was less than 10%. This statement would be made at $P = 0.025$, not $P = 0.05$, for the following reason. Table 11 gives 95% and 99% confidence intervals, so π will exceed the upper limit 2.5% (or 0.5%) of the time, and will lie below the lower limit with the same probability. If it were desired to set an upper (or lower) confidence limit, rather than an interval, and it were essential to set $P = 0.05$ (or 0.01), then Table 11 could not be used and one would have to consult a special table giving 90% (or 98%) confidence intervals, or compute the result in another way.

The normal approximation of the binomial is very useful for larger samples. It was shown above that

$$\sigma_p^2 = \frac{\pi(1 - \pi)}{N}$$

The usual formulation of a sampling distribution applies,

$$x^* = \frac{p - \pi}{\sigma_p}$$

so 95% of all sample p will lie in the interval $\pi \pm 1.96 \sqrt{\frac{\pi(1 - \pi)}{N}}$ and 99% will lie within $\pi \pm 2.58 \sqrt{\frac{\pi(1 - \pi)}{N}}$. In these expressions it does not matter whether proportions or percents are used.

Example 3-4. Estimating confidence interval of π from a sample of moderate size.

Suppose 79 of 360 subjects are found to have a newly discovered blood-cell antigen. Assuming the subjects to be randomly chosen from a particular population, what is the 99% confidence interval for the true incidence of this antigen in the population?

$$p = \frac{79}{360} = 0.219$$

Here we must estimate σ_p^2 from p, since we do not know π.

$$s_p^2 = \frac{0.219(0.781)}{360} = 0.000475$$

$$s_p = \sqrt{0.000475} = 0.0218$$

$$\pi = 0.219 \pm 2.58(0.0218)$$

$$= 0.163 \text{ to } 0.275$$

Table 11 gives practically the same result directly.

Example 3-5. Is a sample p different from a hypothetical π?

Suppose in a toxicity test 40% of a group of 75 mice succumb and the question is whether the true mortality could reasonably be 50%. Using the normal approximation, we have

$$x^* = \frac{p - \pi}{\sigma_p}$$

where $\quad \sigma_p = \sqrt{\dfrac{(50)(50)}{75}} = 5.77$

$$x^* = \frac{40 - 50}{5.77} = -1.73$$

which is smaller than the critical value 1.96, so we conclude that the true mortality could be 50%.

A similar conclusion is reached by consulting Table 11 to see if the 95% confidence limits of π include 0.50 when $p = 0.40$ and $N = 75$. The limits thus found are approximately 0.29 to 0.52.

The difference between two sample proportions (or percents) drawn from the same binomial population is normally distributed, so the null hypothesis may be tested by

$$x^* = \frac{d}{s_d} = \frac{p - p'}{\sqrt{\dfrac{s^2}{N} + \dfrac{s^2}{N'}}}$$

and a confidence interval for the true difference is given by

$$\pi - \pi' = d \pm x^*(s_d)$$

The variance estimate, s^2, is based on a pooled p from both samples.

Example 3-6. **Difference between two sample proportions (or percents).**

Eighty-five patients were treated with a drug, of whom 40% (34 patients) were cured. Seventy were given placebo, of whom only 30% (21 patients) were cured. Was the drug effective?

$$p = 40\%, \quad N = 85 \qquad A = 34$$

$$p' = 30\%, \quad N' = 70 \qquad A' = 21$$

$$\text{Pooled } p = \frac{A + A'}{N + N'} = \frac{55}{155} = 35.5\%$$

$$\text{Pooled } s^2 = 35.5(64.5) = 2{,}290$$

$$s_p^2 = \frac{2{,}290}{85} = 26.9$$

$$s_{p'}^2 = \frac{2{,}290}{70} = 32.7$$

$$s_d^2 = 59.6$$

$$s_d = \sqrt{59.6} = 7.72\%$$

$$x^* = \frac{p - p'}{s_d} = \frac{10\%}{7.72\%} = 1.30$$

and since this falls short of the tabulated 1.64 at $P = 0.05$, in a one-tail test (Table 4), we cannot conclude that the drug was better than placebo.

The 95% confidence interval for the true difference is

$$\pi - \pi' = 10\% \pm 1.96(7.73\%)$$

$$= -5.2\% \text{ to } 25.2\%$$

Thus, although the interval includes zero, it is interesting to note that a true difference as great as 25% in favor of the drug would not have been detected in this experiment. Moreover, a slight adverse effect of the drug (as great as 5.2% decrease in cure rate) would also not have been detected.

CHI-SQUARE TEST:
EXPECTATIONS KNOWN OR ASSUMED

If there are more than two alternative categories of response, the simple methods developed for binomial populations no longer serve. A useful tool that can be applied to various problems involving enumeration data, regardless of sample size or number of categories, is the chi-square test.

The statistic known as chi-square (χ^2) is computed as follows. The items in the various categories of a sample are counted. For each category the difference between the expected number of items ($E = N\pi$) and the number actually observed ($O = Np$) is squared and then divided by the number expected,

$$\frac{(E - O)^2}{E}$$

The computation always involves actual numbers of items, never proportions or percents. χ^2 is then the sum of all such terms, one for each category,

$$\chi^2 = \sum \frac{(E - O)^2}{E}$$

Evidently, the terms $(E - O)^2$ will tend to be small for small samples and large for large samples, since they involve actual differences between numbers of items, but the ratios $(E - O)^2/E$ will be the same regardless of sample size. Clearly too, as the sampling is repeated again and again, since in most samples O will be close to E, small values of χ^2 will predominate and large ones will be rare.

A model population was set up, consisting of a very large number of red and blue beads, in the proportions 0.4 red and 0.6 blue. From this population 20 samples of 25 beads each were drawn, and the frequencies of the different outcomes were recorded. For each outcome the corresponding χ^2 was also computed. The results are shown below.[4]

---

[4]To simplify the explanation at this point, an essential correction (p. 104) is omitted. Consequently each χ^2 is slightly too large.

20 SAMPLES

$$(\pi = 0.40, \ N = 25, \ E = N\pi = 10, \ E' = N(1-\pi) = 15)$$

Number of A in Sample (O)	$\dfrac{(E-O)^2}{E}$	Number of not-A in Sample (O')	$\dfrac{(E'-O')^2}{E'}$	χ^2	Observed Frequency
13	$\dfrac{9}{10}$	12	$\dfrac{9}{15}$	1.50	4
12	$\dfrac{4}{10}$	13	$\dfrac{4}{15}$	0.67	2
11	$\dfrac{1}{10}$	14	$\dfrac{1}{15}$	0.17	5
10	$\dfrac{0}{10}$	15	$\dfrac{0}{15}$	0	2
9	$\dfrac{1}{10}$	16	$\dfrac{1}{15}$	0.17	1
8	$\dfrac{4}{10}$	17	$\dfrac{4}{15}$	0.67	2
7	$\dfrac{9}{10}$	18	$\dfrac{9}{15}$	1.50	3
6	$\dfrac{16}{10}$	19	$\dfrac{16}{15}$	2.67	0
5	$\dfrac{25}{10}$	20	$\dfrac{25}{15}$	4.17	1

χ^2	Frequency	Relative Frequency	Cumulative Relative Frequency
0	2	0.10	0.10
0.17	6	0.30	0.40
0.67	4	0.20	0.60
1.50	7	0.35	0.95
4.17	1	0.05	1.00

Even this limited sampling experiment shows that most χ^2 are in the region 0 to 1, whereas large values are extremely rare. The theoretical distribution of χ^2 values expected in the long run as a result of random sampling has been tabulated.[5] Sufficient for most purposes is Table 9, which gives critical values of χ^2 at $P = 0.05$ and $P = 0.01$, for two-tail and one-tail tests, i.e., values that are exceeded by chance with those probabilities.

The number of categories into which data are classified greatly affects the theoretical distribution of χ^2. If we have a certain number of categories, and a fixed total number of observations, we shall have "freedom" to enter data in all but one category, this last one being filled automatically by items not already entered in the others. For quantitative data, DF was always one less than the sample size. For enumeration data only the *number of categories* is considered, regardless of the number of items in each category, and DF is one less than the number of categories.

In problems involving only two categories, a correction (the Yates correction) is required, to compensate for the fact that whereas the χ^2 distribution is continuous, the enumeration data themselves are integers and therefore discontinuous. The correction is simple: one reduces the absolute magnitude of each difference $(E - O)$ by 0.5 unit. The corrected difference, $(E - O)_c$ is then squared and χ^2 is computed as usual. If the effect of the correction is to reduce $(E - O)$ to zero or below zero, the contribution of that term to χ^2 is zero; one must not proceed to square negative values of $(E - O)_c$.

Finally, the actual sampling distribution will conform to the χ^2 distribution only if samples are not too small, and the "rule of 5," introduced earlier, also applies here: The expected number of items in every category should be at least 5. Otherwise exact binomial probabilities should be computed.

Example 3-7. Application of χ^2 method, E known or hypothesized.

In a disease with 40% mortality we treat 17 patients and only three die. Is the treatment effective?

	Die	Not-die
E	6.8	10.2
O	3	14
$(E - O)$	3.8	3.8
$(E - O)_c$	3.3	3.3
$(E - O)_c^2$	10.89	10.89

$$\frac{(E - O)_c^2}{E} \qquad \frac{10.89}{6.8} + \frac{10.89}{10.2} = \chi^2 = 2.67$$

[5]For example, R. A. Fisher and F. Yates, *Statistical Tables for Biological, Agricultural and Medical Research*, 4th ed. (New York: Hafner Publishing Company, Inc., 1953), Table IV.

Since 2.67 just fails to exceed the tabulated value $\chi^2 = 2.71$ for $P = 0.05$ at 1 DF in a one-tail test (Table 9), we cannot conclude the treatment is effective.

As a matter of fact, if the exact probability is computed for 3 or fewer deaths, from the sum of the last four terms of $(0.4 + 0.6)^{17}$, it will be found to be 0.045. Thus, the χ^2 method gave a somewhat inexact result because even a sample of 17 is rather small.[6] The approximate nature of these methods when applied to small samples should always be borne in mind.

Example 3-8.   *E* too small for χ^2 method.

In the same disease with 40% mortality we treat 10 patients and only 1 dies. Is the treatment effective? Here, since $\pi = 40\%$ and $N = 10$, $E = 4$ so the exact binomial probabilities must be found. Since the cumulative probability of observing "one death or fewer" is desired, the last two terms of the binomial expansion of $(0.4 + 0.6)^{10}$ can be used,

$$10(0.4)(0.6)^9 + (0.6)^{10} = P$$

and with the aid of the table of logarithms (Table 3), the exact probability 0.046 is found. We may therefore conclude, at the 5% level of significance, that the treatment is effective.

The problem, as posed here, requires a one-tail procedure, so Table 11 would not have provided an appropriate shortcut, unless the lower level of significance, $P = 0.025$ were adopted. In that case we would be unable to assert that the treatment is effective, since the upper confidence limit given by Table 11 is 0.44, which exceeds the stated true mortality.

Consider the effect upon χ^2 if the same proportions of A and *not-A* were observed in samples of increasing size. We will assume that $p = 0.2$ in all samples and that we are testing the hypothesis, $\pi = 0.4$.

[6]On the other hand,

$$\pi = 40\%$$
$$N = 17$$
$$p = \frac{3}{17} = 17.6\%$$
$$\sigma_p^2 = \frac{40(60)}{17} = 141$$
$$\sigma_p = \sqrt{141} = 11.9$$
$$x^* = \frac{p - \pi}{\sigma_p} = \frac{17.6 - 40.0}{11.9} = \frac{-22.4}{11.9} = -1.88$$

And reference to Table 4 shows that in both tails of the normal curve, the total area beyond $x^* = \pm 1.88$ is 0.06, so the area beyond -1.88 in one tail is 0.03. Were a continuity correction applied, as in the χ^2 method, the two methods would be identical.

Sample Size	Die	Recover	χ^2	P
10	2	8	0.94	>0.05[7]
20	4	16	2.54	>0.05
40	8	32	5.85	0.01–0.05
100	20	80	15.83	<0.01

It should now be evident that: (1) For a given sample size, the greater the difference between observed and expected numbers, the larger the value of χ^2. (2) For a given p, the greater the sample size, the larger the value of χ^2. (3) For a given absolute difference $(E - O)$, the greater the sample size, the smaller the value of χ^2.

In the commonest type of problem, where there are only two categories (1 DF), the critical values of χ^2 are 3.8 and 6.6 for the 5% and 1% significance levels, respectively, in the two-tail test; 2.7 and 5.4 in the one-tail test, where the question is about a difference from expectation, *in a specified direction*. These four χ^2 values are so often needed that they are well worth remembering; critical values for multiple-category problems can then be looked up as required.

One of the most useful aspects of the χ^2 test is that one can pose any hypothetical expectation and test whether a sample observation is compatible with it or not.

Example 3-9. Hypothetical expectation, χ^2 test.

In a genetic experiment a particular mutant characteristic would occur in the ratio 1 mutant to three wild-type in the generation under study, if it were inherited as a Mendelian recessive. Observation shows 39 wild-type and four mutant. Is this outcome compatible with the postulated mechanism of inheritance?

	Wild	Mutant
E	$3/4 \times 43$	$1/4 \times 43$
	$= 32.2$	$= 10.8$
O	39	4
$(E - O)$	6.8	6.8
$(E - O)_c$	6.3	6.3
$(E - O)_c^2$	39.7	39.7
$\dfrac{(E - O)_c^2}{E}$	1.2 $+$	$3.7 = \chi^2 = 4.9$

[7]E is really too small to justify this computation at all.

And since this exceeds the critical value at $P = 0.05$, we reject the hypothesis that the observed sample was drawn from a population containing the postulated proportion $3:1$.

CHI-SQUARE TEST: CONTINGENCY TABLES

In the examples considered up to this point we have seen how an observed result can be compared with an expected one. It often happens, however, that there is no basis whatsoever for formulating an expectation. Thus, if a drug is being compared with a placebo, nothing may be known in advance about the result to be expected from either. Data of this type are usually presented in *contingency tables*, as in the following example.

Example 3-10. 2 × 2 contingency table.

A double-blind experiment was conducted with 145 subjects, to find out whether or not caffeine delays the onset of sleep. The results are shown in a fourfold (also called "2 × 2") contingency table.

	Placebo	*Caffeine*	*Total*
Delay	*(a)* 8	*(b)* 30	38
No delay	*(c)* 65	*(d)* 42	107
Total	73	72	145

The boxes of the table are identified by letters for easier reference in the following calculations. Here we have four categories: placebo-delay, caffeine-delay, placebo-no-delay, caffeine-no-delay. It is readily ascertained that since all the marginal totals are fixed, once data are entered in any single box, the other boxes are filled automatically by subtraction. Thus, fourfold tables are characterized by 1 DF.

Since there are no *a priori* expectations, we begin by assuming that the drug and placebo results were drawn from the same population (null hypothesis). From the pooled data we can then estimate an expectation for each box of the table. The placebo group was 73/145 of the total, and 38 subjects altogether showed a delay. On the assumption that the drug and placebo do not differ, we should then expect the proportion of subjects showing a delay to be the same in both groups. Thus we expect in box a, $(73/145) \times 38 = 19.1$. The remaining expectations can be filled in by subtraction from the marginal totals: $b = 18.9$, $c = 53.9$, $d = 53.1$.

We now calculate the contribution of each box to χ^2 in the usual way, remembering (since there is only one degree of freedom) to make the Yates correction. In box a for example,

$$(E - O) = (19.1 - 8) = 11.1$$

$$(E - O)_c = 10.6$$

$$(E - O)_c^2 = 112$$

$$\frac{(E - O)_c^2}{E} = 5.9$$

The contributions of boxes b, c, d are similarly computed to be 5.9, 2.1, 2.1, and so $\chi^2 = 16.0$, $P < 0.01$. We therefore reject the null hypothesis and conclude that caffeine did significantly delay the onset of sleep.

A shortcut method of carrying out computations on 2×2 contingency tables proves very useful, for it permits one to make rough-and-ready evaluations of such data wherever they are found and without benefit of any calculating devices. It can be shown mathematically that the following equation for χ^2 is identical with the step-by-step procedure outlined above:

$$\chi^2 = \frac{(|ad - bc| - \frac{1}{2}T)^2(T)}{(T_1)(T_2)(T_3)(T_4)}$$

where ad and bc are the diagonal cross-products of the boxes, T_{1-4} are the marginal totals, and T is the overall total. The diagonal cross-products should be obtained by accurate multiplication and the absolute magnitude of the difference then reduced by $\frac{1}{2}T$ (the Yates correction). The subsequent calculations can be carried out very roughly without greatly disturbing the result. The reason is that if χ^2 is much larger than the critical value for $P = 0.01$, or much smaller than that for $P = 0.05$, its exact numerical value is really immaterial. Only if χ^2 turns out to be close to the critical values must an exact calculation be performed, and even then the shortcut method should be used. Let us recalculate the data of Example 3-10 by the shortcut method, using the roughest kinds of approximation.

$$ad = 8 \times 42 = \quad 336$$

$$bc = 30 \times 65 = 1{,}950$$

$$|ad - bc| \quad 1{,}614$$

$$-\tfrac{1}{2}T = -\frac{145}{2} \cong -73$$

$$1{,}541$$

$$\frac{1{,}541 \times 1{,}541 \times 145}{73 \times 72 \times 107 \times 38} = \chi^2$$

Cancelling roughly, $\dfrac{1{,}541}{73} \cong 20$, $\dfrac{1{,}541}{72} \cong 20$, $\dfrac{145}{107} \cong 1.5$, we obtain $\dfrac{600}{38} \cong 15 \cong \chi^2$. Now this value is not exactly correct (the right value is 16.0) but it yields all the information we require; namely, that $P < 0.01$ so that caffeine may be judged to have caused the delay in onset of sleep.

Example 3-10 could also have been worked by testing the significance of the difference between p in the placebo sample and p' in the caffeine sample. It can be shown that despite the different symbols used, the two methods are really identical; comparison of Tables 9 and 4 will reveal, for example, that χ^2 at 1 DF is simply $(x^*)^2$ at the same P.

$$A = 8, \quad N = 73, \quad p = \frac{8}{73} = 11.0\%$$

$$A' = 30, \quad N = 72, \quad p' = \frac{30}{72} = 41.7\%$$

$$\text{pooled } p = \frac{A + A'}{N + N'} = \frac{38}{145} = 26.2\%$$

$$\text{pooled } s^2 = 26.2(73.8) = 1{,}934$$

$$s_p{}^2 = \frac{1{,}934}{73} = 26.5$$

$$s_{p'}{}^2 = \frac{1{,}934}{72} = 26.8$$

$$s_d{}^2 = \qquad 53.3$$

$$s_d = \sqrt{53.3} = 7.30\%$$

$$x^* = \frac{p - p'}{s_d} = \frac{41.7 - 11.0}{7.30} = 4.20, \quad P < 0.01$$

It is quite often the case that a 2×2 contingency table has one or more boxes in which the expected number is smaller than 5. If all boxes save one contain numbers greater than 5 and that one box contains at least a 1, the discrepancy is not likely to be serious.[8] For more extreme cases, the methods described above are not valid and special tabulations may be consulted[9], which list all possible 2×2 contingency tables, for given marginal totals, and give the exact probability of occurrence of each by random sampling.

If the special tables are not at hand, it is possible to compute exact probabilities without too much difficulty, provided the entries in the table are fairly small. The rationale of the method is simply that for given marginal totals the entries in the boxes may be arranged in a number of different ways. One can write all possible 2×2 tables with fixed marginal totals and calculate the probability of each such table, if the null hypothesis were true. The probability of obtaining the particular table in hand, by chance, is thus obtained. This probability is given by[10]

$$\frac{(a + b)!(c + d)!(a + c)!(b + d)!}{N!\,a!\,b!\,c!\,d!}$$

The desired probability is for obtaining the particular table *or one even more extreme*, so we must sum the probabilities for the table in hand and all more extreme tables.

Example 3-11.

There is some reason to believe that a certain new drug might have value in particular kinds of cancer. However, the drug is quite toxic, so it is not desirable to embark on large-scale clinical trials without some good preliminary evidence of efficacy. Ten patients are assigned randomly to control and treatment groups and their status is evaluated (blind, of course) at the end of six months, with the following result:

[8]A. H. Bowker and G. J. Lieberman, *Engineering Statistics* (Englewood Cliffs, N.J.: Prentice-Hall, Inc., 1959), footnote, p. 366.

[9]For example, E. S. Pearson and H. O. Hartley, *Biometrika Tables for Statisticians*, Vol. 1, (London: Cambridge University Press, 1954), Table 38.

[10]$N!$ means $N(N - 1)(N - 2) \ldots (2)(1)$. Both $1!$ and $0!$ are taken to be unity.

	Control	*Treated*	*Total*
Improved	(a) 0	(b) 4	(a + b) 4
Not improved	(c) 5	(d) 1	(c + d) 6
Total	(a + c) 5	(b + d) 5	(N) 10

Here the expected numbers in all boxes are less than 5, so the exact method is obligatory. To see what tables are possible with these marginal totals, we may focus attention on a single box, e.g., box *a*, and change it systematically. Each number chosen for this box automatically determines the numbers in the other boxes. The possible tables of this kind are:

$$\frac{0 \mid 4}{5 \mid 1} \qquad \frac{1 \mid 3}{4 \mid 2} \qquad \frac{2 \mid 2}{3 \mid 3} \qquad \frac{3 \mid 1}{2 \mid 4} \qquad \frac{4 \mid 0}{1 \mid 5}$$

Then it is evident that the observed table is the most favorable to the treatment, of all the possible tables. Its probability is

$$\frac{4!\,6!\,5!\,5!}{10!\,0!\,4!\,5!\,1!}$$

Cancelling and simplifying, and rembering $0! = 1$ and $1! = 1$, we obtain $P = 0.024$, so the treatment is deemed to be effective at the 5% level of significance.

It is interesting that if this particular problem is worked (inappropriately) by the ordinary χ^2 method, the result is $\chi^2 = 3.75$, which gives almost the same one-tail *P*-value as above. Such agreement, however, cannot be counted on when the "rule of 5" is ignored.

If the numbers involved are large, even after partial cancellation of factorials in the numerator and denominator, the remaining numbers may entail very difficult computations unless logarithms are used. Tables of logarithms of *N*! for various integer *N* are available.[11]

For contingency tables larger than fourfold the shortcut method cannot be used, there will be more than 1 DF, and the Yates correction is not required.[12] The procedure is illustrated in the following example.

[11] E. S. Pearson and H. O. Hartley, *Biometrika Tables for Statisticians*, Vol. 1 (London, Cambridge University Press, 1954), Table 51.

[12] A good explanation is found in R. A. Fisher, *Statistical Methods for Research Workers* (Edinburgh: Oliver and Boyd Ltd., 1950), p. 92.

Example 3-12.   Contingency table greater than 2 × 2.

An investigation was made into fatal poisonings of children by three drugs which were the leading causes of such deaths. In each death, an inquiry was made as to how the child had received the fatal overdose and responsibility for the accident was assessed, as in the following contingency table:

Observations	Drug A	Drug B	Drug C	Total
Child responsible	8	12	13	33
Parent responsible	17	10	9	36
Another person responsible	14	9	10	33
Total	39	31	32	102

It was thought that, since the drugs were not related to each other, and would be found in households for very different reasons, appropriate steps might be taken to reduce the risks, if certain associations could be established. Thus, the above data suggest that the child himself is more prone to take B or C than A, while parents seem more often responsible for accidentally administering fatal dosage of drug A. The question is whether or not these apparent associations are real.

This is a 3 × 3 contingency table, so there are $(3 - 1)(3 - 1) = 4$ DF, since after 2 rows and 2 columns have been filled the remainder follows automatically from the fixed marginal totals. As before, we compute expectations from the pooled data. For child-drug A we have $(39/102) \times 33 = 12.6$, and the remainder of the expectations are found in the same way.

Expectations	Drug A	Drug B	Drug C	Total
Child responsible	12.6	10.0	10.4	33
Parent responsible	13.8	10.9	11.3	36
Other responsible	12.6	10.0	10.4	33
Total	39.0	30.9	32.1	102

$(E - O)$ is then obtained by subtraction in each box. If the signs of the differences are recorded (although they are not really needed), a good check on the work is to add them all together; their sum should be zero. The next two steps are combined below.

$\dfrac{(E - O)^2}{E}$	Drug A	Drug B	Drug C
Child responsible	$\dfrac{21.2}{12.6}$	$\dfrac{4.00}{10.0}$	$\dfrac{6.76}{10.4}$
Parent responsible	$\dfrac{10.2}{13.8}$	$\dfrac{0.81}{10.9}$	$\dfrac{5.29}{11.3}$
Other responsible	$\dfrac{1.96}{12.6}$	$\dfrac{1.00}{10.0}$	$\dfrac{0.16}{10.4}$

Summing the 9 contributions, we find $\chi^2 = 4.28$, which falls far short of the critical value 9.5 for $P = 0.05$ with 4 DF (Table 9). We must conclude that the three drug-fatality groups may well represent the same population, i.e., that the apparent associations may well not be real.

It is not legitimate, having failed to find a significant difference in an overall comparison, to proceed to test the drugs against each other in various pairs. If we make enough such special analyses of random data we expect, of course, to find an effect that is "significant" sooner or later but the result would be quite meaningless. Only if the initial analysis including all the data shows evidence of inhomogeneity, (i.e., of having been drawn from more than one population of values) is it then permissible to seek the source of the inhomogeneity through further comparisons of selected components.

In the case of 2×2 contingency tables, special methods were available to deal with the case where $E < 5$ in some of the boxes. Here, when there are 2 or more DF, a valid significance level is likely to be obtained, provided $E \geq 2.5$ in every box.[13] If this criterion cannot be met, it may be possible to combine rows or columns, in effect pooling categories or treatment groups into a smaller table. In Example 3-12, for instance, if it were necessary, one could combine the categories "Parent responsible" and "Another person responsible," yielding a 2×3 table with "child responsible" and "another person responsible." One might also conceivably decide to compare drug A with the pooled data of B and C. There

[13]See A. H. Bowker and G. J. Lieberman, *Engineering Statistics* (Englewood Cliffs, N.J.: Prentice-Hall, Inc., 1959), footnote, p. 366.

may be other good reasons for consolidating data in this way, and since it introduces no bias into the subsequent analyses, it is an acceptable procedure. The net effect, however, is to lose information that may have been meaningful, and a significant association might even be obscured. One should be especially wary of consolidation which presents a drug or other treatment in a more favorable light than it deserves, as for example, setting up a single category of drug response entitled *"cured or improved"* to obscure the fact that whereas improvement may have been frequent, cure was very rare.

A special case of importance is the *ordered* 2 × *c contingency table*, in which two groups are classified into *ranked* categories. Such a table cannot properly be analyzed by the usual χ^2 technique, for the following reason. Consider an ordinary 2 × 3 contingency table:

	Characteristic A	*Characteristic B*	*Characteristic C*
Control group			
Treated group			

The three characteristics *A, B, C* are independent of each other, and χ^2 simply tests whether the distribution of individuals into the three categories is different from what would be expected by chance. We ask if treatment changes the distribution into categories in any (unspecified) way. However, if the categories are ordered, so that $A > B > C$ or $A < B < C$, then the situation becomes very different. If treatment now has any effect, it will be to shift the entire distribution to right or to left. Suppose, for example, that each item in the treated group were shifted slightly to the right. The result would be to transfer some observations from *A* into *B*, and others from *B* into *C*. Thus a small decrease in box *A*, a small increase in box *C*, and no change at all in box *B*, might indicate a consistent and significant treatment effect. The χ^2 method would often fail to detect such an effect, whereas a method that looked at the whole rank array for both groups might discover it. The case is really the same as a two-sample rank comparison, in which all the observations happen to be involved in ties, there being as many tied groups as there are ordered categories of classification. The proper method is therefore the two-sample rank test (p. 55). As shown in the following example, the correction for ties can, for all practical purposes, be ignored even when the whole array of data consists of tied groups.

Example 3-13. Ordered 2 × c contingency table.

In an experiment on the effectiveness of a teaching machine, a machine-instructed group of students was compared with a teacher-instructed group on an achievement test. The following scores were obtained:

	40–49	50–59	60–69	70–79	80–89	90–99	*Total*
Control	21	40	55	38	10	2	166
Experimental	18	35	42	46	19	4	164
Total	39	75	97	84	29	6	330

We compute U from the control group, multiplying each average rank by the number of items in that rank. (U could just as well be computed from the treated group.) These computations are shown on p. 116.

Sum of ranks for control group $= R = 25{,}843$

$$U = NN' + \frac{N(N+1)}{2} - R$$

$$= 166(164) + \frac{166(167)}{2} - 25{,}843 = 15{,}388$$

$$x^* = \frac{U - \dfrac{NN'}{2}}{\sqrt{\dfrac{NN'(N+N'+1)}{12}}}$$

$$= \frac{15{,}388 - \dfrac{27{,}224}{2}}{\sqrt{\dfrac{27{,}224(331)}{12}}} = 2.05$$

Computations for Example 3-13.

Raw Score	40–49	50–59	60–69	70–79	80–89	90–99
Total in category	39	75	97	84	29	6
Cumulative total	39	114	211	295	324	330
Average rank	$0 + \dfrac{39+1}{2}$ $= 20.0$	$39 + \dfrac{75+1}{2}$ $= 77.0$	$114 + \dfrac{97+1}{2}$ $= 163.0$	$211 + \dfrac{84+1}{2}$ $= 253.5$	$295 + \dfrac{29+1}{2}$ $= 310.0$	$324 + \dfrac{6+1}{2}$ $= 327.5$
Number in control group	21	40	55	38	10	2
Total of ranks for control group	$21 \times 20.0 =$ 410.	3,080.	8,965.	9,633.	3,100.	655.

We see in Table 4 that 2.05 is greater than 1.64, the critical value at $P = 0.05$ in a one-tail test, but less than 2.33, the corresponding value at $P = 0.01$. We may therefore conclude, at the 5% significance level (but not at the 1% level), that machine-instructed students performed better than controls.

It is interesting to note in this example that if the rather elaborate correction for ties is applied, the resulting value of x^* is 2.11, not enough different to affect the interpretation in the least.

If the above example is worked (inappropriately) as though it were an ordinary contingency table, we find $\chi^2 = 6.48$, which does not exceed the critical value 9.24 for the one-tail test at 5 DF (Table 9). This illustrates the weakness of the ordinary χ^2 procedure in an ordered contingency table.

A very common example of an ordered contingency table, that is often not recognized as such, is the kind that summarizes the result of drug therapy by recording the numbers of patients in such categories as, "cured," "much improved," "improved," and so on. If the comparison is between two groups (such as control and drug-treated) the method employed in Example 3-13 should be followed. For a larger number of groups, special procedures are required.[14]

POISSON DISTRIBUTION:
ANALYSIS OF COUNTS

A special kind of enumeration data involves isolated events in a continuum of time or space. Consider the behavior of radioactive atoms. One can detect a certain number of disintegrations per minute but it makes no sense to ask how many "not-disintegrations" occurred. In effect there is only a single category in which items are counted. If we make innumerable replicate counts, minute after minute, the sample counts per minute will converge toward a general mean, λ, and there will be a certain variance of the individual observations. The sampling distribution in a population of isolated events is known as a *Poisson distribution*. As might be expected, it is not unrelated to the binomial and normal distributions.

If the mean occurrence of an isolated event is λ, then the probabilities of its occurrence 0, 1, 2, 3 ... times in a random sample are given by the

[14]M. G. Kendall, *Rank Correlation Methods* (New York: Hafner Publishing Company, Inc., 1955).

successive terms in the expansion[15] of $e^{-\lambda} \cdot e^{\lambda} = 1$. The expansion yields

$$e^{-\lambda}\left(1 + \frac{\lambda}{1} + \frac{\lambda^2}{1 \cdot 2} + \frac{\lambda^3}{1 \cdot 2 \cdot 3} + \frac{\lambda^4}{1 \cdot 2 \cdot 3 \cdot 4} + \cdots\right)$$

The terms are interpreted in the same way as the terms of the binomial expansion (p. 95). Thus the probability of obtaining 0 events in a sample is $e^{-\lambda}$ (1); 1 event, $e^{-\lambda}\left(\dfrac{\lambda}{1}\right)$; 2 events, $\dfrac{e^{-\lambda}\lambda^2}{1 \cdot 2}$; 3 events, $\dfrac{e^{-\lambda}\lambda^3}{1 \cdot 2 \cdot 3}$; and so on. Sample size does not enter these expressions because the "sample" is an arbitrary interval in the time or space continuum, defined by λ. Thus, if a problem happens to deal with hailstones, and $\lambda = 0.6$ per sq ft, the sampling unit is the square foot, and the sampling distribution predicts the relative frequency of 0, 1, 2, 3 ... hailstones per sq ft.

Table 12 is a tabulation of the exponential, $e^{-\lambda}$, for small values of λ, whence the terms of the Poisson distribution may be computed.[16]

Example 3-14. Poisson distribution: Test of randomness by χ^2.

100 agar plates containing an antibiotic were spread with a million bacteria each in order to determine the incidence of antibiotic-resistant mutants. Each such mutant cell gives rise to a single colony. After incubation 58 resistant colonies were found altogether, distributed as follows: 63 plates had no colonies, 22 had 1 colony, 10 had 2 colonies, 4 had 3 colonies, and 1 had 4 colonies. Ascertain if the data are consistent with random sampling, and if so, calculate the frequency of resistant mutants in the bacterial population.

$$\lambda = \frac{58 \text{ colonies}}{100 \text{ plates}} = 0.58 \text{ colonies per plate}$$

$$e^{-\lambda} = 0.560$$

Then the expectations may be calculated from the Poisson distribution, and tabulated, as follows:

[15]$e = 2.718$, the base of natural logarithms.

[16]More extensive tabulation of $e^{-\lambda}$ will be found in any volume of mathematical tables. A source that is readily available to many students is the *Handbook of Chemistry and Physics* (Cleveland: Chemical Rubber Publishing Company). The terms of the Poisson distribution itself may be found directly in E. S. Pearson and H. O. Hartley, *Biometrika Tables for Statisticians*, Vol. 1 (London: Cambridge University Press 1954). Table 39.

Colonies per Plate	Probability	Number of Plates with This Number of Colonies per plate	
		Expected	*Observed*
0	$e^{-\lambda} = 0.560$	56.0	63
1	$e^{-\lambda}(\lambda) = 0.560 \times 0.58 = 0.325$	32.5	22
2	$\dfrac{e^{-\lambda}\lambda^2}{2} = 0.560 \times \dfrac{0.336}{2} = 0.0941$	9.41	10
3	$\dfrac{e^{-\lambda}\lambda^3}{6} = 0.560 \times \dfrac{0.195}{6} = 0.0182$	1.82	4
4 or more		0.27	1
		100.0	100

The differences between the expected and observed occurrences may be tested for significance by χ^2. The calculation (see p. 106) will be left to the reader. The result obtained, 8.9, is less than the tabulated value $\chi^2 = 9.5$ for $P = 0.05$ at 3 DF (Table 9).[17] We therefore conclude that the observations are consistent with random sampling fluctuations. The frequency of resistant mutants may then be calculated as 0.58 per million bacterial cells, or 5.8×10^{-7}.

An interesting and useful feature of the Poisson distribution is that its variance is equal to its mean. This fact can be understood in relation to the binomial variance,

$$\sigma_p{}^2 = \frac{\pi(1 - \pi)}{N}$$

If the observations were expressed as numbers of A per sample ($= Np$) instead of p, the relevant population parameter would be $N\pi$. Since the mean (π) is multiplied by N, the variance will have to be multiplied by N^2 (p. 44). The sampling variance of Np, the number of A per sample, is therefore

$$\sigma_{Np}{}^2 = N^2 \left[\frac{\pi(1 - \pi)}{N} \right] = N\pi(1 - \pi)$$

[17]With five categories it might be thought there would be 4 DF. However, the expectations were computed from a sample estimate of the true parameter λ. Whenever we use an estimate rather than a parameter we lose a degree of freedom.

Now the Poisson distribution may be regarded as a binomial in which π is exceedingly small, and $(1 - \pi)$ is therefore very nearly unity. Then

$$\sigma_L{}^2 \cong N\pi = \lambda$$

where L will denote a sample count drawn from the population with mean count λ.

The commonest application of the Poisson variance is in estimating counting errors. A single count, L, is a random sample from the population of similar counts with known variance equal to the average count, λ. The sampling distribution of L is approximately normal,

$$x^* = \frac{L - \lambda}{\sigma_L} = \frac{L - \lambda}{\sqrt{\lambda}}$$

By making the reasonable assumption that L is a fairly good estimate of λ, we have

$$s_L = \sqrt{L}$$

Then the confidence interval for the average count is

$$\lambda = L \pm x^* \sqrt{L}$$

where x^* is 1.96 or 2.58 for the 95% or 99% confidence intervals, respectively. This estimate will be more correct the larger the number of counts in the sample, as L becomes a better estimate of λ. For low counts (under 100 or so), L estimates λ so poorly that special tables must be consulted to find the exact confidence interval. Table 13 gives 95% and 99% intervals for counts from 0 to 50. For other applications, more extensive tables should be consulted.[18]

[18]For one-sided 95% or 99% confidence limits, see the tabulation under 0.90 and 0.98 in E. S. Pearson and H. O. Hartley, *Biometrika Tables for Statisticians*, vol. 1 (England: The Cambridge University Press, 1954), Table 40. For counts between 50 and 100 or so, if great accuracy is desired, confidence intervals should be computed from the tabulation in R. A. Fisher and F. Yates, *Statistical Tables for Biological, Agricultural and Medical Research* (New York: Hafner Publishing Company, Inc., 1953), Table VIII₁.

Example 3-15. Confidence interval of a count.

In a counting chamber, 470 red blood cells were counted under the microscope, in a volume of 10^{-4} cubic millimeter. What is the 95% confidence interval for the patient's true red blood cell count, per cubic millimeter?

$$L = 470$$

$$s_L = \sqrt{470} = 21.7$$

$$\lambda = L \pm x^*(s_L)$$

$$= 470 \pm 1.96(21.7)$$

$$= 427 \text{ to } 513$$

This is the estimate per 10^{-4} cu mm, so the true count is 4.27 to 5.13 million cells per cu mm.

Example 3-16. Confidence interval of a count (L moderately small).

A mouse was placed in an artificial earth satellite which orbited for 17 hr and was recovered. Serial sections of tissue were examined for the linear streaks of cell destruction caused by high-energy cosmic-ray particles, and 35 were found in the whole mouse. Assuming the bombardment by cosmic rays was random throughout the 17 hr, what is the confidence interval for the number of hits per hour in a mouse?

$$L = 35$$

Note that L is always the *actual number of events observed*, not events per unit time or per unit space. Table 13 gives the 95% confidence interval for λ as 24.38 to 48.68, when $L = 35$. Then the hits per hour will be 24.38/17 to 48.68/17, or 1.43 to 2.86.

Let us compare with the result we would have obtained, had we used the normal approximation, despite the small value of L.

$$L = 35$$

$$s_L = \sqrt{35} = 5.91$$

$$\lambda = 35 \pm 1.96(5.91)$$

$$= 23.4 \text{ to } 46.6, \text{ or } 1.38 \text{ to } 2.74 \text{ per hr}$$

In this case, with $L = 35$, the normal approximation does not lead to very serious error, but the lower and upper confidence limits are both somewhat too small. This effect becomes more serious as L becomes still smaller, as shown in the next example.

Example 3-17.   Confidence interval of a count (L very small).

The spontaneous mutation rate of a gene controlling a visible phenotypic change is known, so that on the average one mutant animal is expected per 48,000. After exposure to a suspected mutagenic chemical, four mutants were found in 20,000 animals examined. What can be said about the mutagenicity of the chemical for this gene?

$$L = 4$$

Table 13 gives the 95% confidence interval $\lambda = 1.09$ to 10.24. Then, per 100,000 animals we have $\dfrac{100,000 \times 1.09}{20,000}$ to $\dfrac{100,000 \times 10.24}{20,000}$, or 5.45 to 51.2, whereas the known spontaneous frequency is $100,000/48,000 = 2.08$. We may therefore correctly conclude that the chemical was mutagenic, but the possible range of its mutagenicity is very large, from 2.6 to 24.6 times the spontaneous frequency.

Now if this problem had been worked (inappropriately) by the normal approximation we would have

$$L = 4$$

$$s_L = \sqrt{4} = 2$$

$$\lambda = 4 \pm 1.96(2)$$

$$= 0.08 \text{ to } 7.92$$

which is so seriously in error, that the mutagen would be adjudged ineffective.

In the case of quantitative data, the variance must be estimated empirically, and replications of the observations serve this purpose. In the case of counts, it is only the total number that matters, but it is nevertheless very desirable to divide this total into two or more replicated observations. The purpose is to ensure the detection of gross mistakes (as contrasted to statistical error) such as might arise from human or instrument malfunction. In that case it may prove convenient to estimate λ from the mean, $\bar{L}$, of N replicate counts. Then, of course,

$$s_L^2 = \frac{\bar{L}}{N}$$

$$s_{\bar{L}} = \sqrt{\frac{\bar{L}}{N}}$$

Example 3-18. Confidence interval of a count, estimated from replicated observations.

A radioactive sample was counted 10 times for 1 min each, with the results shown below. Compute the 99% confidence interval of the true average count per minute.

$$5,450, \ 5,309, \ 5,299, \ 5,250, \ 5,329, \ 5,288, \ 5,292, \ 5,353, \ 5,427, \ 5,437.$$

Total $L = 53,434$ in 10 min.

$$s_L = \sqrt{53,434} = 231$$
$$\pm x^*(s_L) = \pm 2.58(231) = 596$$

$\lambda = 53,434 \pm 596 = 52,838$ to $54,030$ in 10 min. 99% confidence interval $= 5,284$ to $5,403$ per min.

Alternatively, $\bar{L} = 5,343.4$ per min, $N = 10$,

$$s_{\bar{L}} = \sqrt{\frac{5,343.4}{10}} = \sqrt{534.34} = 23.1$$

$$\lambda = 5,343 \pm 2.58(23.1)$$
$$= 5,284 \text{ to } 5,403 \text{ per min}$$

The accuracy of a count depends only upon the number of events counted, and since $s_L = \sqrt{L}$, it follows that the counting accuracy improves as the square root of the count itself. Moreover, the approximation $s_L = \sqrt{L}$, used in place of $\sigma_L = \sqrt{\lambda}$, becomes more reliable as L increases. It follows from the foregoing that one can estimate approximately, for any counting procedure, the minimum number of counts required to achieve any desired degree of accuracy.

Example 3-19. Minimum counts required for a given accuracy.

Red blood cells are to be counted once in a counting chamber, to an error of less than 10%, i.e., the 95% confidence interval of the true count is to be no greater than $\pm 10\%$ of the count itself.
Then,

$$1.96(s_L) \leqq 0.10L$$

$$1.96\sqrt{L} \leqq 0.10L$$

$$19.6 \leqq \frac{L}{\sqrt{L}} \leqq \sqrt{L}$$

$L \geqq 385$, the minimum number of cells that must be counted.

Sometimes the question is whether two observed counts differ significantly from each other. Table 14 shows the smallest significant difference between two counts, at "nominal" probability levels 0.05 and 0.01. The actual P values will be lower than those tabulated, expecially for low counts, because the observations can only assume integer values. Thus, the results given by the table will be somewhat conservative, in that a Type I error will be committed less frequently than 5% or 1% of the time.

Example 3-20. Significance of a difference between two counts.

In an experiment to test the mutagenic properties of the compound described in Example 3-17, no information was available about the spontaneous mutation rate before the experiment began, but concurrently, among 20,000 control animals, no mutants were found. In the same experiment, four mutants occurred among 20,000 treated animals. Is there evidence that the chemical is mutagenic?

Here we consult Table 14 at $L + L' = 4$ and find that even the most extreme difference between the two counts cannot be significant. The smallest counts that could differ significantly are 5 and 0. Therefore we cannot conclude that the chemical is mutagenic. It is interesting to compare this result with that obtained in Example 3-17, where the same number of mutants proved the mutagenicity of the chemical because the true spontaneous expectation was known.

Conformity of a series of counts to the Poisson expectation may be used as a test for the randomness of the events giving rise to the observed counts.

Example 3-21. Test of randomness of counts by χ^2.

Use the 10 counts of Example 3-18 to ascertain if the radioactivity counter is functioning acceptably.

Here we begin with the assumption that radioactive disintegrations are truly random. Then a nonrandom distribution of counts would indicate defective operation of the instrument. χ^2 may be used as in Example 3-14 to test the deviations of each L from $\bar{L}$, which we take to be equivalent to λ, the expected count.

$$\bar{L} = 5{,}343.4$$

The deviations $(E - O)$ are: 106.6, 34.4, 44.4, 93.4, 14.4, 55.4, 51.4, 9.6, 83.6, and 93.6.

$$\chi^2 = \sum \frac{(E - O)^2}{E} = \sum \frac{(E - O)^2}{L} = \frac{45,002.4}{5,343.4} = 8.42$$

which is well below the critical value 16.9 for $P = 0.05$ with 8 DF (*Table* 9).[19] The observed counts are therefore consistent with the expectations of random events and we have no reason to doubt the performance of the counter.

Problems

CHAPTER 3 (ANSWERS ON P. 213)

P3-1.

An insecticide supposed to persist for many weeks was painted on a box and two weeks later 100 houseflies were placed therein. The next day 40 of the flies were dead. Find the lower and upper limits of the true mortality under these conditions. (Cf. p. 98.)

P3-2.

In 400 cadavers studied at autopsy, a peculiar congenital anomaly of the brachial artery is found in 22. Assuming that these cadavers were a random sample, what is the smallest likely incidence of this anomaly in the population? (Cf. p. 99.)

P3-3.

Naive rats were placed in a T-maze and then segregated according to whether they turned left or right at the point of choice. They were then killed, and each right and left cerebral cortex was assayed for its content of serotonin. The animals were thereupon classified into two groups, those whose serotonin content was higher on the left, and those whose content was higher on the right. The data were then tabulated, as follows:

[19] See footnote 17, p. 119.

| Serotonin | Turned toward | |
Higher on	Left	Right
Left	14	8
Right	6	10

It appears that there is a relationship between the serotonin content and the tendency to turn one way or the other in the T-maze. Would this conclusion be justified? (Cf. p. 107.)

P3-4.

Trout eggs are gathered in a stream A and brought to a nearby hatchery. The young fish are later marked and randomized. One large group is released again into stream A, another group of equal size is released into a distant tributary, B, of the same river. Ultimately, when the adult fish make their upstream migration, they are caught near the hatchery in stream A. Of the fish released into stream A, 43 are caught; of those released into B, 28 are caught. If there is a real difference, numerous interpretations might be offered. Is there a real difference? (Cf. p. 124.)

P3-5.

DNA synthesis in bacteria is followed by allowing the organisms to incorporate ^{32}P and then extracting and purifying the DNA. The ^{32}P content of a sample is to be determined to within 1% of the correct value. How many counts must be registered? (Cf. p. 123.)

P3-6.

Replicate counts of virus particles on randomly selected square sections of an electron micrograph gave the following results: 153, 250, 220, 81, 306, 244. Are the particles distributed over the entire field in a reasonably uniform way? (Cf. p. 124.)

P3-7.

A small-scale experiment was conducted to see if a certain mushroom extract causes hallucinations. Thirteen subjects were randomized, then six were given the extract and seven received a placebo. Among the placebo group a single subject reported a hallucinatory experience, among the treated group five subjects so reported. What does the experiment show? (Cf. p. 110.)

P3-8.

Five flavoring agents were tested for their ability to mask the bitter taste of a cough medicine for children. The trial was conducted with proper randomization and blind precautions. Each mother was instructed to administer one of the flavored medications to her child, and then to report simply whether or not it was acceptable. The table shows the numbers of children who found each agent acceptable and not acceptable.

Agent	Acceptable	Not Acceptable
A	14	22
B	12	26
C	20	16
D	13	24
E	17	17

What conclusions can be drawn? (Cf. p. 112.)

P3-9.

A series of patients with low back pain were randomly assigned to two groups. The first group was placed on a regimen of strict rest and the avoidance of all muscular exertion. The second group was given a program of vigorous and increasingly difficult exercises. The status of each patient was evaluated at the start (before his assignment to either group) by a panel of orthopedic surgeons. Several months later the panel reevaluated each patient without knowing what program he had been carrying out. To avoid any bias in evaluation, the patients were instructed not to divulge any information to the panel; thus the panel's judgment would be based on objective tests rather than on information gained through interview. The panel classified each patient into a category determined by the degree of change since the initial evaluation. The results were as follows (numbers of patients):

	Therapeutic Rest	Regimen Exercise
Greatly improved	4	6
Improved	10	11
Slightly improved	19	22
Unchanged	18	13
Slightly-worse	6	2
Worse	2	2
Much worse	0	0
Total	59	56

Is there any real difference between the therapeutic regimens? (Cf. p. 115.)

P3-10

Mice were treated with a neuromuscular blocking agent. Equal groups were given the agent at the same dose by a stomach tube and by subcutaneous injection. Thirty minutes later the two groups of animals were placed on inclined wire screens and the number that fell off in each case was recorded. In the group treated by stomach tube 22 of the 50 lost their footing, and in the group injected subcutaneously 35 of the 50 fell from the screen. Is administration by stomach tube less effective than by subcutaneous injection? (Cf. p. 101.)

P3-11.

Mammalian cells grown in a spinner culture in liquid medium are counted by means of an electronic cell counter. The results obtained for three replicate counts on 0.5-ml samples were 762, 724, 811. What is the 99% confidence interval for the true count, per ml? (Cf. p. 121.)

P3-12.

In the experience of a large hospital, the spontaneous cure rate in a certain disease is known to be 77%. A new therapeutic procedure is tried in 20 patients and all of them recover. Is the new procedure effective? (Cf. p. 106.)

Correlation

LINEAR CORRELATION (LINEAR REGRESSION)

Two different properties of the same system (person, animal, tissue, enzyme preparation, inanimate object, etc.) may be quantitatively related. Age and weight in children, for example, tend to be related in a positive sense; the older a child is, the heavier he tends to be. Similarly, the larger the dose of a drug, the greater the biological effect it produces. A relationship may also be negative. For example, the higher the concentration of a poisonous vapor, the lower the survival rate among exposed subjects. The higher the fluoride concentration in a community's drinking water, the lower the incidence of tooth decay among the children. When observations of two properties are related in such a way that one (y) can be predicted better if the other (x) is known, than if it is not, we say x and y are positively or negatively *correlated*, or *associated*. The simplest kind of correlation is a linear one, to which we shall confine our attention. Methods for dealing with nonlinear and multivariate correlation should be sought elsewhere.[1]

Correlation data can be displayed graphically in a *scatter diagram* by plotting each observation as a point on a grid of x and y coordinates. Quite often a measurement of one kind is chosen independently and then the measurement of the other kind is observed. When this is the case, the independent value is plotted on the x-axis, the dependent one on the y-axis. Figure 4-1 is a typical scatter diagram, depicting the conjugating capacity of guinea-pig liver at different ages. The ages were chosen arbitrarily and the enzyme activity at each age was measured. Therefore age is shown on

[1]See list of references beginning on page 194.

the x-axis, enzyme activity on the y-axis. Each point represents the conjugating capacity of a single animal's liver.

Inspection of the scatter diagram reveals an apparent positive correlation between age and enzyme activity. However, it may be surmised from the

Figure 4–1   Development of the glucuronide conjugating system in guinea pig liver with increasing age. Each point represents the conjugating capacity of a single animal's liver. The rate of conjugation of phenolphthalein with glucuronic acid was measured. (Data of Brown and Zuelzer.*)

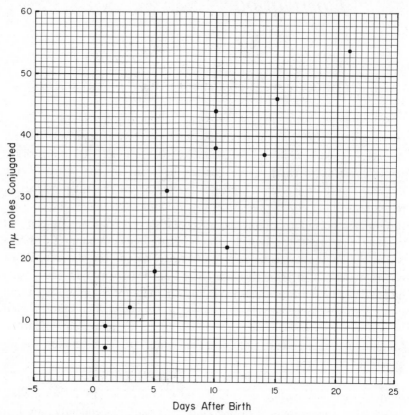

*A. K. Brown and W. W. Zuelzer, *J. Clin. Invest.* **37**: 332(1958).

scatter of the 11 experimental points that a different sample of guinea pig livers would have yielded somewhat different results. The statistical approach to linear correlation data follows familiar principles. For each x-value there is assumed to be a population of y-values from which one or more items have been sampled. If there is indeed a linear correlation between x and y, then the means of these y-populations will all fall exactly

on a straight line, known as the *regression line*. If we knew the equation
of this line, we would have a precise quantitative description of the
correlation. The slope would tell us how much the true value of y changes
for a given change in x, and we could use the line to find an expected
value of y for any given value of x. The problem is to estimate the true
regression line and its confidence limits from the data of a random
sample.[2] With the estimated regression line and its confidence limits in
hand, we will then be able to decide whether an apparent correlation is
real, or whether it might have come about through the chances of sampling from a population in which x and y measurements are really unrelated. We will also be able to decide whether regression lines for two
different samples represent the same or different populations, whether two
slopes differ significantly from each other, and how far apart on the x-axis
two estimated regression lines might really be.

SOME COMMON WAYS OF DISPLAYING CORRELATION DATA

It will be recalled in connection with single-parameter data that the
relevance of reporting either standard deviation or standard error depends
largely upon the purpose the data are to serve. Sometimes one is appropriate, sometimes the other. If the chief concern is with the individual
observations, then some multiple of the standard deviation will be expected
to include a definite fraction of the observations. If, on the other hand,
the main interest is in the true value of the mean, then some multiple of
the standard error of the mean will include the true mean with a known
probability. Very similar considerations apply to correlation data. If
the main question concerns the likely value of a single x,y observation, then
some kind of confidence interval based directly upon the standard
deviations of the various x and y observations will be appropriate. If,
however, one wants to know the true nature of the regression of y on x,
then a confidence range for the regression line as a whole will be desired.
In either case, all the x,y observations contribute information, so the entire
set of correlation data should enter the computations. The appropriate
procedures are presented later in this chapter. Here we shall first consider
briefly some shortcuts that are commonly employed in the graphical
presentation of correlation data.

[2]The problem is analogous to that of estimating μ and its confidence limits from a
sample of x-data.

We should mention first (but only to condemn it) the practice of presenting a regression line fitted to experimental points, without any visible quantitative indication of the validity of the estimate. Experience has shown that intuition is not a reliable guide for assessing the significance of such lines, their slopes, their differences from one another, and so on. Only too often the reader's subjective judgments differ from the author's, so that data which might have been convincing remain ambiguous, or data which are really inconclusive acquire a convincing appearance.

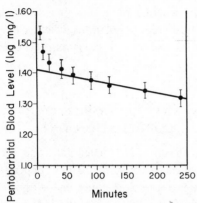

Figure 4–2 Decline of the blood level of pentobarbital with time after a single intravenous injection in dogs. Each point represents the mean of observations on four animals. The vertical lines signify $\pm$ standard error. (Data of Setnikar and Temelcou.*)

*I. Setnikar and O. Temelcou, *J. Pharmacol. Exptl. Therap.* **135**: 213(1962).

Often the observations of y are replicated at each of several x-values. Then for every x there is a sample estimate, $\bar{y}_x$, of the true mean of the y population for that particular x. The most likely regression line will be that from which the sum of squared deviations of all the $\bar{y}_x$ values is a minimum ("least-squares" line). Since the standard error of each $\bar{y}_x$ can be computed readily by single-parameter methods, it is quite usual to portray $\pm$S.E. by a vertical line of appropriate length through each $\bar{y}_x$. A typical illustration of this is seen in Fig. 4-2, where this measure of variability of the mean blood level of a drug is indicated for each time when a blood sample was drawn. Certainly this shows something about the reliability of the data, but it conveys a rather misleading impression of how accurate the estimate really is. One naturally tends to suppose that the parameter being estimated must lie somewhere on each vertical line, but as a matter of fact this could be true only two-thirds of the time at best (since $\pm$S.E. includes only two-thirds of all large-sample means), and

even less often if the sample sizes are small. In the experiment depicted in
Fig. 4-2, for example, one might suppose that the true mean blood level
at 90 min lies, with a fair degree of certainty, between 1.35 and 1.41 units.
Actually, since there were only four observations per group, $t = 3.18$ for
3 DF at $P = 0.05$, so the 95% confidence interval for the blood level at this
particular time will be more than three times greater than the vertical line
suggests.

In Figure 4-3 the standard deviation (rather than the standard error)
was chosen as the measure of variability in a standard curve for the

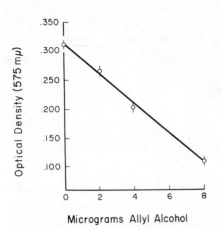

Figure 4–3 Standard calibration curve
for a method of determining allyl alcohol.
Each point is the mean of a number of
determinations whose standard deviation
is shown by the vertical lines. (Adapted
from Kodama and Hine.*)

Micrograms Allyl Alcohol

*J. K. Kodama and C. H. Hine, *J. Pharmacol. Exptl. Therap.* **124**: 97(1958).

assay of allyl alcohol. This choice is correct because here the regression
line would be used for the prediction of a single observation. What we
wish to know is the range of optical densities within which the reading
will lie when we perform a single determination on a given amount of
allyl alcohol. Again, however, the range ±S.D. gives a false
impression, since it will only include two-thirds of the observations.
Moreover, this case presents a further complication. If the regression line
is to be used for the assay of unknown amounts of allyl alcohol, the
problem will be to estimate the unknown from a given optical density
reading, and to attach a confidence interval to such an estimate. This
problem of estimating x from y can only be handled properly by means of
the procedures developed later in this chapter.

Of the various shortcuts for graphic representation of the reliability of
correlation data, the most satisfactory is that illustrated in Fig. 4-4.

Vertical lines are again used, but now the length of each line is made equal to the 95% confidence interval for the true mean y at that value of x. Obviously the true regression line, expressing the general relationship between y and x in the population, must pass through all (or nearly all) such individual confidence ranges. Actually this is a conservative procedure, since the confidence band formed by joining all the upper and

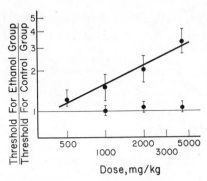

Threshold For Ethanol Group / Threshold For Control Group

Dose, mg/kg

Figure 4–4 Effects of increasing doses of ethanol on electroshock seizure threshold in mice. Two different shock procedures are represented by the two sets of points. Each point is the value determined in a group of 15 – 25 mice. Vertical lines indicate 95% confidence limits. Both the dose scale and the threshold ratio scale are logarithmic. (Adapted from McQuarrie and Fingl.*)

*D. G. McQuarrie and E. Fingl, *J. Pharmacol. Exptl. Therap.* **124**: 264(1958).

lower extremities of the vertical lines is wider than the true 95% confidence band for the regression line as a whole. Thus in the experiment depicted in Fig. 4-4 there is little doubt that seizure threshold was increased significantly by increasing dosage of ethanol with one shock procedure, but not with the other.

MISINTERPRETATIONS OF CORRELATION DATA

False conclusions may be drawn from valid correlation data. First, it must be understood that the mere fact of a correlation implies nothing necessarily about cause and effect. True, the absence of correlation may lead one to reject a hypothesis that y-effects are caused by x. However, even the strongest correlation does not of itself permit one to infer a causal relationship. A correlation may be wholly accidental, as that between the sale of bananas and the death rate from cancer in England.[3] Or y and x effects may be caused independently by other factors that in turn have common causes, as in the correlation over many years between

[3]A. B. Hill, *Principles of Medical Statistics* (New York: Oxford University Press, 1955), p. 185.

the salaries of Presbyterian ministers in Massachusetts and the price of rum in Havana.[4]

A second source of misinterpretation is unwarranted extrapolation. One may never assume without good reason that a regression line will extend beyond the limits of the observational data, and quite often it does not. Figure 4-1 provides a good example. We may perhaps have grounds for supposing that extrapolation back to zero enzyme activity at a few days prior to birth is meaningful, although it is also quite possible that the enzyme increases at a much slower rate during a longer period of prenatal life. Extrapolation in the other direction is clearly unwarranted; as a matter of fact it has been shown experimentally that this enzyme activity does not increase further beyond that attained at 21 days. Mark Twain's[5] wry comment on the shortening of the Lower Mississippi points up the pitfall of extrapolation in a most entertaining way.

> In the space of one hundred and seventy-six years the Lower Mississippi has shortened itself two hundred and forty-two miles. This is an average of a trifle over one mile and a third per year. Therefore, any calm person, who is not blind or idiotic, can see that in the Old Öolitic Silurian Period, just a million years ago next November, the Lower Mississippi River was upward of one million three hundred thousand miles long, and stuck out over the Gulf of Mexico like a fishing-rod. And by the same token any person can see that seven hundred and forty-two years from now the Lower Mississippi will be only a mile and three-quarters long, and Cairo and New Orleans will have joined their streets together. and be plodding comfortably along under a single mayor and a mutual board of aldermen. There is something fascinating about science. One gets such wholesale returns of conjecture out of such a trifling investment of fact.

ESTIMATING A REGRESSION LINE
FROM SAMPLE DATA

Now let us return to a detailed consideration of how correlation data should be treated to obtain a regression line and its confidence limits. Let $\tilde{y}$ be the true value of y at any given value of x. Then the equation of the true regression line will be $\tilde{y} = a + bx$, where a is the intercept on the y-axis at $x = 0$, and b is the slope.[6] The observed y-values will scatter

[4]D. Huff, *How to Lie with Statistics* (New York: W. W. Norton & Company., Inc., 1954), p. 90.
[5]Mark Twain, Life on the Mississippi (New York: Harper & Brothers, 1874), p. 155.
[6]*b* is also known as the *regression coefficient*.

above and below the true line, to yield a set of deviations $(y - \tilde{y})$. As already indicated, we choose as our best estimate, the "least-squares" line, from which the sum of squared deviations $\sum (y - \tilde{y})^2$ will be minimum.

In order to find the values of a and b which will minimize the sum of squared y-deviations from the line, we set

$$\frac{dQ}{da} = 0 \quad \text{and} \quad \frac{dQ}{db} = 0$$

where

$$Q = \sum (y - \tilde{y})^2 = \sum (y - a - bx)^2$$

Solving by partial differentiation yields

$$0 = 2 \left(\sum y - Na - b \sum x \right)$$

$$Na = \sum y - b \sum x$$

$$a = \bar{y} - b\bar{x}$$

Thus, $\tilde{y}$ at $\bar{x}$ is $\bar{y}$; in other words, the least-squares line passes through the general mean $\bar{x}, \bar{y}$ of the observations.

Partial differentiation with respect to b gives

$$0 = 2 \left(\sum xy - a \sum x - b \sum x^2 \right)$$

and substituting now for a,

$$0 = \sum xy - \bar{y} \sum x + b\bar{x} \sum x - b \sum x^2$$

$$b = \frac{\sum xy - \bar{y} \sum x}{\sum x^2 - \bar{x} \sum x} = \frac{\sum xy - \dfrac{(\sum x)(\sum y)}{N}}{\sum x^2 - \dfrac{(\sum x)^2}{N}}$$

$$= \frac{SP_{xy}}{SS_x}$$

An equivalent expression can be obtained[7] which shows somewhat

---

[7]The equation

$$b = \frac{\sum (x - \bar{x})(y - \bar{y})}{\sum (x - \bar{x})^2}$$

is derived by adding and subtracting $\bar{y} \sum x$ in the numerator and $\bar{x} \sum x$ in the denominator. $\sum (x - \bar{x})^2$ is familiar as the SS term for x, which appears in the numerator of the x-variance. $\sum (x - \bar{x})(y - \bar{y})$ is a new term, which is the analogous numerator of an expression known as the *covariance* of x and y, and will be symbolized here by SP_{xy} since it is a sum of products rather than a sum of squares.

more clearly just what the slope represents, but the above equation is more suitable for computations. The required terms, $\sum x, \sum y, \sum xy, \sum x^2$ and (for later use) $\sum y^2$, can all be found automatically on a good calculating machine.

The sign of b may be positive or negative, depending upon whether y-values tend to increase or decrease as x-values become larger. If y-values

Figure 4–5 Diagrammatic representation of the slope of a regression line.

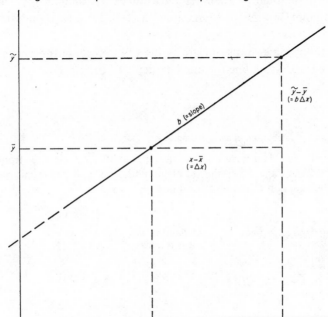

varied without any relation to the associated x-values, there would be no correlation, and the true slope would be zero.

Since we know from the foregoing that the point $\bar{x}, \bar{y}$ lies on the estimated regression line, and since this point is so readily computed, we shall not be concerned further with the intercept, a. Substituting $a = \bar{y} - b\bar{x}$ we obtain a more generally useful equation of the regression line,

$$\tilde{y} = \bar{y} + b(x - \bar{x})$$

Rearranging this expression, we have the reasonable description of slope as the ratio y-deviation to x-deviation, from the point $\bar{x},\bar{y}$

$$b = \frac{\tilde{y} - \bar{y}}{x - \bar{x}}$$

as illustrated in Fig. 4-5.

To draw the estimated regression line, once its equation has been found, plot $(\bar{x},\bar{y})$, as shown. Then add a convenient amount to $\bar{x}$ (preferably as large an amount as possible) and b times this amount to $\bar{y}$, and plot the new point $(\bar{x} + \Delta x, \bar{y} + b\Delta x)$ (see Fig. 4-5). These two points determine the line.

The following example illustrates the full procedure for calculating an estimated regression line for the data depicted in Fig. 4-1.

Example 4-1.   Calculation of a regression line.

The following data were obtained for the ability of liver slices from guinea pigs of different ages to conjugate phenolphthalein with glucuronic acid. Calculate the equation of the regression line.

Age (days)		Millimicromoles Conjugated		
x	x^2	y	y^2	xy
1	1	5.6	31.4	5.6
1	1	8.8	77.4	8.8
3	9	12	144	36
5	25	18	324	90
6	36	31	961	186
10	100	38	1,444	380
10	100	44	1,936	440
11	121	22	484	242
14	196	37	1,369	518
15	225	46	2,116	690
21	441	54	2,916	1,134
$\sum x = 97$	$\sum x^2 = 1,255$	$\sum y = 316.4$	$\sum y^2 = 11,803$	$\sum xy = 3,730.4$

$$b = \frac{940}{400} = 2.4$$

$$\bar{x} = 8.82, \quad \bar{y} = 28.8$$

Then the equation of the regression line is

$$\tilde{y} = 28.8 + 2.4(x - 8.8)$$

The line calculated in the above example is shown as A in Fig. 4-6.

Figure 4-6 Estimated regression line and confidence limits for the data of Figure 4-1.

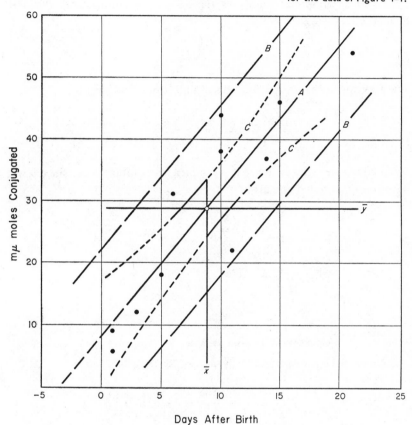

Days After Birth

ESTIMATING THE ERROR VARIANCE AND THE
CONFIDENCE INTERVAL FOR A
REGRESSION LINE

The method of partitioning variances, explained in connection with the analysis of variance (p. 64) is pertinent here. The total variance of y-values about $\bar{y}$ may be broken down into two components. First there is a variance due to the slope of the regression line, so that if all y-values lay exactly on the line, the mean squared deviation of all y from $\bar{y}$ would account for the total variance. Actually there is always a second component, the *error variance*, due to accidental deviations of y-values above and below the regression line. The error variance estimate is designated $s_{y \cdot x}^2$ and is computed simply as the SS for deviations from the line, divided by $(N-2)$.[8]

$$s_{y \cdot x}^2 = \frac{\sum (y - \tilde{y})^2}{N-2}$$

and appropriate substitutions and simplifications lead to[9]

$$s_{y \cdot x}^2 = \frac{1}{N-2}\left\{\sum (y - \bar{y})^2 - \frac{[\sum (x - \bar{x})(y - \bar{y})]^2}{\sum (x - \bar{x})^2}\right\}$$

or an equivalent expression that is simpler for computations, since b will have been computed already:

$$s_{y \cdot x}^2 = \frac{1}{N-2}\left\{\sum y^2 - \frac{(\sum y)^2}{N} - b\left[\sum xy - \frac{(\sum x)(\sum y)}{N}\right]\right\}$$

$$= \frac{1}{N-2}[\text{SS}_y - b(\text{SP}_{xy})]$$

Example 4-2. Computation of the error variance.

Compute the error variance for the data of Example 4-1.

$$s_{y \cdot x^2} = \frac{1}{9}\left\{11{,}803 - \frac{100{,}109}{11} - 2.4\left[3730 - \frac{30{,}691}{11}\right]\right\}$$

$$= 49.56$$

[8]Since two parameters (mean and slope) have been estimated, there are $(N-2)$ DF. Division by $(N-2)$ makes $s_{y \cdot x^2}$ an unbiased estimate of $\sigma_{y \cdot x^2}$ just as division by $(N-1)$ made s^2 an unbiased estimate of σ^2 for the single-parameter case.

[9]Also, note that

$$\sum (y - \tilde{y})^2 = \sum [y - \bar{y} - b(x - \bar{x})]^2$$

$$= \sum (y - \bar{y})^2 - 2b \sum (x - \bar{x})(y - \bar{y}) + b^2 \sum (x - \bar{x})^2$$

Substituting $b = \dfrac{\sum (x - \bar{x})(y - \bar{y})}{\sum (x - \bar{x})^2}$ then gives the result shown.

$s_{y \cdot x}$, the square root of the error variance, is a standard deviation of individual y-values about the regression line. If it were the same at all points on the regression line, we could use it to obtain an approximate confidence interval for individual y-values. Such an approximate 95% interval is demarcated in Fig. 4-6 by parallel lines (B) at vertical distances $\pm 1.96\ s_{y \cdot x}$ from the regression line (where $s_{y \cdot x} = \sqrt{49.56} = 7.04$) and these lines are seen to include all 11 points of the experimental sample. For reasons explained below, such a "confidence interval," bounded by parallel lines, is likely to be too narrow except in the vicinity of $\bar{x}$, $\bar{y}$.

Usually we wish to establish a confidence interval for the true regression line as a whole, rather than for individual y-values. A limited approach may be made by finding a confidence interval for $\bar{y}$ at $\bar{x}$, thus establishing true limits for the regression line in its central region. By analogy to the standard error of a mean in the single-parameter case, we have

$$s_{\bar{y}} = \frac{s_{y \cdot x}}{\sqrt{N}}$$

$$\tilde{y} = \bar{y} \pm t(s_{\bar{y}})$$

where t has $(N - 2)$ DF.

Example 4-3.   Confidence interval for $\bar{y}$ at $\bar{x}$.

Calculate the 95% confidence interval for $\bar{y}$ at $\bar{x}$ from the data of Example 4-1.

From the data,

$$\bar{y} = 28.8$$

$$s_{y \cdot x^2} = 49.56$$

$$s_{\bar{y}}^2 = \frac{49.56}{11} = 4.51$$

$$s_{\bar{y}} = \sqrt{4.51} = 2.12$$

$$\tilde{y} = 28.8 \pm t(2.12)$$

Consulting Table 5 at 9 DF and $P = 0.05$, we find $t = 2.26$, so the limits are $\pm 2.26(2.12) = \pm 4.8$. Then, at $\bar{x}$,

$$\tilde{y} = 24.0 \text{ to } 33.6$$

Lines parallel to the estimated regression line may be drawn through these limits of $\bar{y}$ at $\bar{x}$, as shown by the short solid segments of lines C in Fig. 4-6. In the region close to $\bar{x}$, $\bar{y}$ these will include the true regression line 95 times out of 100. However, such parallel confidence limits cannot be extended beyond the immediate vicinity of $\bar{x}$, $\bar{y}$. The main reason is that even if the variance of y-values about $\bar{y}$ remains the same at all x-values, there is still considerable uncertainty about the true slope of the estimated regression line. The resulting doubt about the true position of the line is very small near $\bar{x}$, $\bar{y}$ but becomes greatly magnified with increasing distance along the line.

Accurate confidence limits will therefore be represented by curves that are convex towards the estimated regression line, the confidence interval becoming wider with increasing distance from $\bar{x}$. This is represented by an equation containing a weighted correction term, $(x - \bar{x})^2$, which increases the magnitude of s_y^2 at increasing distance from $\bar{x}$:

$$s_y^2 = s_{y \cdot x}^2 \left[\frac{1}{N} + \frac{(x - \bar{x})^2}{\sum (x - \bar{x})^2} \right]$$

Only the correction term changes with different x-values; the remaining terms are already known. At $\bar{x}$, where $(x - \bar{x})^2 = 0$, the entire expression reduces to that already used for calculating confidence limits of $\bar{y}$ at $\bar{x}$.

Example 4-4.

Calculate the 95% confidence limits of the true regression line at several representative values of x, for the data of Example 4-1.

At $x = 15$, for example,

$$s_y^2 = 49.56 \left[\frac{1}{11} + \frac{(15 - 8.82)^2}{400} \right]$$

$$= 9.24$$

$$s_y = \sqrt{9.24} = 3.04$$

Then 95% limits are $\pm 2.26(3.04) = \pm 6.9$ from the estimated line, as compared with ± 4.8 at $\bar{x}$.

Similar computation at other x-values leads to the biconvex curves C in Fig. 4-6, which will include the true regression line 95 times out of 100; they should not (and do not) include 95% of the individual points.

In summary, a confidence interval for the true regression line may be found in two ways. A rough approximation that may suffice for some purposes is to estimate a confidence interval for $\tilde{y}$ at $\bar{x}$; through the upper and lower limits of $\tilde{y}$ thus obtained, lines parallel to the least-squares regression line may be drawn. These will approximately bound the true regression line in the immediate vicinity of $\bar{x},\bar{y}$. The accurate method is to find confidence limits of $\tilde{y}$ at several x throughout the pertinent range of observations; this method will yield an hourglass-shaped area, narrowest at $\bar{x},\bar{y}$ and flaring out at a distance, which accurately defines the confidence interval of the true regression line.

CONFIDENCE INTERVAL OF A SLOPE

It has already been pointed out that if y-values varied without any relation to the associated x-values, there would be no correlation and the true slope, β, would be zero. Nevertheless a particular random sample of data might yield a finite positive or negative slope estimate, b. The question whether an apparent correlation is real or not must then be answered by determining with a t-test whether b differs significantly from zero, or better yet, by calculating confidence limits for the true slope, β, and ascertaining whether zero is included in these. It can be shown that the sampling variance of b is given by the following equation:

$$s_b{}^2 = \frac{s_{y\cdot x}{}^2}{\sum (x - \bar{x})^2}$$

and then, as usual,

$$t = \frac{(b - \beta)}{s_b} = \frac{(b - \beta)}{s_{y\cdot x}\sqrt{\dfrac{1}{\sum x^2 - \dfrac{(\sum x)^2}{N}}}}$$

and the confidence interval for β is given by

$$\beta = b \pm \frac{t(s_{y\cdot x})}{\sqrt{SS_x}}$$

where t has $(N - 2)$ DF.

Example 4-5.

Calculate the 95% confidence interval for the slope of the regression line of Fig. 4-6.

$$\beta = 2.4 \pm \frac{2.26(7.04)}{\sqrt{1,255 - \frac{(97)^2}{11}}}$$

$$= 2.4 \pm 0.8$$

$$= 1.6 \text{ to } 3.2$$

Since the limits do not include zero, there is a real positive correlation between age and enzyme activity and the true slope is not less than 1.6 nor greater than 3.2, both statements made at the 5% level of significance.

SIGNIFICANCE OF A DIFFERENCE BETWEEN TWO SLOPES

By analogy to the test of a difference between two sample means, Student's t may be used to test whether or not two slopes differ significantly. In other words this is a test of parallelism. Data will be available upon which two different regression lines are estimated, with two slope estimates, b and b'. A pooled error variance has to be computed,[10] whence t may be calculated in the following equation:

$$t = \frac{b - b'}{s_{y \cdot x}\sqrt{\frac{1}{SS_x} + \frac{1}{SS_{x'}}}}$$

Table 5 is consulted at the desired level of significance, with $(N - 2 + N' - 2)$ DF, and parallelism is rejected if the critical value of t is exceeded.

CORRELATION COEFFICIENT

The absolute magnitude of a slope obviously depends upon the particular units used on the x and y axes, just as the absolute magnitude of a standard deviation depends upon the units of measurement. We can

---

[10]This is legitimate only if the two estimates of error variance are substantially the same just as in pooling variance estimates to compare two sample means, (p. 52).

ascertain whether or not a given slope is significant, but there is no way to decide from the value of b alone whether a correlation is strong or weak. We were able to express standard deviation as a coefficient of variation (p. 36) by relating it to $\bar{x}$, and thus to obtain a comparative measure of the relative homogeneity of data from different normal distributions. Here the problem is similar. We wish to have a measure of slope which is independent of any particular units of measurement, and which will indicate the strength of correlation for any array of data in comparable terms.

The strength of correlation may be defined as the fraction of the total variance (or SS) that is due to regression. The total SS is given by $\sum (y - \bar{y})^2$. The SS due to regression is the total SS less the error SS, or (cf. p. 140),

$$\text{Regression SS} = \sum (y - \bar{y})^2 - \left\{ \sum (y - \bar{y})^2 - \frac{[(x - \bar{x})(y - \bar{y})]^2}{\sum (x - \bar{x})^2} \right\}$$

Then

$$\frac{\text{Regression SS}}{\text{Total SS}} = \frac{[(x - \bar{x})(y - \bar{y})]^2}{\sum (x - \bar{x})^2 \cdot \sum (y - \bar{y})^2}$$

to which we give the symbol r^2. Simplifying, for ease of computation,

$$r^2 = \frac{\left[\sum xy - \frac{(\sum x)(\sum y)}{N} \right]^2}{\left[\sum x^2 - \frac{(\sum x)^2}{N} \right]\left[\sum y^2 - \frac{(\sum y)^2}{N} \right]} = \frac{(\text{SP}_{xy})^2}{(\text{SS}_x)(\text{SS}_y)}$$

Although r^2 gives the strength of correlation directly in terms of a ratio of two variance components, it is nevertheless customary to use the square root, r (known as the *correlation coefficient*) instead. The value of r may vary from zero (no correlation) to -1 or $+1$ (perfect negative or positive correlation).

It can be shown from the above expression for r^2 that r is very directly related to b,

$$r = \left(\frac{s_x}{s_y} \right) b$$

Thus r is really the slope of a universal regression line, plotted on trans-formed coordinates, x and y values being replaced by $\frac{x}{s_x}$ and $\frac{y}{s_y}$. It follows that all correlations which are equally strong will have the same correlation coefficient, regardless of the apparent differences between the slopes of the regression lines based on the original raw data.

The significance of r may be estimated from the expression

$$t = \sqrt{\frac{r^2(N-2)}{1-r^2}}$$

where Table 5 is entered with $(N-2)$ DF. The null hypothesis tested in this way is that r estimated from the sample represents a true correlation coefficient of zero. Obviously, it makes no difference whether the test of significance of a correlation is performed on the actual slope, b, or on the standardized slope, r.

Example 4-6.

Compute r and its significance for the data of Example 4-1.

$$r^2 = \frac{\left[3,730 - \frac{(97)(316.4)}{11} \right]^2}{\left[1,255 - \frac{(97)^2}{11} \right]\left[11,803 - \frac{(316.4)^2}{11} \right]}$$

$$= 0.818$$

$$r = 0.904$$

$$t = \sqrt{\frac{0.818(9)}{0.182}} = 6.36$$

Critical $t = 3.25$ at $P = 0.01$ with 9 DF.

Thus, the apparent positive correlation is real $(P < 0.01)$ and it is very strong, since 82% of the total variance is due to regression.

The distinction between the significance and the strength of a correlation recalls the similar distinction between the significance and the magnitude of a difference between means (p. 29). Here, in a completely analogous way, a correlation may be significant, yet so weak as to be of no practical consequence. On the other hand, it may appear to be strong, yet because of the small sample size or large variability of measurements it may prove not to be significant.

THE LOGARITHMIC TRANSFORMATION AND THE LOG DOSE-RESPONSE CURVE

Because linear regression is so easy to deal with, it is customary to transform nonlinear correlations into linear ones whenever possible. For example, x- or y-values may be plotted as their reciprocals, squares, square roots, ratios, or logarithms. The choice of a particular transformation may have a theoretical basis (as in the Lineweaver-Burk plot in enzymology[11]), or may be purely empirical on the grounds that an approximately linear correlation results.

For biological data the logarithmic transformation is most useful. Many measurements yield skewed frequency distributions when x-values are plotted directly but fit the symmetrical normal distribution better when logarithms of x-values are used. In some cases this can be attributed to a limitation of the possible range of variation in one direction or the other. For example, the mean heart rate in man is about 70 beats per min. Deviations to the left (lower rates) are restricted by a lower limit around 40, whereas possible deviations to the right may be much greater. On a logarithmic scale a deviation of 35 beats per min to the left (log 35/70 = -0.3) will correspond to a deviation of 70 beats to the right (log 140/70 = $+0.3$). It is also true that responses to drugs tend to vary proportionately to log dose rather than to dose, so dose-response correlations are routinely plotted with log-dose rather than dose on the x-axis.

An important type of correlation encountered in several kinds of biological experiment is that between the dose of a drug (or other treatment) and the response elicited. If dose is increased systematically in an isolated tissue or single animal, a *graded response* may be obtained. At first there will be a range of doses so low that no response is manifest. Then a higher range of doses elicits responses of increasing magnitude, and finally a maximal response may be attained which cannot be exceeded at any dose. If log dose is plotted on the x-axis and response on the y-axis, a symmetrical sigmoid curve is characteristically obtained (Fig. 4-7) whose central portion is nearly linear. This means that, over a considerable range of doses, increasing the dose by constant *multiples* causes equal linear *increments* of response.

Figure 4-7 shows three different ways of plotting dose on a logarithmic basis. The upper scale shows actual doses, spaced so that successive geo-

[11]J. S. Fruton and S. Simmonds, *General Biochemistry*, 2 ed. (New York: John Wiley & Sons, Inc., 1958), p. 252.

Figure 4–7 Graded response of cat nictitating membrane to epinephrine injection *in vivo*. Each point is the mean response in 5 cats; the same 5 cats were used for the entire curve. Actual contraction amplitude (after magnification) is shown on the left scale, percent of estimated maximum contraction on the right. (Data of Maxwell et al.*)

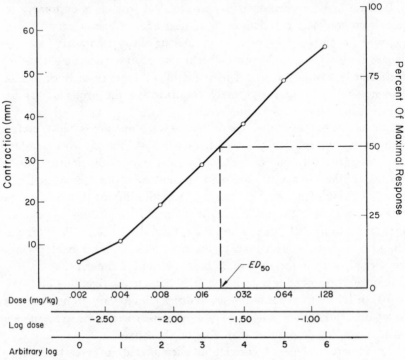

*R. A. Maxwell *et al.*, *J. Pharmacol. Exptl. Therap.* **131**: 355(1961).

metric increases (here doublings) are equally spaced. In the middle scale, actual logarithms are designated. The bottom scale would ordinarily be used only on a working graph, not for the final display of data; it illustrates a transformation that greatly simplifies computations. The ascending doses in the geometric series have been coded by assigning integer numbers beginning with zero. In the present example the actual logarithm of the lowest dose, 0.002, would be $\bar{3}.301$,[12] and this is coded as zero. Since the

[12]Because it simplifies computations we shall employ the established convention of representing negative logarithms as the sum of a negative characteristic and a positive mantissa.

$$\log 2 = 0.301$$
$$\log 20 = 1.301$$
$$\log 0.2 = \bar{1}.301$$

Conversions to and from logarithms may be accomplished with the aid of Table 3.

successive doses are doublings, the coded log units must differ by log $2 = 0.301$. Thus any point on the arbitrary log scale can be decoded by multiplying by 0.301, then adding $\bar{3}.301$. For example, 3.200 on the arbitrary scale would correspond to $(3.200 \times 0.301) + \bar{3}.301 = \bar{2}.264$ in actual log units, and antilog $\bar{2}.264 = 0.0184$ mg/kg, the corresponding dose. The coding and decoding procedures are exactly analogous when

Figure 4–8 Log dose-response curve as a cumulative normal frequency distribution of sensitivities of the individual responsive units.

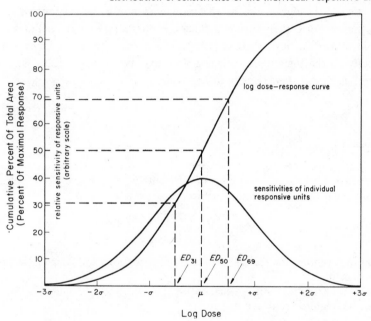

successive doses are not doublings, but differ by any other constant factor k. The arbitrary log units will then differ by log k, and decoding will require multiplying by log k, then adding the actual log of the dose that corresponds to the arbitrary zero.

The log dose-response curve may be regarded for purposes of statistical analysis as a cumulative normal frequency distribution (Fig. 4-8). We consider the responding system to be composed of a population of responsive units whose intrinsic sensitivities to the drug (or other treatment) are distributed normally with respect to log dose. As dose is increased, responsive units of diminishing sensitivity are progressively activated, so that at a given dose all units sensitive to that dose or to any smaller dose respond. The resultant response curve is therefore a plot of the cumulative area of the normal curve from $-\infty$ to $\log x$. When half of the population responds, to produce 50% of the maximal response, we call this median effective dose the ED_{50}. The slope of the log dose-response curve reflects the variance of sensitivities of the responsive units; the steeper the curve, the more homogeneous are the responsive units, i.e., the smaller is their variance. Since the interval $\mu \pm (\sigma/2)$ includes 38% of the area of the normal curve (19% on each side of μ), σ can be estimated directly as the distance on the log-dose axis between the ED_{31} and the ED_{69}, as shown theoretically in Fig. 4-8.

Example 4-7.

For the experiment depicted in Fig. 4-7 estimate the standard deviation of sensitivities of the responsive units in cat nictitating membrane to epinephrine. Maximum contraction was estimated to be 66 mm.

$$31\% \text{ of } 66 = 20.5 \text{ mm}$$

$$69\% \text{ of } 66 = 45.5 \text{ mm}$$

On the arbitrary log scale, these responses correspond to 2.15 and 4.70, or a difference of 2.55.

Each arbitrary log unit is equal to $\log 2 = 0.301$, so 2.55 units $= 0.767$ log units, the required standard deviation.

Often the responsive units are whole animals, and the measured responses are *quantal*, in that an animal either responds or does not. Thus, in toxicity tests groups of animals are exposed to different drug doses and the percent showing the toxic effect at each dose is noted. In clinical trials, the measure of response at each dose level may be the percent of patients cured. If the response measured is death, the curve is known as a *log dose-mortality curve*, and the median lethal dose is called the LD_{50}. If the response measured is cure, the median curative dose may sometimes be called the CD_{50}, but the more general term ED_{50} is preferable.

The two features which characterize any log dose-response curve are its position on the log-dose axis (given by the ED_{50}), and its slope at the ED_{50}. Statistical methods permit one to estimate these, with their confidence limits, from data of a limited random sample. When log dose-response curves for two drugs acting upon the same responsive system are being compared, we wish to know if the two slopes are really the same or

Figure 4–9 Twitch potentiation in cat nerve-muscle preparation. Each line represents the effects of a different drug. Each point is the mean of about 7 observations. Dose is plotted on a logarithmic scale. (Adapted from Kuperman et al.*)

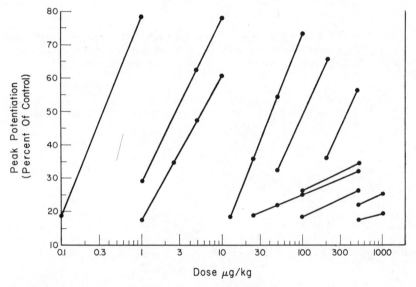

*A. S. Kuperman et al., *J. Pharmacol. Exptl. Therap.* **132**: 65 (1961).

different, and to what extent the two ED_{50} values really differ. If two drugs act by the same mechanism upon the same responsive units, but differ only in potency, the slopes of their curves must be the same. Conversely, different slopes imply different mechanisms of action. If the two curves are equidistant from each other in the horizontal direction at all response levels, it is meaningful to state the difference in potency without further qualification. If the two curves are not parallel, a potency comparison is meaningful only if the particular response level (e.g., the ED_{50}) is specified. Figure 4-9 illustrates some parallel and non-parallel curve segments for different drugs acting upon the same biological system.

The relative potency of two drugs is obaitned as a difference between their two $\log \text{ED}_{50}$ values, and since

$$\log x' - \log x = \log \frac{x'}{x}$$

the comparison is expressed as a *potency ratio*.

Example 4-8.

In Fig. 4-10 are shown the effects of a single drug in depressing the amplitude of contraction of the turtle heart at two different pH values. Estimate by eye the ED_{50} at each pH and the potency ratio for the two pH values.

Figure 4–10 Effects of pH on the action of pentobarbital on the turtle heart. Each point is the mean value from 10 hearts. (Adapted from Hardman et al.*)

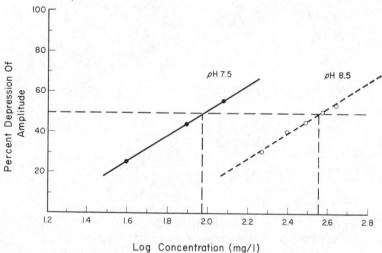

Log Concentration (mg/l)

*H. F. Hardman et al., *J. Pharmacol. Exptl. Therap.* **126**: 136 (1959).

We first draw the 50% response line to intersect both regression lines, as shown, and then drop perpendiculars from each line to the log dose axis. We find, at pH 7.5 $\log \text{ED}_{50} = 1.97$, so $\text{ED}_{50} = 93$ μg/ml; at pH 8.5 $\log \text{ED}_{50} = 2.54$, so $\text{ED}_{50} = 346$ μg/ml. Log potency ratio $= 2.54 - 1.97 = 0.57$, so potency ratio $=$ antilog $0.57 = 3.7$ (or directly, $346/93 = 3.7$).

The confidence limits of a single ED_{50} or of a potency ratio between two ED_{50} values will be equidistant on both sides of the estimated value on the log-dose axis. The limits will therefore not be equidistant from the actual ED_{50} or potency ratio, but will be broader on the high than on the low side. For example, in a careful experimental comparison of two antihistaminic drugs[13] the potency ratio was found to be 3.3, with very

Figure 4–11 Production of tumors in mice following a single subcutaneous injection of a carcinogen. Each point represents the mean of about 20 animals. The dose-response relationship is shown for three different carcinogens, designated A, B, and C. Dose is plotted on a logarithmic scale. (Adapted from Bryan and Shimkin.*)

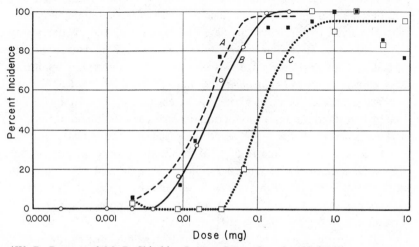

*W. R. Bryan and M. B. Shimkin, *J. Nat. Cancer Inst.* 3: 503 (1943).

unequal 95% confidence limits, 1.6 on the low side and 6.8 on the high side; likewise the confidence range of the ED_{50} for one of the drugs extended from 0.22 below to 0.36 above the estimated value of 0.60 mg/kg.

For many purposes it may suffice to draw the entire log dose-response curve by eye, and to estimate slope, ED_{50}, or potency ratio directly from the approximate curve, without applying any statistical analysis at all. Indeed, biological data may sometimes be unavoidably poor, so that a few rough conclusions with which everyone can agree may be preferable to an elaborate statistical analysis which the experimental observations will not really justify. A good example is presented in Fig. 4-11. Here we see dose-response relationships for three carcinogens given subcutaneously to mice. Now it is quite evident that A and B have about the same slopes

[13]J. T. Litchfield and F. Wilcoxon, *J. Pharmacol. Exptl. Therap.* **96**: 99(1949).

and very nearly equivalent potencies. C, on the other hand, is clearly less potent, but the data are so variable that it is hard to estimate a potency ratio in which we could have much confidence. If these self-evident conclusions are sufficient, then further statistical analysis would serve no useful purpose.

NORMAL EQUIVALENT DEVIATIONS AND PROBITS

Except for rough approximations, the assumption of linearity over any considerable segment of the log dose-response curve is untenable, and a proper analysis requires that the data first be transformed in such a way as to make the curve linear over its entire extent. This can be accomplished by converting the y-values from percents of maximal response to units known as *normal equivalent deviations* (N.E.D.). A "N.E.D." is the response increment brought about by increasing (or decreasing) the log dose by one standard deviation, taking the ED_{50} as starting point (N.E.D. 0). This is shown in Fig. 4-12. Centrally placed on the y-axis at the left is N.E.D. 0, corresponding to 50% of maximal response, or 50% of the cumulative area of the normal curve. Since in the normal distribution an increment of $+\sigma$ from μ includes 34% of the area (Table 4), N.E.D. 1.0 corresponds to $50\% + 34\% = 84\%$ of maximal response. N.E.D. -1.0 corresponds to $50\% - 34\% = 16\%$ of maximal response. Theoretically, such a transformed scale has no upper or lower limit, just as the normal distribution itself is considered to extend from $-\infty$ to $+\infty$. Practically, however, ± 2 N.E.D. are usually sufficient to include the extremes of meaningful data obtained in actual biological experiments.

On the x-axis is a log-dose scale in which log ED_{50} is always chosen as the zero point. All log dose-response curves will therefore intersect at (0,0) in the center of the graph, regardless of relative potencies. Their slopes, however, will differ. In Curve A of Fig. 4-12, for example, increasing log dose by 0.3 (i.e., doubling the dose) raises the response to 84% of maximum, or 1 N.E.D. In other words, the standard deviation of sensitivities of the responsive units to this particular drug is 0.3 log units. Curve B has twice as steep a slope, indicating a standard deviation of only 0.15 log units—i.e., a more homogeneous population of responsive units.

Even more convenient than normal equivalent deviations are units known as *probits*. A probit is identical to a N.E.D. except that zero N.E.D. is defined as 5 probits, thus eliminating negative values. The probit scale is shown at the right of Fig. 4-12. Table 17 permits direct conversion of any percent to the corresponding probit.

Graph paper is available on which actual percentages are shown on the *y*-axis (as in Fig. 4-12), spaced according to the corresponding N.E.D.

Figure 4–12 Transformation of the cumulative normal distribution (log dose-response curve) to normal equivalent deviations and to probits. The scale of percent response is also shown at the left, as it would appear on probability paper.

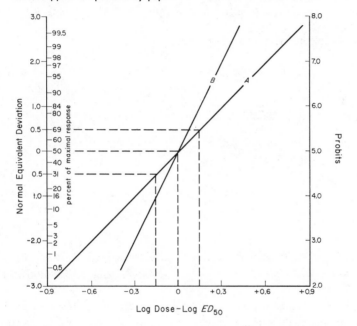

This is known as *probability paper*, or *log-probability paper*, according as the other coordinate scale is linear or logarithmic. Although such special paper is sometimes useful, it is often easiest to convert percent response to probits (by means of Table 17) and dose to log dose (by means of Table 3) or to an arbitrary log scale, and then to use the transformed data both for computations and for plotting on ordinary linear coordinates.

The slope of the regression line of probit (or N.E.D.) on log dose is, as pointed out above, a direct measure of the standard deviation (σ) of logarithms of individually effective doses (i.e., of doses just effective on the individual responsive units). It should be readily apparent that the true slope is equal to $1/\sigma$ when the data are plotted on these transformed coordinates.[14]

Example 4-9.

Doubling the dose of a drug increases the observed effect from 12% to 37% of the maximal response. Assuming these data lie exactly on a normal log dose-response curve, calculate the standard deviation of the logarithms of individual effective doses.

From Table 17 we convert to probits:

$$12\% = 3.82$$
$$37\% = 4.67$$

Since the dose was doubled, and $\log 2 = 0.3$, the slope is

$$\frac{4.67 - 3.82}{0.3} = 2.83 = \frac{1}{\sigma}$$

and $\sigma = 0.35$ log units.

ANALYSIS OF A SINGLE CURVE WITH GRADED RESPONSES

A single log dose-response curve may, for certain purposes, be analyzed in the manner appropriate to any regression line, without transformation of coordinates, provided that responses lying outside the nearly linear central portion of the curve are excluded. Alternatively, if the magnitude of the maximal response is apparent from the observations, then all responses may be expressed as percent of the maximum, and transformation to probits will usually bring all the data into a linear relationship.

The main interest of log dose-response data is usually in the information they provide about potency, expressed as ED_{50} and its confidence limits. This poses a problem quite different from that which we faced in analyzing

[14]In Gaddum's original terminology, λ is used instead of σ. See J. H. Gaddum, *Methods of Biological Assay Depending on a Quantal Response* (London: Medical Research Council, 1933).

ordinary regression data. Here we have an experimentally determined sample of observations which establish an estimated regression of response on log dose, and from which we wish to estimate an x-value (the log ED_{50}) and its confidence limits corresponding to a particular y-parameter (probit 5).[15]

Let $\tilde{m}$ be the log of the true ED_{50}, m be its sample estimate, and let responses be expressed as probits. The slope of any regression line (p. 137, Fig. 4-5) is given by

$$b = \frac{\tilde{y} - \bar{y}}{x - \bar{x}}$$

But here we choose $\tilde{y} = 5.00$ probits, and we designate the corresponding x by m, so

$$b = \frac{5.00 - \bar{y}}{m - \bar{x}}$$

$$m - \bar{x} = \frac{5.00 - \bar{y}}{b}$$

Although the estimate $(m - \bar{x})$ is straightforward, its variance presents difficulties. Evidently, $(m - \bar{x})$ is a ratio of *two* random variables, $(\tilde{y} - \bar{y})$ and b, whereas in ordinary regression problems we have been concerned with the variance and confidence limits of a single random variable, either y or b.

It will be recalled (p. 142) that the variance of y at a chosen x is given by

$$s_y{}^2 = s_{y \cdot x}{}^2 \left[\frac{1}{N} + \frac{(x - \bar{x})^2}{SS_x} \right]$$

Now the variance of $(m - \bar{x})$ can be given *approximately* as this y-variance divided by the square of the slope,

$$s^2{}_{(m-\bar{x})} = \frac{s_{y \cdot x}{}^2}{b^2} \left[\frac{1}{N} + \frac{(x - \bar{x})^2}{SS_x} \right]$$

[15]The method to be described here for graded responses merely uses the probit transformation to achieve a linear regression line. It may not be entirely valid if many responses are at the extremes of the curve, because the variances of the responses are not likely to be constant throughout. For very accurate results a method of weighting the responses must be used, as described by D. J. Finney in *Probit Analysis* (London: Cambridge University Press, 1952), pp. 185–188.

whence the approximate confidence interval would be

$$\tilde{m} - \bar{x} = m - \bar{x} \pm t(s_{(m-\bar{x})})$$

where t has $(N - 2)$ DF. If m is reasonably close to $\bar{x}$, as is often the case in a well balanced experiment, the term $\dfrac{(x - \bar{x})^2}{SS_x}$ in brackets becomes negligible, and the variance simplifies still further, to

$$s^2_{(m-\bar{x})} = \frac{s_{y \cdot x}^2}{b^2 N}$$

whence

$$\tilde{m} - \bar{x} = m - \bar{x} \pm \frac{t(s_{y \cdot x})}{b\sqrt{N}}$$

Although it is true that no exact variance of $(m - \bar{x})$ can be stated, exact confidence limits for the ratio of two random variables are given directly by the solution of a quadratic equation known as *Fieller's Theorem*. For its theoretical basis the reader should consult one of the basic texts cited in the list of references.

A term g must first be computed:

$$g = \frac{t^2(s_{y \cdot x}^2)}{b^2(SS_x)}$$

Then the lower and upper confidence limits (designated by L and U) are

$$(\tilde{m} - \bar{x})_L = \frac{1}{(1 - g)}\left[(m - \bar{x}) - \frac{t(s_{y \cdot x})}{b}\sqrt{\frac{(1 - g)}{N} + \frac{(m - \bar{x})^2}{SS_x}}\right]$$

and

$$(\tilde{m} - \bar{x})_U = \frac{1}{(1 - g)}\left[(m - \bar{x}) + \frac{t(s_{y \cdot x})}{b}\sqrt{\frac{(1 - g)}{N} + \frac{(m - \bar{x})^2}{SS_x}}\right]$$

Now g will be recognized as containing the relationship of the slope to its standard error, since $s_b^2 = \dfrac{s_{y \cdot x}^2}{SS_x}$ (p. 143). Thus, the more certain is the slope estimate, the smaller will be g. If g is small enough (less than about 0.1) it makes a negligible contribution to the above equations, and then the exact equations for confidence limits simplify to those obtained from the approximate variance. Evidently, g will be small under all the conditions that reduce the slope variance: if the error variance is small; if the slope itself is steep; if the dose range is large; and also, if the desired level of confidence is not too rigorous and/or a large number of observations has been made, so that t will be small. Inasmuch as the four terms comprising g have to be found anyway for use in other parts of any data analysis, the actual computation of g will entail almost no additional work and should be performed routinely. If it is found to be smaller than 0.1, it can be dropped; otherwise it is retained, and the full equations for exact confidence limits must be used. If $g \geq 1$, the slope does not differ significantly from zero, and no confidence interval can be found.

Example 4-10.

Estimate the ED_{50} of a drug which produced the following contractions of a piece of rat small intestine suspended in a tissue bath and connected to a device for amplifying and recording the contractions.

Drug Concentration ($\mu g/ml$)	(x) Coded log Concentration	Recorded Contraction mm	Percent of Estimated Maximum	(y) Probit
0.09	0	8	12	3.82
0.27	1	13	20	4.16
0.81	2	19	30	4.48
2.43	3	24	38	4.69
7.29	4	40	62	5.31
21.9	5	47	73	5.61
65.7	6	54	84	5.99
197.	7	63	99	—
591.	8	64	100	—

Since the response increment between the last two doses was negligible, we estimate 64 mm to be the maximum contraction. All the other responses are therefore expressed as percent of 64, and converted to probits. It is wise to exclude responses that are very near zero or maximum, since they cannot be measured reliably, and their conversion to probits would give them a spurious weight in the analysis. For example, the difference between 99.0% and 99.9% of maximal response would hardly be distinguishable in most biological systems, yet the respective probits (7.3 and 8.1) differ considerably. In fact, this probit difference is as great as that between the 34% and 66% responses. For this reason the two highest doses in the example have been excluded. A coded log scale is shown in the second column, as discussed in connection with Fig. 4-7. The transformed data are plotted in Fig. 4-13.

The usual calculations lead to the following:

$$N = 7$$

$$\sum x = 21 \qquad \frac{(\sum x)^2}{N} = 63.0 \qquad \bar{x} = 3$$

$$\sum x^2 = 91$$

$$\sum y = 34.06 \qquad \frac{(\sum y)^2}{N} = 165.73 \qquad \bar{y} = 4.87$$

$$\sum y^2 = 169.51$$

$$\sum xy = 112.42 \qquad \frac{(\sum x)(\sum y)}{N} = 102.18$$

$$b = \frac{112.42 - 102.18}{91.0 - 63.0} = 0.366$$

$$s_{y \cdot x}^2 = \tfrac{1}{5}[169.51 - 165.73 - 0.366(112.42 - 102.18)]$$

$$= 0.006$$

$$s_{y \cdot x} = \sqrt{0.006} = 0.077$$

$$\tilde{y} = \bar{y} + b(x - \bar{x}) = 4.87 + 0.366(x - 3.00)$$

$$m = \frac{5.00 - 4.87}{0.366} + 3.00 = 3.36$$

For 95% confidence interval, we find g is only 0.01 so we proceed with the approximate equation:

$$\tilde{m} - \bar{x} = (m - \bar{x}) \pm \frac{2.57(0.077)}{0.366}\sqrt{\frac{1}{7} + \frac{(0.36)^2}{28}}$$

$$= 0.36 \pm 0.21$$

$$\tilde{m} = 3.36 \pm 0.21$$

Then in coded log units the ED_{50} is 3.36 and its 95% confidence limits are ± 0.21, as shown in Fig. 4-13.

In order to reconvert the coded result to actual log dose, we first note that each dose differed from a previous one by a factor of 3, so the unit of the coded log scale must be $\log 3 = 0.478$. The starting point, zero, on the coded log scale corresponds to log $0.09 = \bar{2}.954$. Therefore we multiply by 0.478 and **add** $\bar{2}.954$; thus log $ED_{50} = 3.36(0.478) + 0.954 - 2 = 0.560$ and $ED_{50} = $ antilog $0.560 = 3.63$ μg/ml.

The 95% confidence limits decode to give $\pm0.21(0.478) = \pm0.100$ log units. Then $0.560 \pm 0.100 = 0.460$ to 0.660 log units, the confidence interval. Limits for the ED_{50} itself are then the antilogs, or 2.88 to 4.57 μg/ml.

Figure 4–13 Working graph for Example 4–10. Hypothetical data on dose-response for contractions of rat intestine. Each open circle represents a single experimental determination. The solid circle is the calculated general mean. Log ED_{50} and its confidence limits are shown at the bottom of the graph.

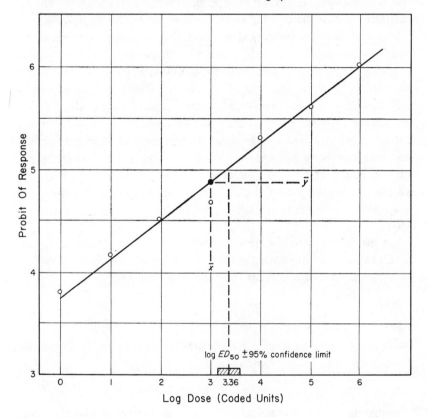

PARALLEL-LINE BIOASSAY WITH GRADED
RESPONSES

The purpose of a *bioassay* is to compare the potency of an unknown with that of a standard, by means of a biological response produced by both substances. The unknown may be the same material as the standard, only its concentration being unknown. This is the case when vitamins, hormones, or vaccines are assayed against preparations of standard activity. Then it is clear that when the unknown and standard are adjusted (by dilution) to give identical biological responses, they will contain the same concentration of the active agent. On the other hand, the potency of a different substance (or crude extract of unknown composition) may be compared with that of a standard material. In that case a generally valid potency comparison can only be made if it is first shown (or known) that the slopes of the two log dose-response curves are the same.

A typical bioassay by graded response does not require the use of a probit transformation, although probits will be useful if they can be employed. There may be good reasons, however, why it is not practical to estimate the maximal response of the system; then it will be impossible to find an ED_{50} and the probit transformation will be out of the question. The method of parallel-line bioassay will be described here in its simplest terms, for a 2×2 assay, with direct measurement of a graded response (e.g., blood pressure increase, in mm of mercury), equal dose-ratios, and equal numbers of observations at each dose. This elementary type of assay has several important limitations, but application of the procedures developed here to more elaborate designs will present no special difficulties.[16]

The procedure is to choose two dose levels of the standard, x_{S_1} and x_{S_2}, and two of the unknown, x_{U_1} and x_{U_2}, in such a way that the ratio of the higher dose to the lower is the same in both cases,

$$\frac{x_{S_2}}{x_{S_1}} = \frac{x_{U_2}}{x_{U_1}}$$

The concentrations of S or U are adjusted so that, as nearly as possible, the responses will be matched,

$$y_{S_1} \cong y_{U_1} \quad \text{and} \quad y_{S_2} \cong y_{U_2}$$

The purpose of the analysis is then to ascertain the potency of U in terms of S, by comparing the two regression lines of response on log dose. If the matching was very good, these two lines will be nearly identical; otherwise they will be parallel but somewhat separated on the x-axis. The statistical problem is to estimate the true *potency ratio*, defined as

[16]More sophisticated designs are well described in D. J. Finney, *Statistical Method in Biological Assay* (New York: Hafner Publishing Company, Inc., 1952).

$\dfrac{\text{dose of } S}{\text{dose of } U}$ for equal effect, and its confidence interval. Since lower effective dosage means higher potency, the magnitude of this ratio expresses the potency of U relative to S.

Figure 4–14 2 × 2 parallel-line bioassay. Each point is the mean of 5 responses at the given dose. Parallel regression lines have been drawn through the respective $\bar{x}$, $\bar{y}$, points with the mean slope calculated from all the data. (Hypothetical data from Example 4–11.)

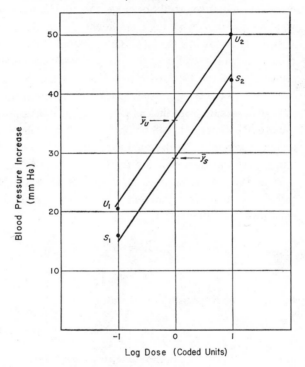

The procedure is illustrated in Fig. 4-14. A standard pressor amine and an unknown extract of adrenal tissue were assayed by injecting intravenously in a cat, and recording the transient rise of blood pressure produced by each injection. Five observations were made at each dose of both preparations (the order of injections being randomized) and the mean responses were plotted as the four points shown on the graph. The two dosages of S and U, whatever they may actually be, are plotted on a coded log scale as -1 and $+1$. The doses of standard pressor amine represent definite weights of a pure chemical substance; the doses of unknown represent definite volumes of a certain dilution of the adrenal extract.

Suppose the matching had been perfect, so that the two regression lines were exactly superimposed. Then in coded units, equal doses produced equal effects, and decoding gives the estimate of the actual potency ratio. Thus, if x_{S_1} were 5 μg of the standard pressor amine and x_{U_1} contained 0.1 ml of the adrenal extract, we would conclude that each ml of extract contained the equivalent of 50 μg of the standard pressor amine. This estimate, of course, would be subject to some uncertainty, which we would want to quantify by giving a confidence interval for the potency ratio.

Now when (as in Fig. 4-14) the matching is not perfect, the estimate of the potency ratio will contain two components, one due to the horizontal separation of the two regression lines on the coded log-dose scale, the other due to the coding itself. Let $\tilde{M}$ be the log of the true potency ratio, M be its estimate from the sample data. Since the dose scale is logarithmic, the coded estimate M_c will be *coded log dose S minus coded log dose U* for identical response. The decoded estimate M will be given by $M_c + (\bar{x}_S - \bar{x}_U)$. Antilog M will then estimate the true potency ratio.

Since the regression lines for S and U are assumed to have the same slope[17] but may have different mean responses, we write two regression equations, as follows:

$$\tilde{y}_S = \bar{y}_S + b(x_S - \bar{x}_S)$$

$$\tilde{y}_U = \bar{y}_U + b(x_U - \bar{x}_U)$$

For the same response, $\tilde{y}_S = \tilde{y}_U$, and

$$\bar{y}_S + b(x_S - \bar{x}_S) = \bar{y}_U + b(x_U - \bar{x}_U)$$

Since $M = x_S - x_U$, for the same response,

$$\bar{y}_U - \bar{y}_S = b[M - (\bar{x}_S - \bar{x}_U)]$$

$$M = \frac{\bar{y}_U - \bar{y}_S}{b} + (\bar{x}_S - \bar{x}_U)$$

---

[17]We shall test this assumption below in an analysis of variance (p. 169). Alternatively, it could be tested by the significance of the difference between the slope estimates $(b_S - b_U)$ from the S and U data, by the method indicated on p. 144.

This equation would apply to the general (uncoded) case. In a symmetrical design with coding, such as represented in Fig. 4-14, $x_S = x_U$ on the coded scale, so in coded units,

$$M_c = \frac{\bar{y}_U - \bar{y}_S}{b}$$

and the actual value of M will be obtained after decoding.

The common slope estimate is given by

$$b = \frac{\sum (x - \bar{x})_U (y - \bar{y})_U + \sum (x - \bar{x})_S (y - \bar{y})_S}{\sum (x - \bar{x})_U{}^2 + \sum (x - \bar{x})_S{}^2}$$

in which the S and U data are pooled to yield the single slope best fitted by all the points.

The error variance is obtained by an equation strictly analogous to the usual one for data of a single regression line, except that there is now one less DF, and the symbols (as above) distinguish between data in the S and U sets.

$$s_{y \cdot x}{}^2 = \frac{1}{N - 3}\left\{ \sum y^2 - \frac{(\sum y_U)^2}{N_U} - \frac{(\sum y_S)^2}{N_S} \right.$$
$$\left. - b\left[\sum (x - \bar{x}_U)(y - \bar{y}_U) + \sum (x - \bar{x}_S)(y - \bar{y}_S) \right] \right\}$$

These equations for slope and for the error variance may also be used with unequal numbers of observations in S and U. For $N_S = N_U$ the various terms may simply be pooled, as illustrated below in Example 4-11.

The estimation of an exact variance of $M - (\bar{x}_S - \bar{x}_U)$ is beset with the same difficulties already pointed out in the case of a single potency estimate (p. 157). An approximate variance is given by an expression of the same form as for $(m - \bar{x})$. Naturally, the error variance, slope, and SS_x are based upon pooled data from both sets, S and U.

$$s^2{}_{[M - (\bar{x}_S - \bar{x}_U)]} = \frac{s_{y \cdot x}{}^2}{b^2}\left[\frac{1}{N_S} + \frac{1}{N_U} + \frac{[M - (\bar{x}_S - \bar{x}_U)]^2}{SS_x} \right]$$

whence approximate confidence limits are given by

$$M - (\bar{x}_S - \bar{x}_U) \pm \frac{t(s_{y \cdot x})}{b}\sqrt{\frac{1}{N_S} + \frac{1}{N_U} + \frac{[M - (\bar{x}_S - \bar{x}_U)]^2}{SS_x}}$$

Exact confidence limits are again given by Fieller's Theorem:

$$\tilde{M} - (\bar{x}_S - \bar{x}_U) = \frac{1}{(1-g)}\Bigg\{ M - (\bar{x}_S - \bar{x}_U)$$

$$\pm \frac{t(s_{y\cdot x})}{b}\sqrt{(1-g)\left(\frac{1}{N_S} + \frac{1}{N_U}\right) + \frac{[M - (\bar{x}_S - \bar{x}_U)]^2}{SS_x}}\Bigg\}$$

where

$$g = \frac{t^2(s_{y\cdot x})^2}{b^2(SS_x)}$$

and may be neglected if it is smaller than about 0.1. In that case the expression reduces to that based on the approximate variance.

In the symmetrical assay, where (in coded units) $\bar{x}_S = \bar{x}_U$, the term $(\bar{x}_S - \bar{x}_U)$ disappears. Moreover, if in a symmetrical 2×2 assay the lower dose is coded as -1 and the higher as $+1$, then $\bar{x} = 0$, each deviation $(x - \bar{x}) = 1$, and $SS_x = \sum (x - \bar{x})^2 = N$ (where N is the total number of observations that are divided equally between N_S and N_U). Then the exact confidence limits become

$$\tilde{M}_c = \frac{1}{(1-g)}\left[M_c \pm \frac{t(s_{y\cdot x})}{b}\sqrt{\frac{4(1-g) + M_c^2}{N}}\right]$$

and if g is small,

$$\tilde{M}_c = M_c \pm \frac{t(s_{y\cdot x})}{b}\sqrt{\frac{4 + M_c^2}{N}}$$

In all problems involving two dose-response lines, t has $(N - 3)$ DF.[18]

Example 4-11.

An extract of adrenal tissue, of unknown pressor amine content, was assayed against a standard pressor amine by injecting into a cat and recording the transient rise of blood pressure. A 2×2 assay was used, with a high/low dose ratio of 3 for both standard and unknown. Five observations were made at each dose of S and U, and the order of injections was randomized. From the data given

[18]One DF is lost in each ED_{50} estimate, and another in the estimate of the common slope.

below, calculate the potency of the extract (and its 95% confidence limits) in terms of the standard. Data are peak blood pressure increases in mm of mercury. Figure 4-14 is the working graph for this example.

	xs_1	xs_2	xu_1	xu_2
	5 μg	15 μg	0.1 ml	0.3 ml
Coded x	−1	+1	−1	+1
	15	41	19	51
	17	47	25	42
	17	35	20	47
	13	50	16	56
	18	38	23	54
N_S, N_U	5	5	5	5
$\sum x$	−5	5	−5	5
$\sum x^2$	5	5	5	5
$\dfrac{(\sum x)^2}{N}$	5	5	5	5
$\sum y$	80	211	103	250
$\sum y^2$	1,296	9,059	2,171	12,626
$\dfrac{(\sum y)^2}{N}$	1,280	8,904.2	2,121.8	12,500
$\sum (y - \bar{y})^2$	16.0	154.8	49.2	126.0
$\bar{y}$	16.0	42.2	20.6	50.0
$\sum xy$	−80	211	−103	250
$\dfrac{(\sum x)(\sum y)}{N}$	−80	211	−103	250

Pooled Data:

	Pooled $S_1 + S_2$	Pooled $S + U$	Pooled $U_1 + U_2$
N	10	20	10
$\sum x$	0	0	0
$\bar{x}$	0	0	0
$\sum x^2$	10	20	10
$\dfrac{(\sum x)^2}{N}$	0	0	0
$\sum (x - \bar{x})^2$	10	20	10
$\sum y$	291	644	353
$\bar{y}$	29.1	32.2	35.3
$\sum y^2$	10,355.0	25,152.0	14,797.0
$\dfrac{(\sum y)^2}{N}$	8,468.1	20,736.8	12,460.9
$\sum (y - \bar{y})^2$	1,886.9	4,415.2	2,336.1
$\sum xy$	131	278	147
$\dfrac{(\sum x)(\sum y)}{N}$	0	0	0
$\sum (x - \bar{x})(y - \bar{y})$	131	278	147

Some of the terms found above will not be required here, but will be used later.

We may now compute b and M_c from the pooled terms above.

$$b = \frac{\text{pooled} \sum (x - \bar{x})(y - \bar{y})}{\text{pooled} \sum (x - \bar{x})^2} = \frac{278}{20} = 13.9$$

$$M_c = \frac{\bar{y}_U - \bar{y}_S}{b} = \frac{35.3 - 29.1}{13.9} = 0.446$$

$$s_{y\cdot x}^2 = \frac{1}{N-3}\{\sum(y-\bar{y})^2 - b[\sum(x-\bar{x})(y-\bar{y})]\}$$

$$= \tfrac{1}{17}[4{,}415.2 - 13.9(278)] = 32.41$$

$$s_{y\cdot x} = \sqrt{32.41} = 5.69$$

$$t_{.05}\ \text{at 17 DF} = 2.11$$

$$t^2 = 4.452$$

$$g = \frac{t^2(s_{y\cdot x}^2)}{b^2\sum(x-\bar{x})^2} = \frac{(4.452)(32.41)}{(193.2)(20)} = 0.04$$

Since g is very small, and the assay is symmetrical 2×2 $(\bar{x}_S = \bar{x}_U)$, the simplest expression may be used for the 95% confidence limits of M_c,

$$\pm\frac{t(s_{y\cdot x})}{b}\sqrt{\frac{4+M_c^2}{N}} =$$

$$\pm\frac{(2.11)(5.69)}{13.9}\sqrt{\frac{4+0.199}{20}} = \pm0.396$$

$$\tilde{M}_c = 0.446 \pm 0.396$$

Now the actual ratio of high-dose/low-dose was 3, corresponding to two coded units; thus, our coded unit corresponds to $1/2 \log 3 = 0.239$.

Then
$$\tilde{M} = (0.239)(0.446) \pm (0.239)(0.396)$$
$$= 0.107 \pm 0.095$$
$$= 0.012 \text{ to } 0.202$$

The actual potency ratio is given by the antilogs of $\tilde{M}$ and of its upper and lower confidence limits. The result is 1.28, with limits 1.03 to 1.59. Then 0.1 ml U is estimated to be 1.28 times more potent than 5 μg S; so 1 ml U contains the equivalent of 64 μg S, with 95% confidence limits 52 to 80 μg.

ANALYSIS OF VARIANCE OF BIOASSAY DATA

As discussed earlier (p. 64), analysis of variance permits one to segregate and examine separately the several components that contribute to the total variability in a system. In parallel-line bioassays the total variance is made up of two components, that due to differences between doses, and that due to error (i.e., the residual within-doses variance). The between-doses variance can be broken down further into four components arising from (1) difference between preparations, (2) regression (i.e., dose-related differences in response), (3) departure from parallelism of the two regression lines, and (4) departure from linearity. Since two points determine a line, departure from linearity can only contribute in assays with more than two points per preparation.[19] Analysis of variance for the data of Example 4-11 is presented below. The respective sums of squares are formed in a manner analogous to that explained on p. 67. It should be recalled that coding in a symmetrical design does not affect the analysis of variance in any way since all the data are changed by addition or subtraction of the same amount.

Calculation of Sums of Squares for Data of Example 4-11.

GRAND TOTAL PER OBSERVATION FOR y:

$$\frac{(\sum y)^2}{N} = \frac{(80 + 211 + 103 + 250)^2}{20} = 20,736.8$$

TOTAL SS: (19 DF)

$$\sum y^2 - \frac{(\sum y)^2}{N} = 1,296 + 9,059 + 2,171 + 12,626 - 20,736.8$$

$$= 4,415.2$$

BETWEEN DOSES: (3 DF)[20]

$$\sum \frac{(\sum y_m)^2}{N_m} - \frac{(\sum y)^2}{N} = \frac{(80)^2 + (211)^2 + (103)^2 + (250)^2}{5} - 20,736.8$$

$$= 4,069.2$$

PREPARATIONS: (1 DF)[21]

$$\frac{(\sum y_s)^2}{N_s} + \frac{(\sum y_U)^2}{N_U} - \frac{(\sum y)^2}{N} = \frac{(291)^2 + (353)^2}{10} - 20,736.8$$

$$= 192.2$$

---

[19]A defect of the 2 × 2 assay is that no information about linearity can be obtained from the data, and serious error may arise if the pairs of points are not in corresponding positions on the two log dose-response curves.

[20]$\sum y_m$ and N_m refer to the individual dose-groups.

[21]$\sum y_s$, N_s and $\sum y_U$, N_U refer to pooled data of both standard groups and both unknown groups, respectively.

REGRESSION: (1 DF) (Pooled slope SS)

$$\frac{[\sum (x - \bar{x})(y - \bar{y})]^2{}_{\text{Pooled}}}{\sum (x - \bar{x})^2{}_{\text{Pooled}}} = \frac{(-80 + 211 - 103 + 250)^2}{20} = 3{,}864.2$$

PARALLELISM: (1 DF) (Difference between separate slopes and pooled slope SS)

$$\frac{[\sum (x - \bar{x})(y - \bar{y})]_s^2}{\sum (x - \bar{x})_s^2} + \frac{[\sum (x - \bar{x})(y - \bar{y})]_U^2}{\sum (x - \bar{x})_U^2} - \frac{[\sum (x - \bar{x})(y - \bar{y})]^2{}_{\text{Pooled}}}{\sum (x - \bar{x})^2{}_{\text{Pooled}}}$$

$$= \frac{(131)^2}{10} + \frac{(147)^2}{10} - 3{,}864.2 = 12.8$$

LINEARITY: 0
ERROR (WITHIN DOSES): (16 DF)
                     Total SS − between-doses SS = 4,415.2 − 4,069.2 = 346.0

ANALYSIS OF VARIANCE (DATA OF EXAMPLE 4-11)			
Source	*DF*	*SS*	*Variance Estimate*
Preparations	1	192.2	192.2
Regression	1	3,864.2	3,864.2
Parallelism	1	12.8	12.8
Between doses	3	4,069.2	
Error (within doses)	16	346.0	21.6
Total	19	4,415.2	

$$\frac{\text{Regression}}{\text{Error}} : F = \frac{3{,}864.2}{21.6} = 179 \ (1, 16 \text{ DF}) \qquad P < 0.01$$

$$\frac{\text{Preparations}}{\text{Error}} : F = \frac{192.2}{21.6} = 8.9 \ (1, 16 \text{ DF}) \qquad P < 0.01$$

$$\frac{\text{Parallelism}}{\text{Error}} : F = \frac{12.8}{21.6} = 0.6 \qquad \text{N.S.}$$

The analysis shows that a very large part (about 88 %) of the total variance is due to regression whereas the unexplained variance (error) is quite small. This is a highly desirable state of affairs; indeed, a relatively low variance estimate due to regression would invalidate the analysis, since it would imply that the dose-response relationship was not reliable enough to serve as the basis of a bioassay. Also satisfactory is the low variance estimate for "parallelism" (meaning "deviations from parallelism"). Were this variance estimate significantly greater than the error variance it would imply that the two regression lines were not really parallel, and since the assumption of parallelism underlies the entire procedure, the validity of thè bioassay would be called into doubt.

The variance estimate for "preparations" (meaning "difference between preparations") requires some explanation. Since the log-dose scales are coded arbitrarily, this variance does not reflect the true potency difference between the preparations. In the kind of bioassay under consideration here we tried to choose doses of S and U whose effects would be closely matched. If the matching were perfect, the variance due to preparations would be zero, and in general, we expect a low variance estimate if the matching is good. The table shows that although the variance due to preparations is not very large, it is nevertheless significantly greater than the error variance. Thus there was some degree of mismatch, as can indeed be seen in Fig. 4-14. Whether or not a given degree of mismatch will have any invalidating effect on the bioassay must be assessed in each case. If it is known, for example, that the four points lie on linear and parallel portions of two log dose-response curves, it may be possible to assert that mismatch makes no difference at all.

SINGLE LOG DOSE-RESPONSE CURVE
WITH QUANTAL RESPONSES

Quantal response curves are based upon enumeration (rather than quantitative) data at each of several dose levels. Every subject is classified as either responding or not responding to the given dose, and the effect of a dose is expressed as the percent of subjects responding. As log dose increases, an ever larger percent of subjects respond, until at some very high dose all subjects respond. These observations on groups of subjects are used to estimate the cumulative frequency distribution of subject sensitivities, as discussed earlier (p. 149), so that a median effective dose (ED_{50}) and its confidence limits, for the population of subjects, can be found. The best example of the use of quantal response data is the determination of toxicity by observing percent of animals killed at various doses, in order to estimate LD_{50}. The methods of probit analysis were specifically developed for handling quantal response data.

The need for special methods arises from the fact that a valid regression line cannot be calculated directly by the same methods that work for graded responses. The reason is that in the case of quantal responses, the y-variances are necessarily different at each response level because the response in every dose group is a sample from a binomial population. It will be recalled (p. 93) that the sampling variance in a binomial population depends upon the true binomial probability, π, in that population. Consequently, the validity with which π can be estimated at a given dose depends not only upon the sample size, but also upon the value of π itself. Since responses at all the dose levels are to be used in estimating a probit regression line, it follows that each response has to be weighted to reflect its relative validity, so that accidental deviant responses will not carry undue weight in determining the line. Responses near the ED_{50} are most reliable, whereas those at the extremes of the log dose-response curve are much less reliable, particularly if each dose is tested on a small number of subjects. Thus the weight to be given a response will be directly proportional to the number of subjects in that group, and inversely proportional to the probit variance at that percent response, thus decreasing the contributions of samples as they deviate more widely from the ED_{50}.

A curious difficulty arises, however. The observed percent responses (and their corresponding probits) are only samples from a population of sensitivities represented by an unknown true regression line. It is not the *sample* probits but the *true* probits that should be used as weights to reflect the sampling variances. These true probits cannot be obtained until the true regression line is found, and the true regression line can only be computed with the aid of the desired weights. This apparently vicious cycle is broken by a process of successive approximation. The essence of the procedure will be outlined briefly, but for details the reader is referred elsewhere.[22]

First, the observed percent response in each dose-group is converted to a probit, and these *empirical probits* are used to fit a *provisional regression line*, usually by eye. From the provisional line is then obtained an *expected*

[22]D. J. Finney, *Probit Analysis* (London: Cambridge University Press, 1952), Chaps. 4–5.

———, *Statistical Method in Biological Assay* (New York: Hafner Publishing Company, Inc., 1952), Chap. 18.

C. W. Emmens, *Principles of Biological Assay* (London: Chapman and Hall Ltd., 1948), Chaps. 15–16.

probit for each dose employed. Now these expected probits will be in error to the extent that the provisional line is not actually the best fit to properly weighted points. By means of Table 18 each expected probit is converted to a *working probit*. This conversion depends upon both the expected probit and the actual sample observation. If a sample response (empirical probit) happens to lie on the line, it will be identical to the expected probit, and the working probit will also be identical. If a sample response deviates from the line, then the working probit will tend to smooth the deviation in a special way that takes account of the relative reliability of the data at different response levels.[23]

The next step is to find, from Table 18, a *weighting coefficient* (w) corresponding to each expected probit, i.e., to the points on the provisional regression line. The number of subjects in each dose group is multiplied by the appropriate weighting coefficient and these weights (Nw) are applied to log dose (x) and to the working probit (y) in each case. The result is that in the subsequent calculations leading to the equation of an *adjusted regression line*, the familiar terms now include weights. Thus, we use $\sum Nwx^2$ instead of $\sum x^2$, $\sum Nwxy$ instead of $\sum xy$, and so on, as illustrated in the following examples.

The adjusted regression line thus obtained is plotted on the same graph as the provisional line. Usually it differs from the provisional line. In that case, the entire procedure is carried through again, for as many cycles as are required, until the line does not change further. Very often the first cycle suffices, and subsequent cycles produce only negligible improvements. The probits given by the final regression line are then used to estimate ED_{50} or potency ratio (in the case of a parallel-line bioassay) and their confidence limits.

Example 4-12.

An antihistaminic drug was used at various doses to protect test animals against a certainly lethal dose of histamine, with the results given below. Estimate the ED_{50} from the probit regression line, and compute its 95% confidence limits. (Data of Litchfield and Wilcoxon.)[24]

[23]An illustration may make this clearer. Suppose that 14% of subjects in a sample respond to a given dose, and that the provisional regression line gives an expected probit of 4.72 at this dose. Since probit of 14% is 3.92, the experimental sample response is lower than would be expected from the responses at other dose levels. We enter Table 18 at $Y = 4.72$ and find (by interpolation) $y_{max} = 6.31$ and $y_{min} = 3.70$. Then the working probit (y) is $0.14(6.31) + 0.86(3.70) = 4.07$, which is an adjustment upward toward the line.

[24]J. T. Litchfield and F. Wilcoxon, *J. Pharmacol. Exptl. Therap.* **96**: 99 (1949).

Dose μg/kg	Log Dose (x)	Alive/ Total	Proportion Alive (p)	Empirical Probit	Expected Probit
1,000	3.0	8/8	1.00	—	—
500	2.7	7/8	0.88	6.18	5.84
250	2.4	4/8	0.50	5.00	5.25
125	2.1	4/8	0.50	5.00	4.67
62.5	1.8	1/8	0.12	3.82	4.09

The empirical probits (from Table 17) are shown plotted against log dose in Figure 4-15, where a provisional regression line has been drawn by eye. Expected probits, read off from the provisional line, have been entered in the last column above.

Weighting coefficients (*w*) are found by interpolation in Table 18, for each expected probit, Nw is obtained for each dose group, then successive multiplications give Nwx and Nwx^2.

Figure 4–15 Working graph for analysis of Example 4–12.

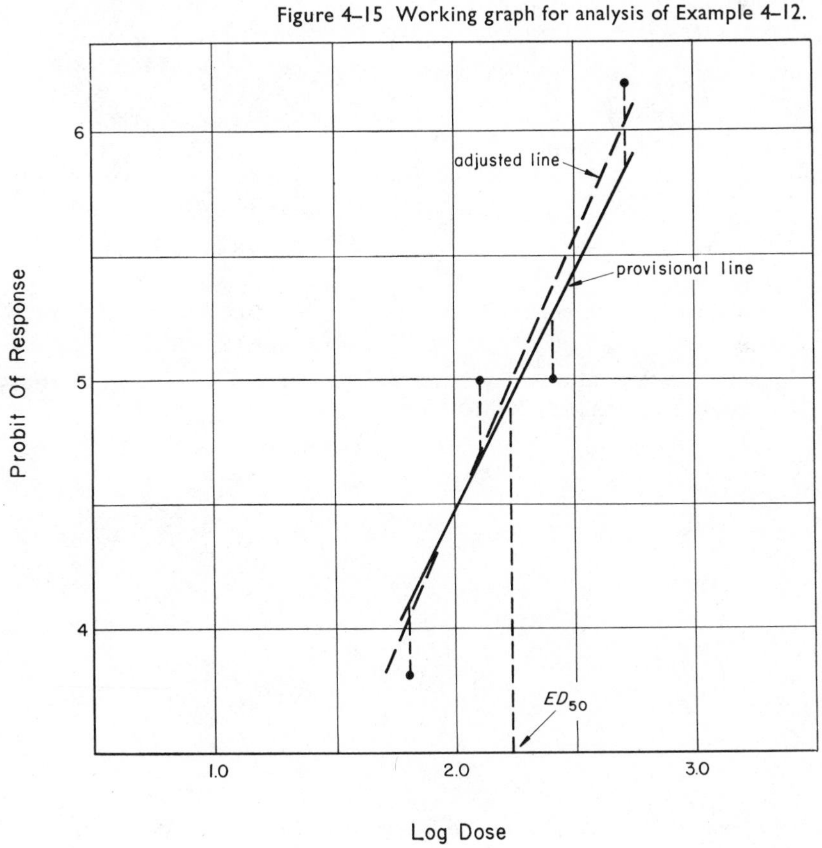

Expected Probit	w	x	N	Nw	Nwx	Nwx^2
5.84	0.490	2.7	8	3.92	10.58	28.57
5.25	0.622	2.4	8	4.98	11.95	28.68
4.67	0.611	2.1	8	4.89	10.27	21.57
4.09	0.468	1.8	8	3.74	6.73	12.11

$$\sum Nw = 17.53$$
$$\sum Nwx = 39.53$$
$$\sum Nwx^2 = 90.93$$

$$\text{Weighted } \bar{x} = \frac{\sum Nwx}{\sum Nw} = \frac{39.53}{17.53} = 2.25$$

Working probits (y) are then obtained by entering Table 18 with each expected probit and using the observed sample proportions (not percents) as indicated. Then Nwy, $Nwxy$ are also computed:[25]

Expected Probit	Observed Proportion (p)	y	Nwy	$Nwxy$
5.84	0.88	6.13	24.03	64.88
5.25	0.50	4.99	24.88	59.64
4.67	0.50	5.01	25.00	52.50
4.09	0.12	3.86	14.44	25.99

$$\sum Nwy = 88.35$$
$$\sum Nwxy = 203.01$$

$$\text{Weighted } \bar{y} = \frac{\sum Nwy}{\sum Nw} = \frac{88.35}{17.53} = 5.04$$

Finally, the slope of the adjusted regression line is given by a weighted equation analogous to that on p. 136:

$$b = \frac{\sum Nwxy - \dfrac{(\sum Nwx)(\sum Nwy)}{\sum Nw}}{\sum Nwx^2 - \dfrac{(\sum Nwx)^2}{\sum Nw}}$$

$$= \frac{203.01 - \dfrac{(39.53)(88.35)}{17.53}}{90.93 - \dfrac{(39.53)^2}{17.53}}$$

$$= \frac{3.85}{1.79} = 2.15$$

[25]For some purposes Nwy^2 may also be required.

The adjusted regression line, with slope 2.15 and passing through the point $(\bar{x},\bar{y}) = (2.25, 5.04)$ is shown in Fig. 4-15, together with the provisional line. One cycle of computation has clearly made some small difference in the line. Another cycle would begin with the adjusted line and proceed exactly as before, to obtain a still better estimate, based on the expected probits given by the new line. In the present case (and quite often with real data) another cycle would alter the adjusted line only by an insignificant amount.

Before accepting the adjusted line as a reasonable fit to the data, a χ^2 test should be made, in order to make sure that the various sample responses are sufficiently homogeneous to be accepted as randomly drawn from a population represented by the adjusted regression line. This goodness-of-fit test is carried out by converting each expected probit (from the new line) back to proportion responding, and then (multiplying by N), to the expected number of subjects responding in each dose group. The difference between expected and observed numbers in each dose group is used to compute χ^2. In this case, however, instead of $\displaystyle\sum \frac{(E-O)^2}{E}$ we use a weighted value $\displaystyle\sum \frac{(E-O)^2}{E(1-\pi)}$, where π is the expected proportion responding. The table of χ^2 (Table 9) is consulted at two less DF than the number of dose groups employed. The following computation, yielding a value of χ^2 far smaller than the critical value at $P = 0.05$, permits us to accept the data as reasonably consistent with the estimated regression line.

x	Expected Probit from Adjusted Line	Expected Proportion Alive	(E) Expected Number Alive	(O) Observed Number Alive
2.7	6.00	0.841	6.7	7
2.4	5.35	0.637	5.1	4
2.1	4.70	0.382	3.1	4
1.8	4.05	0.171	1.4	1

$(E-O)$	$(1-\pi)$	$(E-O)^2$	$E(1-\pi)$	$\dfrac{(E-O)^2}{E(1-\pi)}$
0.3	0.16	0.09	1.07	0.084
1.1	0.36	1.21	1.84	0.658
0.9	0.62	0.81	1.92	0.422
0.4	0.83	0.16	1.16	0.138
				$\chi^2 = 1.302$

Having thus gained some confidence in the validity of the regression line we may use it to estimate the log ED_{50} graphically by dropping a perpendicular from probit 5.00 on the line (as shown in Fig. 4-15). We may accomplish the same thing more accurately by substituting $y = 5.00$ in the equation of the line, to obtain the corresponding log dose, as on p. 160:

$$m = \frac{5.00 - \bar{y}}{b} + \bar{x} = \frac{5.00 - 5.04}{2.15} + 2.25 = 2.23$$

The approximate variance of $(m - \bar{x})$ is given by an expression very similar to that encountered in connection with graded responses (p. 157), except for the inclusion of weights and the absence of an "error variance" (since that is fixed in a binomial population):

$$s_{(m-\bar{x})^2} = \frac{1}{b^2}\left[\frac{1}{\sum Nw} + \frac{(m - \bar{x})^2}{\sum Nw(x - \bar{x})^2}\right]$$

Then,

$$\tilde{m} - 2.25 = \frac{1}{(1 - 0.464)}\left[(2.23 - 2.25) \pm \frac{1.96}{2.15}\sqrt{\frac{(1 - 0.464)}{17.5} + \frac{(-0.02)^2}{1.79}}\right]$$

$$= \frac{1}{0.536}(-0.02 \pm 0.16)$$

$$= -0.04 \pm 0.30$$

$$= -0.34 \text{ to } + 0.26$$

and so

$$\tilde{m}_L = -0.34 + 2.25 = 1.91 \qquad (\text{antilog} = 81)$$

$$\tilde{m}_U = +0.26 + 2.25 = 2.51 \qquad (\text{antilog} = 324)$$

Then $ED_{50} = $ antilog $m = 170$ $\mu g/kg$, with 95% confidence interval 81–324 $\mu g/kg$. In this problem, use of the approximate variance would have given somewhat narrower limits, 102–282 $\mu g/kg$.

PARALLEL-LINE BIOASSAY WITH QUANTAL RESPONSES

Here the equations are again similar to those employed with graded responses (p. 165), except for the presence of weighting coefficients and the absence of an explicit error variance.

$$b = \frac{\sum Nw(x - \bar{x})(y - \bar{y})}{\sum Nw(x - \bar{x})^2}, \text{ the common slope of both lines}$$

$$g = \frac{x^{*2}}{b^2 \sum Nw(x - \bar{x})^2}$$

Confidence limits of $M - (\bar{x}_S - \bar{x}_U)$ are

$$\frac{1}{(1-g)}\left\{M-(\bar{x}_S-\bar{x}_U)\right.$$

$$\pm\frac{x^*}{b}\sqrt{(1-g)\left(\frac{1}{\sum N_S w}+\frac{1}{\sum N_U w}\right)+\frac{[M-(\bar{x}_S-\bar{x}_U)]^2}{\sum Nw(x-\bar{x})^2}}\right\}$$

In all these equations, $\sum Nw(x-\bar{x})(y-\bar{y})$ and $\sum Nw(x-\bar{x})^2$ are pooled terms from the S and U data, and x^* is the normal (two-tail) deviate. The usual simplification results when g is less than about 0.1.

It should be noted that when quantal response data are analyzed by the probit method, even though the design is symmetrical, and the doses of S and U are set equal on a coded log scale, the differing weights assigned to the several responses will usually make the weighted means, $\bar{x}_S$ and $\bar{x}_U$ unequal. For this reason the term $(\bar{x}_S-\bar{x}_U)$ will not, in general, drop out.

Example 4-13.

The acute toxicities of two drugs, A and B, were tested by intravenous injection into mice. Each drug was given at different doses to four groups of 20 mice, and deaths were recorded 5 min later. Calculate, from the results given below, the LD_{50} and its 95% confidence limits for each drug, as well as the potency ratio and its 95% confidence limits. Figure 4-16 is the working graph for this example.

Dose mg/kg	Coded log Dose (x)	Dead/ Total	Propor- tion Dead	Empiri- cal Probit	Expec- ted Probit	w	Nw	Nwx	Nwx²
				DRUG A					
2	−1	2/20	0.10	3.72	3.7	0.336	6.72	−6.72	6.72
4	0	9/20	0.45	4.87	4.7	0.616	12.32	0	0
8	1	14/20	0.70	5.52	5.7	0.532	10.64	10.64	10.64
16	2	19/20	0.95	6.64	6.7	0.208	4.16	8.32	16.64
						$\sum$	33.84	12.24	34.00
				DRUG B					
0.3	−1	1/20	0.05	3.36	3.4	0.238	4.76	−4.76	4.76
0.6	0	6/20	0.30	4.48	4.4	0.558	11.16	0	0
1.2	1	14/20	0.70	5.52	5.3	0.616	12.32	12.32	12.32
2.4	2	17/20	0.85	6.04	6.3	0.336	6.72	13.44	26.88
						$\sum$	34.96	21.00	43.96

Expected Probit	Observed Proportion (p)	Working Probit (y)		Nwy	Nwxy
		DRUG A			
3.7	0.10	3.72		25.00	−25.00
4.7	0.45	4.88		60.12	0
5.7	0.70	5.52		58.73	58.73
6.7	0.95	6.64		27.62	55.24
			$\sum$	171.47	88.97
		DRUG B			
3.4	0.05	3.36		15.99	−15.99
4.4	0.30	4.48		50.00	0
5.3	0.70	5.52		68.01	68.01
6.3	0.85	5.98		40.19	80.38
			$\sum$	174.19	132.40

For convenience in applying the equations, designate drug A as S and drug B as U.

	DRUG A (S)	DRUG B (U)
$\bar{x}$	$\dfrac{12.24}{33.84} = 0.362$	$\dfrac{21.00}{34.96} = 0.601$
$(\bar{x}_S - \bar{x}_U)$	$0.362 - 0.60\bar{1} = 1.761$	
$\sum Nwx^2$	34.00	43.96
$\dfrac{(\sum Nwx)^2}{\sum Nw}$	$\dfrac{(12.24)^2}{33.84} = 4.43$	$\dfrac{(21.00)^2}{34.96} = 12.61$
$\sum Nw(x - \bar{x})^2$	$34.00 - 4.43 = 29.57$	$43.96 - 12.61 = 31.35$
Pooled $\sum Nwxy$	$88.97 + 132.40 = 221.37$	
Pooled $\dfrac{(\sum Nwx)(\sum Nwy)}{Nw}$	$\dfrac{(12.24 + 21.00)(171.47 + 174.19)}{33.84 + 34.96} = 166.95$	

Pooled $\sum Nw(x - \bar{x})(y - \bar{y})$ $221.37 - 166.95 = 54.42$

Pooled b $\qquad\qquad \dfrac{54.42}{29.57 + 31.35} = 0.89$

$\bar{y}$ $\qquad\qquad \dfrac{171.47}{33.84} = 5.07$ $\qquad\qquad \dfrac{174.19}{34.96} = 4.98$

Regression line: $y =$ $\qquad 5.07 + 0.89(x - 0.362)$ $\qquad 4.98 + 0.89(x - 0.601)$

Figure 4–16 Parallel-line bioassay with quantal responses. Working graph for Example 4–13. Solid circles are data for Drug A, open circles are for Drug B. Solid lines A and B are provisional parallel regression lines fitted by eye. Broken lines have been adjusted on the basis of the first cycle of computations.

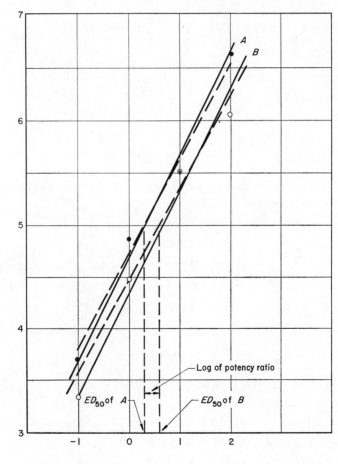

Log Dose (Coded Units)

The adjusted lines with slope 0.89 and passing through $(\bar{x},\bar{y})$ in each case, are shown in Fig. 4-16. They differ but slightly from the provisional lines and although a high degree of accuracy would require that another cycle of approximation be performed, we shall ordinarily be content with a single adjustment. The test of homogeneity by χ^2 is performed with each set of data and the adjusted lines, exactly as on p. 177; the result is an acceptably low value of χ^2. Here, if there seems to be any doubt that the data describe two parallel lines, a test for parallelism should also be performed.[26]

Once we have satisfied ourselves that the observations are reasonable samples from the populations represented by the two adjusted lines, implying also that a linear regression is a reasonable representation, and that parallelism is a reasonable assumption, we may proceed to the actual estimates required.

$$(S) \qquad\qquad (U)$$

$$m_c = \frac{5.00 - 5.07}{0.89} + 0.362 = 0.283 \qquad \bigg| \qquad \frac{5.00 - 4.98}{0.89} + 0.601 = 0.623$$

$$M_c = m_S - m_U = 0.283 - 0.623 = \bar{1}.660$$

Alternatively,

$$M_c = \frac{\bar{y}_U - \bar{y}_S}{b} + (\bar{x}_S - \bar{x}_U) = \frac{4.98 - 5.07}{0.89} + (0.362 - 0.601)$$

$$= \bar{1}.660$$

First we compute the confidence interval for each LD_{50} separately.

FOR S (DRUG A):

$$g = \frac{(1.96)^2}{(0.89)^2(29.6)} = 0.164$$

$$\tilde{m}_c - 0.362 = \frac{1}{0.936}\left[-0.079 \pm \frac{1.96}{0.89}\sqrt{\frac{0.936}{33.8} + \frac{(-0.079)^2}{29.6}} \right]$$

$$= -0.478 \text{ to } +0.309$$

$$(-0.478 + 0.362) < \tilde{m}_c < (+0.309 + 0.362)$$

$$-0.116 < \tilde{m}_c < +0.671$$

So $\tilde{m}_c$ is estimated to be 0.283, with 95% confidence limits -0.116 and $+0.671$.

FOR U (DRUG B):

$$g = \frac{(1.96)^2}{(0.89)^2(31.4)} = 0.155$$

[26]As, for example, D. J. Finney, *Probit Analysis* (London: Cambridge University Press, 1952) pp. 69–71.

$$\tilde{m}_c - 0.601 = \frac{1}{0.845}\left[0.623 - 0.601 \pm \frac{1.96}{0.89}\sqrt{\frac{0.845}{35.0} + \frac{(0.022)^2}{31.4}}\right]$$

$$= -0.384 \text{ to } +0.436$$

$$(-0.384 + 0.601) < \tilde{m}_c < (+0.436 + 0.601)$$

$$0.217 < \tilde{m}_c < 1.037$$

So $\tilde{m}_c$ is estimated to be 0.623, with 95% confidence limits 0.217 and 1.037.

SUMMARY

	DRUG A (S)	DRUG B (U)
m_c	0.283	0.623
95% conf. lim.		
Lower limit	−0.116	0.217
Upper limit	0.671	1.037
Decode by	$\times \log 2 + \log 4$	$\times \log 2 + \log 0.6$
m	0.686	$\bar{1}.965$
95% conf. lim.		
Lower limit	0.567	$\bar{1}.843$
Upper limit	0.804	0.090
$LD_{50} = $ antilog m	4.85 mg/kg	0.92 mg/kg
Lower limit	3.68	0.70
Upper limit	6.37	1.23

$M = 0.686 - \bar{1}.965 = 0.721$ and drug B is estimated to be 5.3 times more toxic than drug A.

Confidence limits of $\tilde{M}_c$ are obtained as follows:

$$g = \frac{(1.96)^2}{(0.89)^2(29.57 + 31.35)} = 0.08, \text{ which is}$$

sufficiently small (less than 0.1) to be dropped.

Then the limits of $M_c - (\bar{x}_S - \bar{x}_U)$ are

$$\bar{1}.660 - \bar{1}.761 \pm \frac{1.96}{0.89}\sqrt{\frac{1}{33.84} + \frac{1}{34.96} + \frac{(\bar{1}.66 - \bar{1}.76)^2}{(29.57 + 31.35)}}$$

$$= \bar{1}.899 \pm 0.530$$

Upper limit 0.429

Lower limit $\bar{1}.369$

Then $\tilde{M}_c$ is estimated to be $\bar{1}.660$, with the following limits:

$$\text{Upper limit:} \quad 0.429 + \bar{1}.761 = 0.190$$

$$\text{Lower limit:} \quad \bar{1}.369 + \bar{1}.761 = \bar{1}.130$$

To decode, we must multiply by log 2, to which the unit of our coded scale corresponds, and then add the difference in actual log dose between the two preparations at the same coded x. This difference, $\log S_0 - \log U_0 = \log 2 - \log 0.3 = 0.824$.

		antilog
$M = \bar{1}.660(0.301) + 0.824 = 0.722$		5.3
Upper limit $= 0.190(0.301) + 0.824 = 0.881$		7.6
Lower limit $= \bar{1}.130(0.301) + 0.824 = 0.562$		3.6

Thus potency ratio drug A/drug B is 5.3. Drug B is 5.3 times more toxic than drug A, with limits 3.6 and 7.6 times. Since 1.0 is not included in the limits, we may also conclude that drug B is significantly ($P < 0.05$) more toxic than drug A.

Finally, it should be noted that there are several alternative (and sometimes more convenient) procedures for estimating ED_{50} and potency ratio with their confidence limits, in quantal-response bioassays. Among these, the most widely used has been the method of Litchfield and Wilcoxon[27] which employs a set of nomograms to supplant many of the calculations demonstrated here.

CONFIDENCE INTERVAL OF A RATIO[28]

Quite often in biological experimentation one wishes to estimate a ratio from a set of observations on the numerator (y) and another set of observations on the denominator (x). Now these may be paired observations, each item in a sample supplying a value of y and a value of x, so that there may be some degree of correlation between the two. On the other hand,

[27]J. T. Litchfield and F. Wilcoxon, *J. Pharmacol. Exptl. Therap.* **96**: 99 (1949).
[28]For acquainting me with the method described here I am indebted to Dr. Rupert G. Miller. The actual procedure is the same as that described by E. Paulson, *Ann. Math. Stat.* **13**: 440 (1942).

the y and x estimates may be made on wholly independent samples, so that no question of a correlation arises.

Both cases may be illustrated by alternative versions of the same experiment. Suppose the protein content of cells per unit DNA is to be determined. If the cells in question are growing in replicate bottles, we may determine both DNA and protein on the contents of each bottle, or alternatively, we may determine DNA on some bottles and protein on others. What we require in either case is an estimate (with confidence limits) of the true value of the ratio DNA/protein.

Now in the first case, replicate estimates of the desired ratio will be available, so it might be thought that a confidence interval could be found by merely treating each estimate y/x as though it were a single observation, by single-parameter methods. However, this would not be at all correct. The appropriate limits of the true ratio, R $(=\mu_y/\mu_x)$, whose estimate is $\bar{y}/\bar{x}$, are given by Fieller's Theorem (cf. p. 158) as the roots of a quadratic equation,

$$-\left[\bar{x}^2 - t^2\left(\frac{s_x^2}{N}\right)\right]R^2 + 2\left[\bar{x}\bar{y} - \frac{t^2 r s_x s_y}{N}\right]R - \left[\bar{y}^2 - t^2\left(\frac{s_y^2}{N}\right)\right] = 0$$

$$(a) \qquad\qquad (b) \qquad\qquad (c)$$

where r is the sample correlation coefficient, N is the number of paired observations in the sample, s_x^2 and s_y^2 are the respective variances, and t is the two-tail value found in Table 5 at $(N-1)$ DF. The confidence limits are therefore

$$\frac{-b \pm \sqrt{b^2 - 4ac}}{2a} =$$

$$\frac{\left(\bar{x}\bar{y} - \frac{t^2 r s_x s_y}{N}\right) \pm \sqrt{\left(\bar{x}\bar{y} - \frac{t^2 r s_x s_y}{N}\right)^2 - \left[\bar{x}^2 - t^2\left(\frac{s_x^2}{N}\right)\right]\left[\bar{y}^2 - t^2\left(\frac{s_y^2}{N}\right)\right]}}{\bar{x}^2 - t^2\left(\frac{s_x^2}{N}\right)}$$

Example 4-14.   Confidence limits of a ratio; correlated observations on x and y.

From a set of replicate cell cultures were randomly chosen seven bottles. Methods of analysis were employed that permitted protein and DNA to be determined on each bottle, with the following results:

	(x)	(y)
Bottle	*Protein*	*DNA*
1	5	12
2	7	14
3	3	12
4	3	12
5	8	13
6	6	13
7	4	13

The units of measurement are not given because they are unimportant in the statistical analysis. We wish to find the true DNA/protein ratio. The customary computations yield $N = 7$, $\sum x = 36$, $\sum x^2 = 208$, $\sum y = 89$, $\sum y^2 = 1,135$, $\sum xy = 464$. Then $\bar{x} = 5.1$, $\bar{y} = 12.7$, $\bar{y}/\bar{x} = 2.5$, $SS_x = 22.9$, $SS_y = 3.43$, $SP_{xy} = 6.29$, $s_x^2 = 3.82$, $s_y^2 = 0.572$, $s_x = 1.95$, $s_y = 0.756$

$$r^2 = \frac{(6.29)^2}{(22.9)(3.43)} = 0.504$$

$$r = 0.71$$

$$t = 2.45 \text{ at } P = 0.05 \text{ with 6 DF}$$

$$t^2 = 6.00$$

Then the 95% confidence limits are

$$\frac{\left[(5.1)(12.7) - \dfrac{(6.00)(0.71)(1.95)(0.756)}{7}\right]}{(5.1)^2 - (6.00)\left(\dfrac{3.82}{7}\right)}$$

$$\pm \frac{\sqrt{(63.9)^2 - (22.7)\left[(12.7)^2 - 6.00\left(\dfrac{0.572}{7}\right)\right]}}{22.7}$$

$$= 2.8 \pm 0.9 = 1.9 \text{ to } 3.7$$

So the ratio DNA/protein (in the appropriate units of measurement) is estimated to be 2.5, with 95% confidence limits 1.9 to 3.7.

In the alternative case, where x and y are estimated on wholly independent samples, the confidence limits are obtained from the same expression, with $r = 0$:

$$\frac{\bar{x}\bar{y} \pm \sqrt{(\bar{x}\bar{y})^2 - \left[\bar{x}^2 - t^2\left(\frac{s_x^2}{N_x}\right)\right]\left[\bar{y}^2 - t^2\left(\frac{s_y^2}{N_y}\right)\right]}}{\bar{x}^2 - t^2\left(\frac{s_x^2}{N_x}\right)}$$

Now N_x and N_y may be unequal, and DF is equal to $(N_x - 1)$ or $(N_y - 1)$, whichever is smaller.[29]

Example 4-15. Confidence limits of a ratio; independent observations on x and y.

In the same system as described in the preceding example, seven bottles were chosen for DNA assays and 10 others for protein determinations. The DNA results were 12, 15, 13, 14, 15, 12, 12 and the protein results were, 5, 7, 7, 6, 4, 3, 5, 3, 7, 4. Find the DNA/protein ratio and its 95 % confidence limits.

Here $N_x = 10$, $N_y = 7$, $\sum x = 51$, $\sum x^2 = 283$, $SS_x = 22.9$, $s_x^2 = 2.544$, $\sum y = 93$, $\sum y^2 = 1{,}247$, $SS_y = 11.43$, $s_y^2 = 1.905$, $\bar{x} = 5.10$, $\bar{y} = 13.28$, $\bar{y}/\bar{x} = 2.60$.

$$t = 2.45 \text{ at } P = 0.05 \text{ with 6 DF}$$

$$t^2 = 6.00$$

Then the limits are

$$(5.10)(13.28) \pm \frac{\sqrt{\left[(5.10)(13.28)\right]^2 - \left[(5.10)^2 - 6.00\left(\frac{2.54}{10}\right)\right]\left[(13.28)^2 - 6.00\left(\frac{1.90}{7}\right)\right]}}{\left[(5.10)^2 - 6.00\left(\frac{2.54}{10}\right)\right]}$$

$$= 2.77 \pm 0.71 = 2.06 \text{ to } 3.48$$

So the estimate of DNA/protein is 2.60, with 95 % confidence limits 2.06 to 3.48.

[29]As shown by W. G. Cochran (*Biometrics* 7:17, 1951), a requirement that must be met is that

$$\frac{\bar{x}^2(N_x)}{s_x^2} < t^2$$

This test can be made routinely before proceeding, but the condition will certainly be satisfied for any reasonable coefficient of variation of the observations, for all but the very smallest samples, and for the values of t corresponding to $P = 0.05$ or 0.01.

Problems

CHAPTER 4 (ANSWERS ON P. 220)

P4-1.

In an experiment on the effect of light upon the development of retinal enzymes, two groups of animals were used. The control group was reared in the dark from birth; the experimental group was reared in the light. Each week for 6 weeks animals of the control group were killed, and the activity of a particular retinal enzyme was determined, with the following results:

Week		Enzyme Activity			
1	0.5,	0.4,	0.4,	0.5,	0.4
2	1.1,	0.9,	1.0,	0.9,	1.1
3	1.4,	1.5,	1.4,	1.3,	1.4
4	1.8,	2.0,	1.9,	1.7,	1.7
5	2.1,	2.2,	2.1,	1.9,	2.0
6	2.2,	2.3,	2.2,	2.0,	2.1

Plot a scatter diagram and find the equation of the least-squares regression line for the data of the first 4 weeks only. Draw the line. Find the confidence interval for the true rate of increase of the enzyme activity during the first 4 weeks. Also find the correlation coefficient and interpret its meaning. (Cf. pp. 138, 146.)

P4-2.

In the experiment described in the preceding problem, there were 10 animals in the group exposed to light during development. These animals were killed at three different times, with the following results:

Week	Enzyme Activity
1	0.6, 0.5, 0.5
2.5	1.6, 1.4, 1.4, 1.5
4	2.1, 2.1, 2.0

Does exposure to light, under these conditions, increase the rate of enzyme development, as compared with the controls raised in the dark? (Cf. p. 144.)

P4-3.

The clam heart was used to assay an unknown amount of a certain ester. Small amounts of the ester caused an increase in amplitude of the spontaneous rhythmic contractions, which were recorded on a polygraph. The pen deflection was shown to be a linear function of the contraction amplitude. The effects were measured directly on the polygraph record, with the following result:

Dose, $m\mu g$	Contraction, mm
10	2, 0, 0, 1
31.6	15, 17, 16, 16
100	32, 27, 30, 33
316	44, 42, 46, 47
1,000	61, 63, 63, 61

Plot a regression line of mm contraction on log dose for the four highest doses, ignoring the lowest dose (which barely elicited a response). Find the dose (and its 99% confidence limits) that would be expected to cause a mean contraction of 35 mm in this system. (Cf. pp. 135, 158.)

P4-4.

In the preceding problem, suppose it were ascertained, by giving yet higher doses, that the maximal response is about 67 mm contraction. Plot the regression line of probit on log dose, and estimate the ED_{50} and its 99% confidence interval. (Cf. p. 158.)

P4-5.

For the data of Prob. 4-4, compute the standard deviation (in log units) of the sensitivities of individual responsive units in the clam heart. (Cf. p. 154.)

P4-6.

From the toxicity data presented below, compute the LD_{50} and its 95% confidence interval.

Dose mg/kg	Number Dead/Total
5	0/10
10	2/10
20	6/10
40	7/10
80	10/10

(Cf. p. 172 ff.)

P4-7.

An experiment was conducted to see how the frequency of amphibian heart beats was related to the ambient temperature. For the data given below, plot the regression line and show the accurate 95% confidence band for the true regression of heartbeat on temperature over the range of the observations.

Temperature, °C	Frequency
2	9, 12, 15
5	10, 17, 22
10	16, 27, 23, 25
15	42, 48
20	60, 68, 66

(Cf. p. 142.)

P4-8.

An experiment sought to determine whether or not there was a difference between the activity of the enzyme cholinesterase per mg of protein in hemolyzed erythrocytes and in nerve trunks. Since there is considerable variation between animals, a determination of enzyme from both sources was made in each animal. From the following data compute the mean ratio erythrocyte/nerve cholinesterase activity and ascertain whether or not the 95% confidence interval includes 1.00.

Animal	Erythrocyte	Nerve
1	425	375
2	510	450
3	475	460
4	325	330
5	580	420
6	610	580

(Cf. p. 185.)

P4-9.

Two anticonvulsant drugs were compared by administering them to mice which were then given electric shock under conditions that caused all control mice to convulse. From the following data, find the potency ratio estimate and its 95% confidence interval, after constructing a working graph.

	DRUG A		DRUG B
Dose mg/kg	*Convulsed/Total*	*Dose mg/kg*	*Convulsed/Total*
10	13/15	200	12/15
30	9/15	600	6/15
90	4/15	1,800	2/15

(Cf. p. 178 ff.)

References for Further Reading

TABLES

Fisher, R. A., and F. Yates. *Statistical Tables for Biological, Agricultural and Medical Research*, 4th ed. New York: Hafner Publishing Company, Inc., 1953.

Pearson, E. S., and H. O. Hartley. *Biometrika Tables for Statisticians*, vol. I. London: Cambridge University Press, 1954.

These two collections of tables are the most complete and generally useful available, from which most of the tables in the present book were derived.

The RAND Corporation. *A Million Random Digits*. New York: The Free Press of Glencoe, 1955.

The most extensive table of random numbers, from which Table 1 of the present book was taken.

Hodgman, C. D., et al. *Handbook of Chemistry and Physics*, 41st ed. Cleveland: Chemical Rubber Publishing Company, 1959–60.

The mathematics section of this handbook contains a number of useful tables such as logarithms, exponentials, areas, and ordinates of the normal curve.

EXPERIMENTAL DESIGN

Cochran, W. G., and G. M. Cox. *Experimental Designs*. New York: John Wiley & Sons, Inc., 1950.

Finney, D. J. *Experimental Design and its Statistical Basis*. Chicago: University of Chicago Press, 1955.

Fisher, R. A. *The Design of Experiments*. Edinburgh and London: Oliver & Boyd, Ltd., 1935.

These three books approach the problem of experimental design from the statistician's point of view.

Beveridge, W. I. B. *The Art of Scientific Investigation*. New York: W. W. Norton & Company, Inc., 1951.

Wilson, E. B., Jr. *An Introduction to Scientific Research.* New York: McGraw-Hill Book Company, Inc., 1952.

These two books present in an interesting narrative style the essentials of good experimental design from the research worker's point of view.

Huff, D. *How To Lie with Statistics.* New York: W. W. Norton & Company, Inc., 1954.

A lively and humorous presentation, which makes good use of exaggeration to highlight common pitfalls in the application of statistics to problems of daily life.

Modell, W. "Problems in the Evaluation of Drugs in Man," *J. Pharm. Pharmacol.,* **11**: 577 (1959).

Sheps, M. C. "The Clinical Value of Drugs: Sources of Evidence," *J. Public Health,* **51**: 647 (1961).

Wolf, S. "The Pharmacology of Placebos," Pharmacol. Revs. **11**: 689(1959).

Three articles, out of many that could have been cited, which illuminate some of the difficulties of conducting and interpreting controlled experiments in man.

OTHER ELEMENTARY TEXTS

Li, J. C. R. *Introduction to Statistical Inference.* Lancaster, Pa.: The Science Press, Inc., 1957.

A thorough treatment, in which actual sampling experiments play a large part in developing the theme. Intended as a textbook for a rather intensive elementary college course. Contains numerous problem exercises taken from published data in the biological and chemical literature.

Moroney, M. J. *Facts from Figures.* Baltimore: Penguin Books, Inc., 1951.

An unusually lucid presentation directed to the general reader. This little book is remarkably successful in conveying the spirit of the statistical approach through the use of lively everyday examples.

Alder, H. L., and E. B. Roessler. *Introduction to Probability and Statistics.* San Francisco: W. H. Freeman and Company, 1960.

Dixon, W. J., and F. J. Massey, Jr. *Introduction to Statistical Analysis.* New York: McGraw-Hill Book Company, Inc., 1951.

Wallis, W. A., and H. V. Roberts. *Statistics: A New Approach.* New York: The Free Press of Glencoe, 1956.

These three books employ different approaches. The exercises in Wallis and Roberts may be useful, but none of the three stresses biological applications.

Bailey, N. T. J. *Statistical Methods in Biology.* New York: John Wiley & Sons, Inc., 1959.

This book has had a well-deserved popularity among recent texts directed toward students of biology and medicine.

Hill, A. B. *Principles of Medical Statistics.* London: Oxford University Press, 1955.
  The author played a major role in advancing the use of sound statistical methods in medicine. The book reflects this interest but does not stress the small-sample procedures needed in laboratory research.

Bancroft, H. *Introduction to Biostatistics.* New York: Paul B. Hoeber, Inc., 1957.
Batson, H. C. *An Introduction to Statistics in the Medical Sciences.* Minneapolis: Burgess Publishing Company, 1956.
Croxton, F. E. *Elementary Statistics with Applications in Medicine.* Englewood Cliffs, N.J.: Prentice-Hall, Inc., 1953.
Mainland, D. *Elementary Medical Statistics.* Philadelphia: W. B. Saunders Company, 1952.
  Among these four, Mainland is unique by virtue of the many illustrative examples drawn from the field of medicine. It also contains special nomograms for finding confidence limits of proportions from binomial samples.

MORE ADVANCED TEXTS

Anderson, R. L., and T. A. Bancroft. *Statistical Theory in Research.* New York: McGraw-Hill Book Company, Inc., 1952.
Bennett, C. A., and N. L. Franklin. *Statistical Analysis in Chemistry and the Chemical Industry.* New York: John Wiley & Sons, Inc., 1954.
Bowker, A. H., and G. J. Lieberman. *Engineering Statistics.* Englewood Cliffs, N.J.: Prentice-Hall, Inc., 1959.
Eisenhart, C., M. W. Hastay, and W. A. Wallis. *Techniques of Statistical Analysis.* New York: McGraw-Hill Book Company, Inc., 1947.
Fisher, R. A. *Statistical Methods for Research Workers.* Edinburgh and London: Oliver & Boyd, Ltd., 1950.
Kendall, M. G. *Rank Correlation Methods.* New York: Hafner Publishing Company, Inc., 1955.
Mood, A. M. *Introduction to the Theory of Statistics.* New York: McGraw-Hill Book Company, Inc., 1952.
Scheffé, H. *The Analysis of Variance.* New York: John Wiley & Sons, Inc., 1959.
Siegel, S. *Nonparametric Statistics for the Behavioral Sciences.* New York: McGraw-Hill Book Company, Inc., 1956.
  Most of the titles above are self-descriptive. Fisher is considered a classic in the field of biostatistics. Bowker and Lieberman, although written with reference to problems in engineering, offers much sound mathematical derivation that is applicable to the analysis of problems in many other fields. Scheffé and Kendall are specialized treatises for the sophisticated.

BIOASSAY

Bliss, E. I. *The Statistics of Bioassay.* New York: Academic Press, Inc., 1952.
Burn, J. H., D. J. Finney, and L. G. Goodwin. *Biological Standardization.* London: Oxford University Press, 1950.
Emmens, C. W. *Principles of Biological Assay.* London: Chapman & Hall, Ltd., 1948.

Finney, D. J. *Probit Analysis*. London: Cambridge University Press, 1952.

————. *Statistical Method in Biological Assay*. New York: Hafner Publishing Company, Inc., 1952.

Gaddum, J. H. *Methods of Biological Assay Depending on a Quantal Response*. London: Medical Research Council, 1933.

Litchfield, J. T., Jr., and F. Wilcoxon. "A Simplified Method of Evaluating Dose-Effect Experiments," *J. Pharmacol. Exptl. Therap.*, **96**:99 (1949).

The list above contains the principal works on the theory of bioassay. All will be useful primarily to the advanced student or mature investigator. The Gaddum monograph is of historical interest for its importance in the development of methods for dealing with quantal-response data. The method described by Litchfield and Wilcoxon has been adopted very widely; the article contains nomograms that simplify many of the otherwise laborious computations required to analyze dose-effect data.

Answers to Problems

CHAPTER 1

PI-I.

This is a good instance of the lack of a concurrent control, but rather more subtle than the one cited in the text. Here the clinical trials were well done and left no doubt that a patient with pulmonary tuberculosis has a greater probability of cure and of a shortened period of illness if he receives the drug than if he does not. But proving it reduces the overall morbidity and mortality from the disease is not exactly the same thing, although it may be related. A proper control for the effect of streptomycin on tuberculosis morbidity would be practically impossible to devise. If two otherwise identical countries, or sections of a country, could be compared, one might imagine using the drug for many years in one but not in the other, yet this is obviously out of the question. It is just as well to recognize that some experiments simply cannot be done. Curiously, the morbidity and mortality rates from tuberculosis have shown a continuous decline since long before the introduction of streptomycin. Presumably the drug (and others developed later) plays some part in the most recent decline, but from the earliest days to the present, economic and social conditions of life (especially housing and nutrition) probably have played the major role. An experiment nearly always contains more treatments than meet the eye!

PI-2.

The basic point here is that the method of assigning mice to groups is seriously defective. The most likely result of drawing 25 mice arbitrarily out of a group of 50 is that the most sluggish, least active mice will be easily caught. Anyone who has handled mice knows how varied are their temperaments and their abilities to elude the investigator's grasp. Therefore, apart from any drug effect, we shall probably see less activity in the group that was removed to a new cage than in the residual group. If the drug is inert and is given to the removed mice, it will appear to be a tranquilizer; if the residual mice receive the inert drug, it will appear to have stimulant properties. Both effects may seem to be very striking, and statistical analysis may show them highly significant, but they are false. If the drug really is a tranquilizer, its action may be greatly exaggerated in case (*a*), and wholly masked in case (*b*). A misleading experiment is worse than useless. Randomization would have avoided the difficulties.

PI-3.

Draw up a sequential list of 50 numbers that will represent the order in which mice are going to be drawn out of stock for assignment to cage A or B. To avoid having to discard all the numbers greater than 50 as meaningless, designate the first mouse to be drawn by 01 or 51, the second mouse by 02 or 52, and so on. Then find the 25 random assignments to cage A by entering Table 1 and reading out a set of 25 digit pairs. Suppose the numbers 02, 54, and 05 occurred among this set but 01 (or 51), 03 (or 53), and 06 (or 56) did not. Then the beginning of the list might look like this:

Mouse Order

1st	2nd	3rd	4th	5th	6th
01	02	03	04	05	06
51	52	53	54	55	56
	A		A	A	

When 25 assignments to A have been entered on the list, as above, B is entered for the remaining 25. Then the first mouse is removed from stock, the list is consulted, and the animal is placed in the appropriate cage (in this instance, B). The distribution of mice continues in the same way until completed; this part of the procedure is a mere physical execution of the specified plan of randomization in which no characteristic of the mice plays any role whatsoever.

PI-4.

The law of randomization was violated. The letter with which his last name begins is certainly a "characteristic of a subject" and it has in this case determined into which group he is placed. This might seem a ridiculous objection, but deeper thought will reveal that many experiences in life, which could influence one's response to a psychological test, may be related to one's name and its rank in the alphabet. It is not necessary to cite any particular respect in which a name is likely to influence an experimental outcome. The point is that as long as *some* characteristic of a person influences his assignment to a group, a suspicion is introduced, that the groups may not be as equivalent as they should be.

P1-5.

Experimental Day

		1	2	3	4	5
	1	A	B	C	D	E
Location	2	B	C	D	E	A
	3	C	D	E	A	B
	4	D	E	A	B	C
	5	E	A	B	C	D

Here each letter represents a different attractant. Since there are five positions, if the experiment is to be balanced it must be conducted on five different occasions, so each position can be occupied by every attractant at some time. Many other 5×5 Latin squares could have been chosen. The results obtained will be numbers of flies trapped, and there will be a number in each of the 25 boxes of the table. The attractants will be compared by computing the mean numbers for all A, for all B, and so on. Any difference between locations will be given by a comparison between the row means, any difference between days by a comparison between column means.

P1-6.

Hypothesis: The systolic blood pressure is not abnormally elevated. *Decision rule*: Measure systolic blood pressure. If it does not exceed 130, accept; otherwise reject. Many definitions of the normal state of health are necessarily of a statistical nature. Large deviations from the norm imply underlying disease, but there is often a considerable region of uncertainty, where health and disease are both to be found. Thus in the present problem, some rule has to be adopted. Among all recruits who are rejected because of blood pressure above 130 there will be some who are really quite healthy. The decision rule may reject all recruits with disease manifested by high blood pressure (if so, then $\beta = 0$) and it will certainly reject 1 % of all healthy recruits (since $\alpha = 0.01$).

P1-7.

If you see X, the chances are 2 to 1 that the other side is also X. This is because there are three X symbols in all; on the obverse side of one of these is a 0, of two of them an X. The decision rule is therefore: If X is seen, accept; if 0 is seen, reject. Now if 0 is seen, and we reject, we will be wrong once in three trials, because with that frequency the other side is indeed X, so $\alpha = 0.33$. But if X is seen, and we accept, we will also be wrong once in three trials, so $\beta = 0.33$.

P1-8.

The null hypothesis states that the samples of data from the alcohol-treated group and from the control group were drawn from the same population, i.e., that alcohol had no effect. Since we are dealing with score differences, the null hypothesis is that the true score difference is zero, i.e., that the sample of score differences was drawn from a population with mean difference equal to zero. The null hypothesis will be tested by comparing the observed mean difference with its sampling distribution (about which we will need some information) to see how rare it is. If the probability of its being drawn by chance from the hypothetical null population is less than our chosen value of P, we will reject the null hypothesis and conclude that alcohol was detrimental to driving ability. Otherwise we shall be unable to conclude that alcohol is detrimental.

PI-9.

When we reject a null hypothesis, we conclude that the two samples were drawn from different populations, i.e., that treated and control groups really differed. This is the same as finding that the confidence interval of a difference does not include zero. Accepting a null hypothesis, however, may merely mean we had insufficient data to reject it. It certainly does not mean it is true. While β may be reasonably small with respect to some specified alternative hypothesis, other alternatives can usually be postulated for which β is very large. A real but small difference between two parameters might only be detectable by samples too large to be practical. The confidence interval for the difference would, in this case, include zero, but the limits would specify how large a real difference might exist without being detected. The confidence interval approach is therefore much more informative.

PI-10.

Not necessarily. The level of significance should not be confused with an estimate of the true magnitude of an effect. The results mean that it is more *certain* that B is effective, in the sense that there is one chance in 20 that A may really be inert, but only one chance in 100 that B is inert. It is entirely possible, however, that A is the more effective vaccine. For example, it might have been tried on a smaller sample than B, so that the results were less decisively different from the control. Again a confidence interval for the potency difference would be more informative than the mere statement of effectiveness.

PI-11

The defect in this experimental design is that each medication was labeled distinctively. It is true that the investigators, nursing staff, and patients could not know which medications were represented by A, B, and C. However, opinions soon form as to which is which, and these in turn bias further observations. The merits of A, B, and C are sure to be discussed among the patients and among the staff. Any observed effect (favorable, unfavorable, or neutral) of one drug, though it may be manifested in but a single patient, becomes common knowledge, and that drug (be it A, B, or C) acquires special properties throughout the experimental group and for the remainder of the experimental period.

For these reasons the drugs to be administered to each subject must be coded individually and without clue as to their relationship to any other subject's medications. Random serial numbers may be employed; or the entire sequence of medications for a given subject may be labeled with that subject's name, and numbered serially.

CHAPTER 2

P2-1.

Since the data are paired for each subject, the procedure should make use of the pairing. We therefore calculate the score difference, placebo minus drug, for each of the 10 subjects. This gives the following set of differences:

$$+14, \quad +26, \quad +19, \quad -26, \quad -4, \quad -6, \quad +17, \quad -29, \quad +5, \quad +10$$

Inspection of the signs of these differences makes it seem unlikely that the drug causes any significant improvement. Certainly six positive and four negative signs in a group of 10 is entirely compatible with the $5+$, $5-$ expected on a chance basis in a population with true difference zero.

The signed-ranks test would require a preliminary rearrangement in rank order without regard to sign, as follows:

d	-4,	$+5$,	-6,	$+10$,	$+14$,	$+17$,	$+19$,	$(+26$,	$-26)$,	-29
Rank	1	2	3	4	5	6	7	8.5		10

Then the sum of the negative ranks is 22.5, the sum of the positive ranks is 32.5, Table 16 shows that at $P = 0.05$ for one tail and $N = 10$, the smaller sum may not exceed 10.8. We could not, therefore, assert a significant drug effect from this test either.

Had we chosen to employ a t-test, we would find, for the set of 10 differences,

$$\sum x = +26 \qquad\qquad \sum x^2 = 3{,}216.$$

$$\frac{(\sum x)^2}{N} \longrightarrow 67.6$$

$$SS = 3{,}148.4$$

$$\bar{x} = +2.6$$

$$s^2 = \frac{3{,}148.4}{9} = 349.8$$

$$s_{\bar{x}}^2 = \frac{349.8}{10} = 34.98$$

$$s_{\bar{x}} = \sqrt{34.98} = 5.92$$

$$t = \frac{\bar{x}}{s_{\bar{x}}} = \frac{+2.60}{5.92} = \quad 0.439$$

which Table 5 shows to be not significant.

To answer how great an improvement or decrement might be attributable to the drug yet not discernible here (Type II error), we establish 95% confidence limits for μ, the true difference. Table 5 shows $t = 2.26$ for $P = 0.05$ at 9 DF.

$$\mu = +2.6 \pm 2.26(5.92) = +2.6 \pm 13.4$$
$$= -10.8 \text{ to } +16.0$$

These are the limits within which the true drug effect probably lies. Since zero is included in them, the drug may be entirely ineffectual as already shown. It is also clear, that if the drug does have a beneficial effect, this is on the average no greater than $+16$ points on a base score of about 300, in other words, no greater than about 6% improvement. Moreover, although the drug could also be having a detrimental effect, that effect would be no worse than about a 4% decrement from the original score.

P2-2.

Here C.V. $= \dfrac{100s}{\bar{x}} = 15$ and $\bar{x} = 282$, so

$$s = \frac{15(282)}{100} = \quad 42.3$$

$$\begin{aligned} s^2 &= \quad 1{,}789 \\ s_{\bar{x}}^2 &= \quad 89.45 \text{ for the group initially} \\ s_{\bar{x}'}^2 &= \quad 89.45 \text{ since we were told the C.V. did not change} \end{aligned}$$

$$\begin{aligned} s^2_{(\bar{x}-\bar{x}')} &= \quad 178.9 \\ s_{(\bar{x}-\bar{x}')} &= \quad 13.4 \\ \bar{x} - \bar{x}' &= \quad 282 - 240 = 42 \end{aligned}$$

Then $t = \dfrac{(\bar{x} - \bar{x}')}{s_{(\bar{x}-\bar{x}')}} = \dfrac{42}{13.4} = 3.13$

This exceeds critical value 2.55 for one tail at $P = 0.01$ with 18 DF (Table 5), so the fall in heart rate is highly significant.

For the 95% confidence limits of the true change in heart rate, $t_{.05}$ with 18 DF is 2.10

$$(\bar{x} - \bar{x}') \pm t_{.05}(s_{\bar{x}-\bar{x}'}) = 42 \pm 2.10(13.4)$$
$$= 14 \text{ to } 70$$

P2-3.

Code by subtracting 40. Then

x_c	x_c^2
0.2	0.04
-1.3	1.69
1.6	2.56
0.5	0.25
3.2	10.24
-0.6	0.36

$$\sum x_c = +3.6 \qquad\qquad \sum x_c^2 = 15.14$$

$$\frac{(\sum x_c)^2}{N} = \frac{12.96}{6} = \longrightarrow 2.16$$
$$\mathrm{SS} = 12.98$$

$$\bar{x}_c = \frac{+3.6}{6} = +0.6 \qquad\qquad s^2 = \frac{12.98}{5} = 2.60$$

$$s_{\bar{x}}^2 = \frac{2.60}{6} = 0.433$$

$$s_{\bar{x}} = 0.658$$

Decoding,

$$\bar{x} = +0.6 + 40 = 40.6$$

$$\text{C.V.} = \frac{100s}{\bar{x}} = \frac{100\sqrt{2.60}}{40.6} = 4.0\%$$

For 99% confidence interval, $t_{.01}(5 \ \mathrm{DF}) = 4.03$
$$\mu = 40.6 \pm 4.03(0.658) = 37.9 \text{ to } 43.3$$

P2-4.

The obvious question in this problem is whether or not caffeine affected the scores on each criterion. We begin by inspection of the data. It appears that the "alertness" scores are improved, and that the "relaxation" scores are decreased; but it is obvious that "nervousness" scores are not consistently changed and nothing would be gained by analyzing them. The first step, then, is to perform an analysis of variance on the "alertness" scores.

Placebo		150 mg		300 mg		
x	x^2	x	x^2	x	x^2	
0	0	1	1	2	4	
0	0	2	4	4	16	
1	1	4	16	4	16	
1	1	2	4	3	9	
0	0	1	1	3	9	
2		10		16		$T = 28$
4		100		256		$T^2 = 784$

Preliminary Calculations

Grand total $= 784/15 = 52.3$ per observation
Between doses: $360/5 = 72.0$,,   ,,
Observations: $82 \ \ = 82.0$,,   ,,

ANALYSIS OF VARIANCE

	SS	DF	Variance Estimate	F
Between doses	$72.0 - 52.3 = 19.7$	2	9.85	11.8**
Within doses (error)	By diff. $= 10.0$	12	0.833	
Total	$82.0 - 52.3 = 29.7$	14		

Table 7 gives $F_{01} = 6.93$ at 2,12 DF, so the between-doses effect is highly significant. We are then justified in going further.

A summary of "alertness" score differences for each subject provides the following:

caffeine (150 mg) minus placebo	caffeine (300 mg) minus placebo	caffeine (300 mg) minus caffeine (150 mg)
1, 2, 3, 1, 1	2, 4, 3, 2, 3	1, 2, 0, 1, 2

Since all the differences are positive, and since Table 10 shows that if there are no signs of one kind in a sample of 5, $P < 0.05$, there is no difficulty in observing that both doses differ from placebo. In the last set of data, however, elimination of the zero leaves $N = 4$, too small for the sign test or the signed-ranks test. However, a t-test is appropriate, and yields $\sum x = 6$, $\bar{x} = 1.2$, $\sum x^2 = 10$, $(\sum x)^2/N = 7.2$, SS $= 2.8$, $s^2 = 0.700$, $s_{\bar{x}}^2 = 0.140$, $s_{\bar{x}} = 0.374$, $t = 1.2/0.374 = 3.21$ and $t_{.05}$ at 4 DF (Table 5) $= 2.13$ in a one-tail test. Thus we may reject the null hypothesis of zero difference between the two doses.

Proceeding similarly, we find that analysis of variance on the "relaxation" scores provides no evidence of heterogeneity, since variance estimate between doses $= 2.45$, error $= 0.833$, $F = 2.94$ and $F_{.05}$ (2,12 DF) $= 3.89$, which is not exceeded. We cannot, therefore, properly go further with comparison of the "relaxation" scores. There is, however, some clear indication that caffeine does reduce "relaxation" scores, and it is not unlikely that this effect would prove significant if a larger number of subjects were used.

We therefore conclude that caffeine increases "alertness" scores as compared to placebo, and that there is a real dose effect. Caffeine may reduce "relaxation" scores, but this could not be established in the present experiment. There appears to be no effect on "nervousness" scores.

P2-5.

The problem is solved by constructing the analysis of variance. It is convenient to code the data by subtracting 50. Decoding is not required.

	Obs	(Obs)²		Obs	(Obs)²		Obs	(Obs)²	Total		
Y	−10	100	R	12	144	G	−35	1,225	−33	1,089	
R	20	400	G	−29	841	Y	−12	144	−21	441	
G	−21	441	Y	1	1	R	8	64	−12	144	
Total	−11			−16			−39		−66		
	121			256			1,521		$T^2 = 4,356$		

Colors
$\sum Y$	−21	441	
$\sum R$	40	1,600	
$\sum G$	−85	7,225	
		9,266	

PRELIMINARY CALCULATIONS

Type of Total	Total of Squares	Number of Items Squared	Number of Observations per Squared Item	Total of Squares per Observation
Grand	4,356	1	9	484
Rows	1,674	3	3	558
Columns	1,898	3	3	632.7
Colors	9,266	3	3	3,089
Observations	3,360	9	1	3,360

ANALYSIS OF VARIANCE

Source	SS		DF	Variance Estimate	F	
Rows	558 − 484 =	74	2	37	1.52	N.S.
Columns	632.7 − 484 =	148.7	2	74.35	3.06	N.S.
Colors	3,089 − 484 =	2,605	2	1,302	53.6	*
Error	by difference =	48.6	2	24.3	—	
Total	3,360 − 484 =	2,876	8			

Table 7 shows at 2, 2 DF that $F_{.05} = 19.0$ and $F_{.01} = 99.0$. Therefore the colors differ significantly in their attractiveness to the birds and there are no significant position effects in the experiment.

P2-6.

The problem really asks for an upper tolerance limit for observations on individual body temperatures in this illness. We are required to find a temperature so high that if it were exceeded, a "serious doubt" would be raised that the observation came from the same population. The definition of "serious doubt" is somewhat arbitrary. Let us find that temperature below which 99% of the observations would be expected to lie, and let us make our assertion at $P = 0.05$. For $N = 15$, Table 6 indicates $K = 3.52$. The data themselves are readily coded by subtracting 100:

$$1.2, \quad 0.6, \quad 0.6, \quad 1.8, \quad 1.0, \quad 1.2, \quad 0.4, \quad 2.2, \quad 0.8,$$
$$1.6, \quad 1.0, \quad 0.8, \quad 2.0, \quad 1.6, \quad 1.6$$

$\sum x_c = 18.4$	$\sum x_c^2 = 26.80$
$\dfrac{(\sum x_c)^2}{N} \quad \longrightarrow$	22.57
	$SS = 4.23$
$\bar{x}_c = 1.23$	$s^2 = \dfrac{4.23}{14} = 0.302$
$\bar{x} = 101.23$	$s = 0.550$

$\bar{x} + K(s) = 101.2 + 3.52(0.550) = 103.2$, the required upper limit.

P2-7.

This problem is solved directly by the two-sample rank test. The number of items is small enough to make it practical to obtain U directly by counting. Evidently there is a preponderance of X preceding C, so the smaller U will probably be found by counting C preceding X. In the following diagram the number of C preceding each X is indicated.

```
                                            C
        C  C      X              C          C
X  X  X  C  X  X  C  C  X  C  X  C  X  C  X  C  C  C  C
                             X     X

0   0  0.5      3  3        5     6.5        9       11
                   3                6.5       9
```

The sum of C preceding X is therefore 56.5. We next confirm that this is the smaller U by $U = NN' - U' = 12(15) - 56.5 = 123.5$, which is larger than the value we obtained. Then consulting Table 15, we find that at $P = 0.05$ the value of U must be 55 or less for these sample sizes. Therefore we canot quite assert, at the 5% significance level, that the supplemented diet improved pelt quality. The nearly significant result, however, suggests it might be unwise to accept the null hypothesis unequivocally. The farmer would have to decide whether or not the matter was worth further (and perhaps more refined) experimentation.

P2-8.

Code the data by subtracting 200, then dividing by 10. No decoding will be necessary because addition and subtraction do not affect variances; and although multiplication and division do affect variances, they will not change F, which is a ratio of two variances.

	10°	20°	30°	Total	(Total)²
I	−5, −4 (−9)	5, 3 (8)	0, 0 (0)	−1	1
II	−3, −5 (−8)	6, 8 (14)	−1, −5 (−6)	0	0
III	0, 1 (1)	7, 8 (15)	−9, −6 (−15)	1	1
Total	−16	37	−21	$T = 0$	
(Total)²	256	1,369	441		$T^2 = 0$

PRELIMINARY CALCULATIONS

Type of Total	Total of Squares	Number of Items Squared	Number of Observations per Squared Item	Total of Squares per Observation
Grand	0	1	18	0
Light	$1 + 0 + 1 = 2$	3	6	0.333
Temperature	$256 + 1,369 + 441$ $= 2,066$	3	6	344.3
Combinations	$(-9)^2 + (8)^2 + \cdots + (-15)^2$ $= 892$	9	2	446
Observations	$(-5)^2 + (-4)^2 + \cdots + (-6)^2$ $= 466$	18	1	466

ANALYSIS OF VARIANCE

Source	SS			DF	Variance Estimate	F
Light	0.333 −	0 =	0.333	2	0.167	<1
Temperature	344 −	0 =	344.	2	172.	77.5**
Light × temperature	by diff.		= 101.4	4	25.4	11.4**
Error	466 −	446 =	20.0	9	2.22	—
Total	466 −	0 =	466.0	17		

Table 7 shows $F_{.01}$ (2,9 DF) $= 8.02$, $F_{.01}$ (4,9 DF) $= 6.42$ so there is a highly significant difference between the temperatures and also a highly significant interaction between light and temperature. Thus the apparent finding that at 10° the organisms grow better at light intensity III than at I, whereas the reverse is true at 30°, is not a mere random sampling variation but is significant. Light intensity itself in this experiment could not be said to have any consistent effect apart from the temperature-dependent effect already described.

P2-9.

This is a five-sample comparison, to which we want to apply a one-way analysis of variance. First code by subtracting 5.

	A	B	C	D	E	
	0.6	0.9	−0.8	2.2	0	
	0.2	1.7	−0.9	2.5	0.7	
	0.8	1.4	−0.2	1.1	−0.2	
	1.0	0.8	0.3	1.8	0.3	
	0.3	1.1	0.3	0.9	0.6	
Total	2.9	5.9	−1.3	8.5	1.4	$T = 17.4$
(Total)²	8.41	34.81	1.69	72.25	1.96	$T^2 = 302.76$
$\bar{x}_c$	0.58	1.18	−0.26	1.70	0.28	

PRELIMINARY CALCULATIONS

Type of Total	Total of Squares	Number of Items Squared	Number of Observations per Squared Item	Total of Squares per Observation
Grand	302.76	1	25	12.11
Varieties	119.12	5	5	23.82
Observations	28.64	25	1	28.64

ANALYSIS OF VARIANCE

Source	SS	DF	Variance Estimate	F
Between varieties	$23.82 - 12.11 = 11.71$	4	2.93	12.2**
Within varieties (error)	$28.64 - 23.82 = 4.82$	20	0.241	
Total	$28.64 - 12.11 = 16.53$	24		

The null hypothesis, that all the varieties belong to the same population, is rejected. Then we apply the studentized range factor from Table 8. At $P = 0.01$, $k* = 5.29$ for five samples and 20 DF. We use the error variance estimate 0.241, found above.

$$k = 5.29 \sqrt{\frac{0.241}{5}} = 1.16$$

which is the least significant range. Then arranging the five means in rank order, we can indicate by a solid line, all means that do not differ by this minimum amount.

C	E	A	B	D
-0.26	0.28	0.58	1.18	1.70

We conclude, at the 1% significance level, that D is superior to E and C, and that B is superior to C. Other pairs, such as B and E, A and C, D and A, may not really be different from each other. Had we adopted the 5% level of significance, however, we would have found, in addition, that D is superior to A. Note that the entire analysis was performed without decoding.

P2-10.

First code by subtracting 100, then dividing by 10.

	5	6	15	
	2	4	16	
	10	4	12	
Total	17	14	43	$\sum 74$
(Total)^2	289	196	1,849	$(74)^2 = 5,476$

	15	0	5	
	4	−1	3	
	5	5	9	

Total	24	4	17	$\sum 45$
(Total)^2	576	16	289	$(45)^2 = 2,025$
Total	41	18	60	$T = \quad 119$
(Total)^2	1,681	324	3,600	$T^2 = 14,161$

PRELIMINARY CALCULATIONS

Type of Total	Total of Squares	Number of Items Squared	Number of Observations per Squared Item	Total of Squares per Observation
Grand	14,161	1	18	786.7
Sexes	7,501	2	9	833.4
Study conditions	5,605	3	6	934.2
Combinations	3,215	6	3	1,071.7
Observations	1,229	18	1	1,229

ANALYSIS OF VARIANCE

Source	SS	DF	Variance Estimate	F	
Sexes	$833.4 - 786.7 = 46.7$	1	46.7	3.56	N.S.
Study conditions	$934.2 - 786.7 = 147.5$	2	73.75	5.63	*
Sexes × study conditions	by difference $= 90.8$	2	45.4	3.47	N.S.
Error	$1,229 - 1,071.7 = 157.3$	12	13.1	—	
Total	$1,229 - 786.7 = 442.3$	17			

Table 7 shows $F_{.05}$ (1,12 DF) $= 4.75$, $F_{.05}$ (2,12 DF) $= 3.89$. So there is no significant overall difference between men and women students, but there is a significant effect of at least one kind of music upon the learning tested in this experiment. Further examination of the coded data indicates that the significant differences between conditions of study arise from a detrimental effect of folk songs and a beneficial effect of chamber music in both men and women. The magnitudes of these effects appear to be different in the two groups, i.e., there appears to be an interaction of study conditions and sex. However, the analysis of variance shows that the interaction can not be regarded as significant.

P2-11.

The observations are coded conveniently by dividing by 10; no decoding will be required. The coded observations may then be set down in a tabular grid corresponding to the original one. One should then obtain systematic totals, first for each of the three observations on each subject, then for the subjects within each family, then for the families within each racial group, and finally the grand total. Independent subject totals will be required for male subjects and for female subjects. The preliminary calculations then consist in squaring and summing each of these, beginning with the grand total and ending with the individual observations.

PRELIMINARY CALCULATIONS

Type of Total	Total of Squares	Number of Items Squared	Number of Observations per Squared Item	Total of Squares per Observation
Grand	98,282	1	60	1,638
Races	$\dfrac{7,140}{27} + \dfrac{52,441}{33}$			1,853
Sexes	$\dfrac{39,204}{27} + \dfrac{13,340}{33}$			1,856
Families	$\dfrac{441}{12} + \dfrac{1,190}{9} + \dfrac{841}{6} + \dfrac{11,025}{9} + \dfrac{5,112}{15} + \dfrac{2,756}{9}$			2,180
Subjects	7,177	20	3	2,392
Observations	2,431	60	1	2,431

Note that when groups are of unequal size, the total of squares per observation is found for each group and these are added.

The best way to be certain of constructing the analysis of variance correctly is to think through each step. First, let us consider the major partition of SS into between-subjects and within-subjects portions.

$$SS$$

$$
\begin{array}{lll}
\text{Between subjects} & 2,392 - 1,638 = & 754 \\
\text{Within subjects} & 2,431 - 2,392 = & 39 \\
\text{(error)} & & \\
\hline
\text{Total} & 2,431 - 1,638 = & 793
\end{array}
$$

The remainder of the procedure is directed toward accounting further for the between-subjects SS. Now subjects might differ partly because of race difference, and also partly because of sex difference, so these components will be segregated first.

$$SS$$

Races	$1,853 - 1,638 = 215$	
Sexes	$1,856 - 1,638 = 218$	

These are seen to account for a good deal of the between-subjects SS, leaving unexplained between-subjects SS $= 754 - 215 - 218 = 321$. Now part of this may be due to differences between families. However, part of the differences between families may itself be due to race and sex differences, which we have already segregated. Let us find an SS for families which does not include race and sex effects.

Families SS $= 2,180 - 1,638 = 542$, of which races account for 215, sexes for 218. So the remaining families SS $= 542 - 215 - 218 = 109$. Then

Unexplained between-subjects SS	321
SS due to families after race and sex effects removed	109
Residual between-subjects SS	212

This is the SS between-subjects that can not be attributed to any factor in the experiment.

ANALYSIS OF VARIANCE

Source	SS	DF	Variance Estimate	F	
Between-subjects	754	19	3.97	4.07	**
Races	215	1	215.	221.	**
Sexes	218	1	218.	224.	**
Families	109	5	21.8	22.4	**
Subjects residual	212	12	17.7	18.2	**
	754	19			
Within-subjects (error)	39	40	0.975	—	
Total	793	59			

Table 7 shows that all the F-ratios marked ** are significant at the 1% level. The conclusion is that the capacity to metabolize this drug is distributed in a very heterogeneous manner. Males differ from females, whites from Negroes, and there are also highly significant differences between families irrespective of race and sex differences. Moreover, even after these specified sources of variation have been taken account of, there still remain unexplained highly significant individual differences between subjects.

P2-12.

Totals are formed for hospitals (50, 44, 85), surgeons (23, 14, 13, 20, 14, 10, 28, 25, 32), detergents (53, 81, 45), combinations (7, 11, 5, 4, 7, 3, ... 10, 13, 9), and these are squared and summed, as are also the 54 individual observations.

PRELIMINARY CALCULATIONS

Type of Total	Total of Squares	Number of Items Squared	Number of Observations per Squared Item	Total of Squares per Observation
Grand	32,041	1	54	593.4
Detergents	11,395	3	18	633.1
Hospitals	11,661	3	18	647.8
Surgeons	4,023	9	6	670.5
Combinations	1,447	27	2	723.5
Observations	743	54	1	743.0

It is instructive to form SS first as though no separate hospitals were involved:

		SS	DF
Surgeons	$670.5 - 593.4 =$	77.1	8
Detergents	$633.1 - 593.4 =$	39.7	2
Surgeons × detergents	by difference $=$	13.3	16
Error	$743 \quad - 723.5 =$	19.5	27
Total	$743 \quad - 593.4 = 149.6$		53

The DF were obtained as follows. For 9 surgeons there must be 8 DF; and for 3 detergents, 2 DF. The interaction DF is always the product of the inter-acting DF, $8 \times 2 = 16$. The error DF is evident in the design, since there were 27 duplicate observations.

Now we know that part of the SS between surgeons may be due to variation between hospitals. We may segregate a "Surgeons within hospitals" SS by subtraction, as follows:

		SS	DF
Surgeons (as above)		77.1	8
Hospitals	$647.8 - 593.4 =$	54.4	2
Surgeons within hospitals	$= $	22.7	6

ANALYSIS OF VARIANCE

Source	SS	DF	MS	F	
Hospitals	54.4	2	27.2 ⎫	32.7	**
Surgeons within hospitals	22.7	6	3.78 ⎬	4.55	**
Detergents	39.7	2	19.8 ⎭	23.8	**
Interactions	13.3	16	0.831 ⎫	1.15	N.S.
Error	19.5	27	0.722 ⎭		
Total	149.6	53			

This is obviously a mixed model. Detergents A, B, and C are fixed factors, since we will wish to draw conclusions about these three detergents. Hospitals and surgeons are random factors, since we presumably are not interested in these particular surgeons or hospitals but rather wish to extend any conclusions about the detergents to hospitals in general or to surgeons in general. We therefore test the interactions against the error variance, and find them not significant. The main effects are then tested against the interaction variance estimate, as shown above. All three are found (Table 7) to be highly significant.

We conclude, then, as follows: (1) The three detergents do differ in their irritating properties. B is evidently the most irritating but there seems to be no great difference between A and C. (2) The hospitals differ in the scores they assign to the detergents, and surgeons differ from each other in this respect, even within each hospital. These effects may or may not be of interest. Surgeons (and hospitals), despite their lack of uniformity in scoring, nevertheless agree on the ranking of the detergents. If they did not, there would have been a significant interaction variance estimate.

CHAPTER 3

P3-1.

The problem is to find the 95% confidence interval for π from $p = 0.40$ with $N = 100$. Table 11 gives this directly as 0.31 to 0.51.

P3-2.

We are asked to state a value of π such that the probability is only 0.05 that the true value will be smaller than the stated value. In other words we want to find the lower bound of a 90% confidence interval, since the upper limit will also be exceeded with probability 0.05. Table 11 will not be useful unless we wish to find the lower bound of a 95% confidence interval.

The best way to solve the problem is by the normal approximation.

$$p = 22/400 = 0.055$$
$$N = 400$$
$$s_p^2 = \frac{0.055(0.945)}{400} = 0.000130$$
$$s_p = 0.0113$$

$\pi = p \pm x^*(s_p)$, where we want the one-tail value of x^* at $P = 0.05$. Table 4 gives this as 1.64. Then,

$$\text{Lower limit} = 0.055 - 1.64(0.0113) = 0.036$$

So the smallest incidence of this anomaly in the population is 36 per thousand, and this statement is made at the 5% level of significance.

P3-3.

14	8	22
6	10	16
20	18	38

By the rough shortcut,

$$
\begin{array}{r}
(14 \times 10) = 140 \\
-(8 \times 6) = 48 \\
\hline
92 \\
-\dfrac{38}{2} = 19 \\
\hline
73
\end{array}
$$

$$\frac{(73)(73)(38)}{(20)(18)(16)(22)}$$

$$\frac{38}{22} \cong 2 \qquad \frac{73}{16} \cong 4 \qquad \frac{73}{18} \cong 4$$

$$\frac{(2)(4)(4)}{(20)} \cong \frac{16}{10} \cong 1.6 \cong \chi^2$$

Since this falls so far short of the critical value 3.8 at $P = 0.05$, it is apparent that the observed outcome might well have come about by chance, and offers no support to a hypothesis relating the behavior to the serotonin content. The exact value of χ^2 in this 2×2 contingency table happens to work out to the same value, 1.60.

P3-4.

We are asked here for the significance of a difference between two counts.

$$L + L' = 71$$
$$\text{Smaller count} = 28.$$

Table 14 shows directly that for this sum of the two counts, $P \leq 0.05$ that the smaller count will be 28 or less, if the null hypothesis is true. The null hypothesis may therefore be rejected, and we conclude that there is a real difference.

P3-5.

The 95% confidence interval for the true count λ is given by $L \pm 1.96(s_L)$ and it is required that $1.96(s_L) = 0.01\lambda \cong 0.01L$. Then, since $s_L = \sqrt{L}$, $1.96\sqrt{L} = 0.01$ L, $\sqrt{L} = 196$, $L = 38{,}416$ total counts. This might best be achieved by timing four replicate counts of 10^4 each. The replication ensures that no malfunction of the instrument is overlooked. The counts per minute are then obtained by dividing the total count by the total time, whence the ^{32}P content may be calculated.

P3-6.

$$
\begin{array}{r}
153 \\
250 \\
220 \\
81 \\
306 \\
244 \\
\hline
\sum \quad 1{,}254 \\
L \quad 209
\end{array}
$$

We may consider 209 to be a reasonably good estimate of λ, and examine the deviations from this expectation by χ^2.

O	$O-E$	$(O-E)^2$
153	-56	3,136
250	$+41$	1,681
220	$+11$	121
81	-128	16,384
306	$+97$	9,409
244	$+35$	1,225
	0	31,956

$$\chi^2 = \Sigma \frac{(O-E)^2}{E} = \frac{\Sigma (O-E)^2}{E} = \frac{31,956}{209} = 153$$

At $P = 0.01$ and 5 DF, Table 9 gives 15.1 as the critical value of χ^2. So it may be concluded that there is a marked heterogeneity in the distribution of particles over the electron micrograph field. In other words there has been local aggregation or dispersion so that the overall distribution is not at all what would be expected if the same number of particles had been uniformly sprayed over the same area.

P3-7.

	Hallucinations	No Hallucinations	Total
Placebo	1	6	7
Treated	5	1	6
Total	6	7	13

Since this 2×2 table has boxes containing expectations smaller than 5, the special method must be used. We first write the most extreme table with the same marginal totals, then the next most extreme,

0	7		1	6
6	0		5	1

Since the second table is identical to the one observed, we find the probabilities for both these tables, if the null hypothesis were true. For the observed table we have

$$\frac{7!6!6!7!}{13!1!6!5!1!} = \frac{7}{22(13)} = 0.0245$$

and for the more extreme one,

$$\frac{7!6!6!7!}{13!0!7!6!0!} = \frac{2}{(24)(11)(13)} = 0.0006$$

The sum of these, $P = 0.025$, is the probability we wish. So we reject the null hypothesis and conclude that the extract did have hallucinogenic properties.

P3-8.

Let us rewrite the data as a standard 2×5 contingency table and apply the χ^2 test.

	A	B	C	D	E	Total
Acceptable	14	12	20	13	17	76
Not acceptable	22	26	16	24	17	105
Total	36	38	36	37	34	181

EXPECTED FREQUENCIES:

A	B	C	D	E	Total
15.1	16.0	15.1	15.5	14.3	76
20.9	22.0	20.9	21.5	19.7	105
36	38	36	37	34	181

$E - O$:

A	B	C	D	E	Total
1.1	4.0	-4.9	2.5	-2.7	0
-1.1	-4.0	4.9	-2.5	2.7	0

$(E - O)^2$:

A	B	C	D	E
1.21	16.0	24.0	6.25	7.29
1.21	16.0	24.0	6.25	7.29

$\dfrac{(E - O)^2}{E}$:

A	B	C	D	E
0.08	1.00	1.59	0.40	0.51
0.06	0.73	1.15	0.29	0.37

$$\chi^2 = \Sigma \frac{(E - O)^2}{E} = 6.18$$

At $P = 0.05$ with 4 DF, Table 9 gives 9.49 as the critical value of χ^2. The null hypothesis may therefore not be rejected, and we cannot conclude that there is any real difference between the flavoring agents. In other words, the apparent superiority of C and inferiority of B may well be the result of the chances of random sampling from a population in which all the agents are equally acceptable.

P3-9.

The important thing to recognize is that this problem calls for the two-sample rank test, and not a χ^2 test, because the data form an *ordered* contingency table.

Data	4r,6e	10r,11e	19,22	18,13	6,2	2,2
Rank	5.5	21.	52.	88.	107.5	113.5

Then the sum of r ranks is

$$4(5.5) + 10(21) + 19(52) + 18(88) + 6(107.5) + 2(113.5) = 3,676$$

and as a check we find the sum of e ranks,

$$6(5.5) + 11(21) + 22(52) + 13(88) + 2(107.5) + 2(113.5) = 2,994$$

Compute U from the sum of r ranks:

$$U = NN' + \frac{N(N+1)}{2} - R$$

$$= 59(56) + \frac{59(60)}{2} - 3,676 = 1,398$$

Compute U from the sum of e ranks:

$$U = 56(59) + \frac{56(57)}{2} - 2,994 = 1,906$$

$$U' = NN' - U = 56(59) - 1,398 = 1,906$$

Thus verifying the computations.

Now choosing either U and applying the normal approximation,

$$x^* = \frac{\left| U - \frac{NN'}{2} \right|}{\sqrt{\frac{NN'(N+N'+1)}{12}}}$$

$$= \frac{\left| 1,906 - \frac{3,304}{2} \right|}{\sqrt{\frac{3,304(116)}{12}}} = \frac{254}{179} = 1.42$$

and since this is smaller than 1.96 (Table 4), we cannot conclude that there was any difference between the two groups.

P3-10.

$$p = \frac{22}{50} = 0.44 \qquad N = 50 \qquad A = 22$$

$$p' = \frac{35}{50} = 0.70 \qquad N' = 50 \qquad A' = 35$$

$$\text{Pooled } p = \frac{22 + 35}{50 + 50} = 0.57$$

$$\text{Pooled } s^2 = 0.57(0.43) = 0.245$$

$$s_p{}^2 = \frac{0.245}{50} = 0.00490$$

$$s_p{}'^2 = 0.00490$$

$$s_d{}^2 = 0.00980$$

$$s_d = 0.0990$$

$$x^* = \frac{p - p'}{s_d} = \frac{-0.26}{0.0990} = -2.63$$

This exceeds the critical value 2.33 at $P = 0.01$ in a one-tail test (Table 4) so we conclude that the drug is indeed less effective by stomach tube than by subcutaneous injection.

P3-11.

The total count was 2,297. Then $s_L = \sqrt{2,297} = 47.9$. Table 4 gives $x^* = 2.58$ for both tails at $P = 0.01$. So $\lambda = 2,297 \pm 2.58(47.9) = 2,297 \pm 124$. This is the interval for the number of cells in $3(0.5) = 1.5$ ml. Then the desired 99% confidence interval is $\frac{2,297}{1.5} \pm \frac{124}{1.5}$ per ml, or $1,531 \pm 83$, or 1,448 to 1,614 cells per ml.

P3-12.

	Cured	Not Cured
Observed	25	0
Expected	19.25	5.75
$(E - O)$	5.75	5.75
$(E - O)_c$	5.25	5.25
$(E - O)_c^2$	27.56	27.56
$\dfrac{(E - O)_c^2}{E}$	1.43	4.79

$$\chi^2 = 6.22$$

Since this exceeds the critical value 5.41 at $P = 0.01$ with 1 DF in a one-tail test (Table 9), we conclude that the new procedure is effective.

CHAPTER 4

P4-1.

For the data of the first 4 weeks only, let x be weeks, y be weights.

$$\sum x = 5(1 + 2 + 3 + 4) = 50 \qquad\qquad \bar{x} = \frac{50}{20} = 2.50$$

$$\sum x^2 = 5(1 + 4 + 9 + 16) = 150 \qquad\qquad \frac{(\sum x)^2}{N} = 125$$

$$\sum y = 23.3 \qquad\qquad \bar{y} = \frac{23.3}{20} = 1.16$$

$$\sum y^2 = 32.5 \qquad\qquad \frac{(\sum y)^2}{N} = 27.1$$

$$\sum xy = 69.6$$

$$b = \frac{69.6 - \dfrac{(50)(23.3)}{20}}{150 - 125} = \frac{11.4}{25} = 0.454$$

Then the equation of the line is

$$\tilde{y} = 1.16 + 0.454(x - 2.50)$$

The line is drawn by plotting the point at $\bar{x}$, $\bar{y} = 2.50$, 1.16, then choosing a higher x, for example 4.00. The second point on the line is therefore

$$\tilde{y} = 1.16 + 0.454(4.00 - 2.50) = 1.84 \text{ at } x = 4.00$$

Now $\quad s_{y\cdot x}^2 = \dfrac{1}{N-2}\left\{ \sum y^2 - \dfrac{(\sum y)^2}{N} - b\left[\sum xy - \dfrac{(\sum x)(\sum y)}{N}\right] \right\}$

$$= \frac{1}{18}\left\{ 32.5 - 27.1 - 0.454\left[69.6 - \frac{(50)(23.3)}{20}\right] \right\}$$

$$= 0.01$$

$$s_{y\cdot x} = \sqrt{0.01} = 0.1$$

For the 95% confidence interval,

$$\beta = b \pm \frac{t(s_{y \cdot x})}{\sqrt{\sum x^2 - \frac{(\sum x)^2}{N}}}$$

$$= 0.454 \pm \frac{2.10(0.1)}{\sqrt{150 - 125}}$$

$= 0.454 \pm 0.04 = 0.42$ to 0.50 units per week, the 95% confidence interval for the true rate.

$$r^2 = \frac{\left[\sum xy - \frac{(\sum x)(\sum y)}{N} \right]^2}{\left[\sum x^2 - \frac{(\sum x)^2}{N} \right]\left[\sum y^2 - \frac{(\sum y)^2}{N} \right]}$$

$$= \frac{(11.4)^2}{(25)(5.4)} = 0.96$$

So 96% of the total variance is due to regression, a remarkably homogeneous set of data.

$$r = \sqrt{0.96} = 0.98$$

P4-2.

The question is whether two slopes differ significantly from each other.

$$\sum x = 25 \qquad \sum x^2 = 76.0 \qquad \sum y = 13.7 \qquad \sum y^2 = 22.41$$

$$\frac{(\sum x)^2}{N} = \xrightarrow[\text{SS}_x]{} \frac{62.5}{13.5} \qquad \frac{(\sum y)^2}{N} = \xrightarrow[\text{SS}_y]{} \frac{18.77}{3.64}$$

$$\sum xy = 41.15$$

$$\frac{(\sum x)(\sum y)}{N} = 34.25$$

$$\text{SP}_{xy} \quad 6.90$$

$$b = \frac{6.90}{13.5} = 0.511$$

To compute a pooled error variance we require SS_x, SS_y, and SP_{xy} from Prob. 4-1. Then we pool as follows:

	SS_x	SS_y	SP_{xy}	DF
Dark controls	25	5.33	11.35	18
Light exposed	13	3.64	6.90	8
Pooled	38	8.97	18.25	26

$$s_{y \cdot x}^2 = \frac{1}{26}\left[8.97 - \frac{18.25}{38.0}(18.25)\right] = 0.00808$$

$$s_{y \cdot x} = 0.0899$$

$$t = \frac{0.454 - 0.511}{0.0899\sqrt{\dfrac{1}{25} + \dfrac{1}{13}}} = -1.86$$

and since this exceeds the value 1.71 at $P = 0.05$ with 26 DF in a one-tail test, we may conclude that the enzyme developed faster in the animals exposed to light. Although the difference is significant, it should be noted that it is really quite small; the estimate is that there was an increase of 13% in the rate of enzyme development.

P4-3.

Dose	x_c	y
31.6	−1	15, 17, 16, 16
100	0	32, 27, 30, 33
316	+1	44, 42, 46, 47
1,000	+2	61, 63, 63, 61

$$N = 16$$

$$\sum x = 8 \qquad \sum x^2 = 24 \qquad \sum y = 613 \qquad \sum y^2 = 28{,}173$$

$$\frac{(\sum x)^2}{N} \longrightarrow 4 \qquad\qquad \frac{(\sum y)^2}{N} \longrightarrow 23{,}486$$

$$\qquad\qquad SS_x = 20 \qquad\qquad\qquad\qquad SS_y = 4{,}687$$

$$\bar{x} = 0.500 \qquad\qquad \sum xy = 611 \qquad\qquad \bar{y} = 38.3$$

$$\frac{(\sum x)(\sum y)}{N} = 306.5$$

$$SP_{xy} = 304.5$$

$$b = \frac{SP_{xy}}{SS_x} = \frac{304.5}{20} = 15.2$$

$$\tilde{y} = 38.3 + 15.2(x - 0.500)$$

Rearranging, and substituting $\bar{y} = 35$, as required,

$$x_c = \frac{35 - 38.3 + 15.2(0.500)}{15.2} = 0.283$$

The confidence interval for this x_c is given by the same equations used to estimate a confidence interval of m ($= x$ corresponding to $\bar{y} = 5.00$ probits):

$$g = \frac{t^2(s_{y \cdot x}^2)}{b^2(SS_x)} = \frac{(2.98)^2(4.73)}{(15.2)^2(20)} = 0.01$$

The value of t is that for 14 DF at $P = 0.01$ (Table 5). Since g is so small, we may proceed with the simplified variance and confidence interval equations,

$$s_m^2 = \frac{s_{y \cdot x}^2}{b^2}\left[\frac{1}{N} + \frac{(m - \bar{x})^2}{\sum(x - \bar{x})^2}\right]$$

$$\tilde{m} = m \pm t(s_m)$$

Here we will let $m = x_c = 0.283$

$$s_{y \cdot x}^2 = \frac{1}{N-2}\left[SS_y - b(SP_{xy})\right]$$

$$= \frac{1}{14}[4{,}687 - 15.2(304)] = 4.73$$

$$s_m^2 = \frac{4.73}{(15.2)^2}\left[\frac{1}{16} + \frac{(0.283 - 0.500)^2}{20}\right] = 0.00123$$

$$s_m = 0.035$$

Then the 99% confidence interval for the true value of x_c is

$$0.283 \pm 2.98(0.035) = 0.179 \text{ to } 0.387 \text{ coded units}$$

To decode, we note that each coded unit represented a 3.16-fold dose increase, or 0.500 log units; and that the true log corresponding to zero on the coded scale is 2.000. Then, from Table 3,

Coded dose	Actual Log Dose	Actual Dose $m\mu g$
0.283	0.283(0.500) + 2.000 = 2.142	139.
0.179	0.179(0.500) + 2.000 = 2.090	123.
0.387	0.387(0.500) + 2.000 = 2.194	156.

So the dose that would produce a mean contraction of 35 mm is estimated to be 139, with 99% confidence limits 123 to 156 mμg.

P4-4.

Dose	Coded Log Dose, x_c	Contraction, mm	Contraction, Percent of Maximal	Probit (y)
31.6	−1	15, 17, 16, 16	22.4, 25.4, 23.9, 23.9	4.24, 4.34, 4.29, 4.29
100	0	32, 27, 30, 33	47.8, 40.3, 44.8, 49.3	4.94, 4.76, 4.86, 4.98
316	+1	44, 42, 46, 47	65.7, 62.7, 68.7, 70.1	5.40, 5.32, 5.49, 5.52
1,000	+2	61, 63, 63, 61	91.0, 94.0, 94.0, 91.0	6.34, 6.55, 6.55, 6.34

$$\sum x_c = 8 \qquad \sum x_c^2 = 24 \qquad \sum y = 84.21 \qquad \sum y^2 = 453.37$$

$$\frac{(\sum x_c)^2}{N} \longrightarrow 4 \qquad\qquad \frac{(\sum y)^2}{N} \longrightarrow 443.21$$
$$\mathrm{SS}_x = 20.0 \qquad\qquad \mathrm{SS}_y = 10.16$$

$$\bar{x}_c = 0.500 \qquad\qquad \sum xy = 56.13 \qquad\qquad \bar{y} = 5.26$$

$$\frac{(\sum x)(\sum y)}{N} = 42.10$$

$$\mathrm{SP}_{xy} = 14.03$$

$$b = \frac{14.0}{20.0} = 0.700$$

$$\tilde{y} = 5.26 + 0.700(x - 0.500)$$

$$m_c = \frac{5.00 - 5.26}{0.700} + 0.500 = 0.129$$

$$s_{y \cdot x}^2 = \frac{1}{14}[10.16 - 0.700(14.0)] = 0.0257$$

$$s_{m_c}^2 = \frac{0.0257}{0.490}\left[\frac{1}{16} + \frac{(0.129 - 0.500)^2}{20.0}\right] = 0.00364$$

$$s_{m_c} = 0.0603$$

$$\tilde{m}_c = 0.129 \pm 2.98(0.0603) = -.051 \text{ to } 0.309$$

Decoding, these limits are $-0.051(0.500) + 2$ to $0.309(0.500) + 2 = 1.97$ to 2.15 and $m = 0.129(0.500) + 2 = 2.06$.

Then $\mathrm{ED}_{50} = $ antilog $2.06 = 115$ mμg with 99% confidence limits 93 to 141.

P4-5.

$b = 0.700$ in coded units. Since each coded x unit is 0.5 log units, the slope of the regression of probit on log dose will be twice as steep, or 1.40. Then $\sigma = 1/1.40 = 0.714$ log units. Then ± 0.357 log units from the ED_{50} should include responses from 31% to 69% of maximal. This can be verified by inspection of a graph of the probit of response on log dose.

P4-6.

A provisional line is first drawn as indicated by the column of expected probits.

Dose (mg/kg)	Coded Log Dose	Dead/ Total	Percent Dead	Empirical Probit	Expected Probit
5		0/10			
10	−1	2/10	20.	4.16	4.31
20	0	6/10	60.	5.25	5.04
40	+1	7/10	70.	5.52	5.76
80		10/10			

Expected Probit	w	x	N	Nw	Nwx	Nwx²
4.31	0.535	−1	10	5.35	−5.35	5.35
5.04	0.636	0	10	6.36	0	0
5.76	0.515	+1	10	5.15	5.15	5.15

$$\sum Nw = 16.86$$

$$\sum Nwx = -0.20$$

$$\sum Nwx^2 = 10.50$$

$$\text{Weighted } \bar{x} = \frac{-0.20}{16.86} = -0.0119$$

Expected Probit	Observed Proportion (p)	Working Probit (y)	Nwy	Nwxy
4.31	0.20	4.17	22.31	−22.31
5.04	0.60	5.25	33.39	0
5.76	0.70	5.50	28.32	28.32

$$\sum Nwy = 84.02$$

$$\sum Nwxy = 6.01$$

$$\text{Weighted } \bar{y} = \frac{84.02}{16.86} = 4.98$$

$$b = \frac{6.01 - \dfrac{(-0.20)(84.02)}{16.86}}{10.50 - \dfrac{(-0.20)^2}{16.86}} = 0.668$$

The adjusted line is drawn through $(-0.01, 4.98)$ with slope 0.668. At $\Delta x = 1$, $\Delta y = 0.67$; so the line passes through a point 0.99, 5.65. When the adjusted line is drawn we see it is so close to the original one that a further cycle of computation would be useless.

χ^2 TEST OF FIT:

Expected Probit (Adjusted Line)	Expected Proportion Dead	(E) Expected Number Dead	(O) Observed Number Dead	$(E - O)(1 - \pi)$	$(E - O)^2$	$E(1 - \pi)$
4.30	0.242	2.42	2.	0.42	0.758	0.176	1.83
4.98	0.493	4.93	6.	1.07	0.507	1.15	2.50
5.65	0.743	7.43	7.	0.43	0.257	0.185	1.91

$$\chi^2 = \Sigma \frac{(E - O)^2}{E(1 - \pi)} = 0.66$$

So the adjusted line is an acceptable fit to the data.

$$m_c = \frac{5.00 - 4.98}{0.668} - 0.01 = 0.01$$

$$g = \frac{(1.96)^2}{(0.668)^2 (10.5)} = 0.820$$

Then,

$$\tilde{m}_c - \bar{x} = \frac{1}{(1 - 0.820)} \left[0.01 + 0.01 \pm \frac{1.96}{0.668} \sqrt{\frac{(1 - 0.820)}{16.9} + \frac{(0.01 + 0.01)^2}{10.5}} \right]$$

$$\tilde{m}_c - (-0.01) = 0.11 \pm 1.68$$

$$(-1.57 - 0.01) < \tilde{m}_c < (+1.79 - 0.01)$$

$$-1.58 < \tilde{m}_c < +1.78$$

Since each dose increment was a doubling, the coded unit is $\log 2 = 0.301$, and log dose at coded zero $= \log 20 = 1.301$. Then $m = 0.01(0.301) + 1.301 = 1.30$, with lower 95% confidence limit $= -1.58(0.301) + 1.301 = 0.82$, and upper 95% confidence limit $= -1.78(0.301) + 1.301 = 1.84$. Then the actual LD$_{50}$ and its confidence limits are the respective antilogs,

$$LD_{50} = 20 \, mg/kg \, (6.6 \text{ to } 69 \, mg/kg)$$

In this case the magnitude of g indicates a very considerable uncertainty about the true slope, which results in a confidence interval so wide as to be rather uninformative. The unsatisfactory outcome should suggest the advisability of improving the experimental procedures, by attention to methods that will reduce the variability, and by increasing the number of animals at each dose level. Here, use of the approximate variance would have led to a serious underestimate of the width of the confidence interval, as 12 to 32 mg/kg.

P4-7.

$$\sum x = 151 \qquad \sum x^2 = 2{,}137 \qquad\qquad \sum y = 460 \qquad \sum y^2 = 20{,}110$$

$$\frac{(\sum x)^2}{N} \;\text{------}\rightarrow\; 1{,}520 \qquad \frac{(\sum y)^2}{N} \;\text{------}\rightarrow\; 14{,}107$$

$$\text{SS}_x = \;\; 617 \qquad\qquad\qquad\qquad \text{SS}_y = \;\; 6{,}003$$

$$\bar{x} = 10.1 \qquad\qquad \sum xy = 6{,}457 \qquad\qquad \bar{y} = 30.7$$

$$\frac{(\sum x)(\sum y)}{N} = 4{,}631$$

$$\text{SP}_{xy} = 1{,}826$$

$$b = \frac{1{,}826}{617} = 2.96$$

$$\tilde{y} = 30.7 + 2.96(x - 10.1)$$

$$s_{y\cdot x}^2 = \frac{1}{13}\left[6{,}003 - 2.96(1{,}826)\right] = 46.0$$

$$s_y^2 = 46.0\left[\frac{1}{15} + \frac{(x - 10.1)^2}{617}\right]$$

We compute s_y^2 at different values of x. From Table 5 we obtain $t = 2.16$ at $P = 0.05$ with 13 DF.

x	y	s_y^2	s_y	$\pm t(s_y)$	Lower y	Upper y
2	6.7	7.96	2.82	6.1	0.6	12.8
5	15.6	5.01	2.24	4.8	10.8	20.4
10	30.4	3.08	1.76	3.8	26.6	34.2
15	45.2	4.88	2.21	4.8	40.4	50.0
20	60.0	10.40	3.23	7.0	53.0	67.0

P4-8.

Let erythrocyte be y, nerve be x, the desired ratio y/x. Code by dividing all data by 100.

$$\sum x = 26.15 \quad \sum x^2 = 117.64 \qquad\qquad \sum y = 29.25 \quad \sum y^2 = 148.05$$

$$\frac{(\sum x)^2}{N} \longrightarrow 113.97 \qquad\qquad \frac{(\sum y)^2}{N} \longrightarrow 142.59$$

$$SS_x = \quad 3.67 \qquad\qquad SS_y = \quad 5.46$$

$$s_x{}^2 = \quad 0.734 \qquad\qquad s_y{}^2 = \quad 1.09$$

$$\bar{x} = 4.36 \qquad\qquad\qquad \bar{y} = 4.88$$

$$s_x = \quad 0.857 \qquad\qquad\qquad s_y = \quad 1.04$$

$$\sum xy = 131.20$$

$$\frac{(\sum x)(\sum y)}{N} = 127.48$$

$$SP_{xy} = \quad 3.72$$

$$r^2 = \frac{(3.72)^2}{(3.67)(5.46)} = 0.690$$

$$r = 0.830$$

$$t = 2.57 \text{ at } P = 0.05 \text{ with 5 DF}$$

$$t^2 = 6.60$$

$$\frac{\left[(4.36)(4.88) - \dfrac{(6.60)(0.830)(0.857)(1.04)}{6} \right]}{(4.36)^2 - 6.60\left(\dfrac{0.734}{6}\right)} = 1.13$$

$$\pm \frac{\sqrt{420 - (18.2)\left[(4.88)^2 - \dfrac{(6.60)(1.09)}{6} \right]}}{18.2} = 0.04$$

Then the mean ratio is estimated to be $4.88/4.36 = 1.12$, with 95% confidence limits $1.13 - 0.04$ and $1.13 + 0.04 = 1.09$ to 1.17. Since these limits do not include 1.00, we may also conclude that there is a real difference in enzyme activity per mg protein in the two tissues.

P.4-9

Coding and computations are shown below. Provisional parallel regression lines are indicated by the data in the column of expected probits.

Dose, mg/kg	Coded Log Dose (x)	Con- vulsed Total	Propor- tion Convulsed (p)	Empiri- cal Probit	Expec- ted Probit	w	Nw	Nwx	Nwx^2
				DRUG A					
10	−1	13/15	0.867	6.12	6.23	0.360	5.40	−5.40	5.40
30	0	9/15	0.600	5.25	5.25	0.622	9.33	0	0
90	+1	4/15	0.267	4.38	4.28	0.526	7.89	7.89	7.89
							22.62	2.49	13.29
				DRUG B					
200	−1	12/15	0.800	5.84	5.81	0.500	7.50	−7.50	7.50
600	0	6/15	0.400	4.75	4.83	0.629	9.44	0	0
1,800	+1	2/15	0.133	3.89	3.86	0.391	5.86	5.86	5.86
							22.80	−1.64	13.36

Expected Probit	Observed Proportion (p)	Working Probit (y)	Nwy	Nwxy
		DRUG A		
6.23	0.867	6.09	32.89	−32.89
5.25	0.600	5.25	48.98	0
4.28	0.267	4.38	34.56	34.56
			116.43	1.67
		DRUG B		
5.81	0.800	5.84	43.80	−43.80
4.83	0.400	4.74	44.75	0
3.86	0.133	3.89	22.79	22.79
			111.34	−21.01

	Drug A (S)	Drug B (U)
$\bar{x}$	$\dfrac{2.49}{22.62} = 0.110$	$\dfrac{-1.64}{22.80} = -0.072$
$\bar{x}_S - \bar{x}_U$	$0.110 + 0.072 = 0.182$	
$\sum Nwx^2$	13.29	13.36
$\dfrac{(\sum Nwx)^2}{\sum Nw}$	$\dfrac{(2.49)^2}{22.62} = 0.274$	$\dfrac{(-1.64)^2}{22.80} = 0.118$
$\sum Nw(x - \bar{x})^2$	13.02	13.24
Pooled $\sum Nwxy$	$1.67 + (-21.01) = -19.34$	
Pooled $\dfrac{(\sum Nwx)(\sum Nwy)}{\sum Nw}$	$\dfrac{(2.49 - 1.64)(116.4 + 111.3)}{(22.62 + 22.80)} = 4.27$	
Pooled $\sum Nw(x - \bar{x})(y - \bar{y})$	$-19.34 - 4.27 = -23.61$	
Pooled b	$\dfrac{-23.61}{(13.02 + 13.24)} = -0.899$	
$\bar{y}$	$\dfrac{116}{22.6} = 5.13$	$\dfrac{111}{22.8} = 4.87$

Adjusted lines,

$\tilde{y} =$	$5.13 - 0.899(x - 0.110)$	$4.87 - 0.899(x + 0.072)$

The working graph will show that the adjusted lines differ but slightly from the provisional ones first chosen, and moreover, that both $\bar{x}$ are quite close to the intersection of the respective lines with probit 5. Simplifications may therefore be employed. Inspection of the working graph reveals that the lines pass so nearly through all the points that a χ^2 test would be redundant, and a special test for parallelism seems hardly worthwhile. Proceeding,

	Drug A (S)	Drug B (U)
m_c	$\dfrac{5.00 - 5.13}{-0.899} + 0.110$	$\dfrac{5.00 - 4.87}{-0.899} - 0.072$
	$= 0.255$	$= -0.217$

M_c

$$0.255 - (-0.217) = 0.472$$

g

$$\frac{(1.96)^2}{(-0.899)^2(13.02 + 13.24)} = 0.18$$

and g must be retained in the computations since it exceeds 0.1.

Then 95% confidence limits of $M_c - (\bar{x}_S - \bar{x}_U)$ are

$$\frac{1}{0.82}\left[0.472 - 0.182 \pm \frac{1.96}{-0.899}\sqrt{0.82\left(\frac{1}{22.62} + \frac{1}{22.80}\right) + \frac{(0.472 - 0.182)^2}{(13.02 + 13.24)}}\right.$$
$$= 0.354 \pm 0.732 = \bar{1}.622 \text{ to } 1.086$$

Thus, $\tilde{M}_c$ is estimated to be 0.472, with

$$\text{Upper limit} = 1.086 + 0.182 = 1.268$$
$$\text{Lower limit} = \bar{1}.622 + 0.182 = \bar{1}.804$$

To decode, since each dose increment was threefold, we must multiply the coded estimates of log potency difference by log 3 ($= 0.477$), and then add the difference in actual log dose between the two preparations at $x_c = 0$. This difference, $\log S_0 - \log U_0 = \log 30 - \log 600 = \bar{2}.699$.

	Antilog
$M = 0.472(0.477) + \bar{2}.699 = \bar{2}.924$	0.0839
$\text{Upper limit} = 1.268(0.477) + \bar{2}.699 = \bar{1}.304$	0.201
$\text{Lower limit} = \bar{1}.804(0.477) + \bar{2}.699 = \bar{2}.606$	0.0404

Thus potency ratio drug A/drug B is 0.0839, so drug A is $\dfrac{1}{0.0839}$ or 11.9 times more potent than drug B, with 95% confidence limits $\dfrac{1}{0.201} = 5.0$ and $\dfrac{1}{0.0404} = 24.7$ times.

232 Blank

Tables

TABLE 1

RANDOM DIGITS*

94847	47234	47635	39600	38350	14352	18217	06657
27966	59562	27413	06107	80168	54049	46815	07519
55445	48728	64878	05431	64646	05415	80237	50680
61296	22008	86504	25890	05825	38212	48280	89409
37962	03156	74748	54940	54198	34085	02577	81058
18588	97277	12791	63404	22158	13066	70177	75499
35781	86725	28967	99246	13355	01006	74893	63387
87543	59897	54070	48761	40751	77248	33808	26225
23193	62074	05410	46649	76559	17401	02722	93108
57145	05208	84640	56960	30100	56606	67985	37387
04292	35897	84499	14717	70221	23504	57596	03816
97400	74677	73008	45774	10097	46147	25385	89324
59183	83434	38211	67643	19292	47887	63225	51478
44030	37229	73277	32481	66191	29929	65645	03294
28320	06610	78988	51642	10641	00674	21045	74789
95523	16893	48247	03407	31665	66917	98339	69569
62477	35693	90285	00994	74594	90414	80392	86873
57327	96854	12771	31236	89768	32495	67307	16957
41636	48701	55198	93603	58155	89862	55728	80036
69743	71852	38521	70835	21981	20370	40829	38049
27583	54945	40301	09374	64651	87504	46483	54700
43193	77444	60036	96246	56872	23543	71399	46681
74121	08564	82161	68832	23596	93906	44956	42941
32155	01757	32402	01704	13312	93761	79236	70219
24415	95858	89258	11388	42821	07595	90003	02631

* Extracted from The Rand Corporation, *A million random digits with* 100,000 *normal deviates.* (New York: The Free Press of Glencoe, 1955), p. 89.

TABLE 2

SQUARES OF NUMBERS*

	0	1	2	3	4	5	6	7	8	9
10	10000	10201	10404	10609	10816	11025	11236	11449	11664	11881
11	12100	12321	12544	12769	12996	13225	13456	13689	13924	14161
12	14400	14641	14884	15129	15376	15625	15876	16129	16384	16641
13	16900	17161	17424	17689	17956	18225	18496	18769	19044	19321
14	19600	19881	20164	20449	20736	21025	21316	21609	21904	22201
15	22500	22801	23104	23409	23716	24025	24336	24649	24964	25281
16	25600	25921	26244	26569	26896	27225	27556	27889	28224	28561
17	28900	29241	29584	29929	30276	30625	30976	31329	31684	32041
18	32400	32761	33124	33489	33856	34225	34596	34969	35344	35721
19	36100	36481	36864	37249	37636	38025	38416	38809	39204	39601
20	40000	40401	40804	41209	41616	42025	42436	42849	43264	43681
21	44100	44521	44944	45369	45796	46225	46656	47089	47524	47961
22	48400	48841	49284	49729	50176	50625	51076	51529	51984	52441
23	52900	53361	53824	54289	54756	55225	55696	56169	56644	57121
24	57600	58081	58564	59049	59536	60025	60516	61009	61504	62001
25	62500	63001	63504	64009	64516	65025	65536	66049	66564	67081
26	67600	68121	68644	69169	69696	70225	70756	71289	71824	72361
27	72900	73441	73984	74529	75076	75625	76176	76729	77284	77841
28	78400	78961	79524	80089	80656	81225	81796	82369	82944	83521
29	84100	84681	85264	85849	86436	87025	87616	88209	88804	89401

TABLE 2—continued

	0	1	2	3	4	5	6	7	8	9
30	90000	90601	91204	91809	92416	93025	93636	94249	94864	95481
31	96100	96721	97344	97969	98596	99225	99856	100489	101124	101761
32	102400	103041	103684	104329	104976	105625	106276	106929	107584	108241
33	108900	109561	110224	110889	111556	112225	112896	113569	114244	114921
34	115600	116281	116964	117649	118336	119025	119716	120409	121104	121801
35	122500	123201	123904	124609	125316	126025	126736	127449	128164	128881
36	129600	130321	131044	131769	132496	133225	133956	134689	135424	136161
37	136900	137641	138384	139129	139876	140625	141376	142129	142884	143641
38	144400	145161	145924	146689	147456	148225	148996	149769	150544	151321
39	152100	152881	153664	154449	155236	156025	156816	157609	158404	159201
40	160000	160801	161604	162409	163216	164025	164836	165649	166464	167281
41	168100	168921	169744	170569	171396	172225	173056	173889	174724	175561
42	176400	177241	178084	178929	179776	180625	181476	182329	183184	184041
43	184900	185761	186624	187489	188356	189225	190096	190969	191844	192721
44	193600	194481	195364	196249	197136	198025	198916	199809	200704	201601
45	202500	203401	204304	205209	206116	207025	207936	208849	209764	210681
46	211600	212521	213444	214369	215296	216225	217156	218089	219024	219961
47	220900	221841	222784	223729	224676	225625	226576	227529	228484	229441
48	230400	231361	232324	233289	234256	235225	236196	237169	238144	239121
49	240100	241081	242064	243049	244036	245025	246016	247009	248004	249001
50	250000	251001	252004	253009	254016	255025	256036	257049	258064	259081
51	260100	261121	262144	263169	264196	265225	266256	267289	268324	269361
52	270400	271441	272484	273529	274576	275625	276676	277729	278784	279841
53	280900	281961	283024	284089	285156	286225	287296	288369	289444	290521
54	291600	292681	293764	294849	295936	297025	298116	299209	300304	301401

	0	1	2	3	4	5	6	7	8	9
55	302500	303601	304704	305809	306916	308025	309136	310249	311364	312481
56	313600	314721	315844	316969	318096	319225	320356	321489	322624	323761
57	324900	326041	327184	328329	329476	330625	331776	332929	334084	335241
58	336400	337561	338724	339889	341056	342225	343396	344569	345744	346921
59	348100	349281	350464	351649	352836	354025	355216	356409	357604	358801
60	360000	361201	362404	363609	364816	366025	367236	368449	369664	370881
61	372100	373321	374544	375769	376996	378225	379456	380689	381924	383161
62	384400	385641	386884	388129	389376	390625	391876	393129	394384	395641
63	396900	398161	399424	400689	401956	403225	404496	405769	407044	408321
64	409600	410881	412164	413449	414736	416025	417316	418609	419904	421201
65	422500	423801	425104	426409	427716	429025	430336	431649	432964	434281
66	435600	436921	438244	439569	440896	442225	443556	444889	446224	447561
67	448900	450241	451584	452929	454276	455625	456976	458329	459684	461041
68	462400	463761	465124	466489	467856	469225	470596	471969	473344	474721
69	476100	477481	478864	480249	481636	483025	484416	485809	487204	488601
70	490000	491401	492804	494209	495616	497025	498436	499849	501264	502681
71	504100	505521	506944	508369	509796	511225	512656	514089	515524	516961
72	518400	519841	521284	522729	524176	525625	527076	528529	529984	531441
73	532900	534361	535824	537289	538756	540225	541696	543169	544644	546121
74	547600	549081	550564	552049	553536	555025	556516	558009	559504	561001
75	562500	564001	565504	567009	568516	570025	571536	573049	574564	576081
76	577600	579121	580644	582169	583696	585225	586756	588289	589824	591361
77	592900	594441	595984	597529	599076	600625	602176	603729	605284	606841
78	608400	609961	611524	613089	614656	616225	617796	619369	620944	622521
79	624100	625681	627264	628849	630436	632025	633616	635209	636804	638401

TABLE 2—continued

	0	1	2	3	4	5	6	7	8	9
80	640000	641601	643204	644809	646416	648025	649636	651249	652864	654481
81	656100	657721	659344	660969	662596	664225	665856	667489	669124	670761
82	672400	674041	675684	677329	678976	680625	682276	683929	685584	687241
83	688900	690561	692224	693889	695556	697225	698896	700569	702244	703921
84	705600	707281	708964	710649	712336	714025	715716	717409	719104	720801
85	722500	724201	725904	727609	729316	731025	732736	734449	736164	737881
86	739600	741321	743044	744769	746496	748225	749956	751689	753424	755161
87	756900	758641	760384	762129	763876	765625	767376	769129	770884	772641
88	774400	776161	777924	779689	781456	783225	784996	786769	788544	790321
89	792100	793881	795664	797449	799236	801025	802816	804609	806404	808201
90	810000	811801	813604	815409	817216	819025	820836	822649	824464	826281
91	828100	829921	831744	833569	835396	837225	839056	840889	842724	844561
92	846400	848241	850084	851929	853776	855625	857476	859329	861184	863041
93	864900	866761	868624	870489	872356	874225	876096	877969	879844	881721
94	883600	885481	887364	889249	891136	893025	894916	896809	898704	900601
95	902500	904401	906304	908209	910116	912025	913936	915849	917764	919681
96	921600	923521	925444	927369	929296	931225	933156	935089	937024	938961
97	940900	942841	944784	946729	948676	950625	952576	954529	956484	958441
98	960400	962361	964324	966289	968256	970225	972196	974169	976144	978121
99	980100	982081	984064	986049	988036	990025	992016	994009	996004	998001

* Table 2 is abridged from Table XXVII of Fisher & Yates: *Statistical Tables for Biological, Agricultural and Medical Research* published by Oliver & Boyd Ltd., Edinburgh, and by permission of the authors and publishers.

TABLE 3

FOUR-PLACE LOGARITHMS*

N	0	1	2	3	4	5	6	7	8	9
1.0	.0000	.0043	.0086	.0128	.0170	.0212	.0253	.0294	.0334	.0374
1.1	.0414	.0453	.0492	.0531	.0569	.0607	.0645	.0682	.0719	.0755
1.2	.0792	.0828	.0864	.0899	.0934	.0969	.1004	.1038	.1072	.1106
1.3	.1139	.1173	.1206	.1239	.1271	.1303	.1335	.1367	.1399	.1430
1.4	.1461	.1492	.1523	.1553	.1584	.1614	.1644	.1673	.1703	.1732
1.5	.1761	.1790	.1818	.1847	.1875	.1903	.1931	.1959	.1987	.2014
1.6	.2041	.2068	.2095	.2122	.2148	.2175	.2201	.2227	.2253	.2279
1.7	.2304	.2330	.2355	.2380	.2405	.2430	.2455	.2480	.2504	.2529
1.8	.2553	.2577	.2601	.2625	.2648	.2672	.2695	.2718	.2742	.2765
1.9	.2788	.2810	.2833	.2856	.2878	.2900	.2923	.2945	.2967	.2989
2.0	.3010	.3032	.3054	.3075	.3096	.3118	.3139	.3160	.3181	.3201
2.1	.3222	.3243	.3263	.3284	.3304	.3324	.3345	.3365	.3385	.3404
2.2	.3424	.3444	.3464	.3483	.3502	.3522	.3541	.3560	.3579	.3598
2.3	.3617	.3636	.3655	.3674	.3692	.3711	.3729	.3747	.3766	.3784
2.4	.3802	.3820	.3838	.3856	.3874	.3892	.3909	.3927	.3945	.3962
2.5	.3979	.3997	.4014	.4031	.4048	.4065	.4082	.4099	.4116	.4133
2.6	.4150	.4166	.4183	.4200	.4216	.4232	.4249	.4265	.4281	.4298
2.7	.4314	.4330	.4346	.4362	.4378	.4393	.4409	.4425	.4440	.4456
2.8	.4472	.4487	.4502	.4518	.4533	.4548	.4564	.4579	.4594	.4609
2.9	.4624	.4639	.4654	.4669	.4683	.4698	.4713	.4728	.4742	.4757
3.0	.4771	.4786	.4800	.4814	.4829	.4843	.4857	.4871	.4886	.4900
3.1	.4914	.4928	.4942	.4955	.4969	.4983	.4997	.5011	.5024	.5038
3.2	.5051	.5065	.5079	.5092	.5105	.5119	.5132	.5145	.5159	.5172
3.3	.5185	.5198	.5211	.5224	.5237	.5250	.5263	.5276	.5289	.5302
3.4	.5315	.5328	.5340	.5353	.5366	.5378	.5391	.5403	.5416	.5428
3.5	.5441	.5453	.5465	.5478	.5490	.5502	.5514	.5527	.5539	.5551
3.6	.5563	.5575	.5587	.5599	.5611	.5623	.5635	.5647	.5658	.5670
3.7	.5682	.5694	.5705	.5717	.5729	.5740	.5752	.5763	.5775	.5786
3.8	.5798	.5809	.5821	.5832	.5843	.5855	.5866	.5877	.5888	.5899
3.9	.5911	.5922	.5933	.5944	.5955	.5966	.5977	.5988	.5999	.6010
4.0	.6021	.6031	.6042	.6053	.6064	.6075	.6085	.6096	.6107	.6117
4.1	.6128	.6138	.6149	.6160	.6170	.6180	.6191	.6201	.6212	.6222
4.2	.6232	.6243	.6253	.6263	.6274	.6284	.6294	.6304	.6314	.6325
4.3	.6335	.6345	.6355	.6365	.6375	.6385	.6395	.6405	.6415	.6425
4.4	.6435	.6444	.6454	.6464	.6474	.6484	.6493	.6503	.6513	.6522
4.5	.6532	.6542	.6551	.6561	.6571	.6580	.6590	.6599	.6609	.6618
4.6	.6628	.6637	.6646	.6656	.6665	.6675	.6684	.6693	.6702	.6712
4.7	.6721	.6730	.6739	.6749	.6758	.6767	.6776	.6785	.6794	.6803
4.8	.6812	.6821	.6830	.6839	.6848	.6857	.6866	.6875	.6884	.6893
4.9	.6902	.6911	.6920	.6928	.6937	.6946	.6955	.6964	.6972	.6981
5.0	.6990	.6998	.7007	.7016	.7024	.7033	.7042	.7050	.7059	.7067
5.1	.7076	.7084	.7093	.7101	.7110	.7118	.7126	.7135	.7143	.7152
5.2	.7160	.7168	.7177	.7185	.7193	.7202	.7210	.7218	.7226	.7235
5.3	.7243	.7251	.7259	.7267	.7275	.7284	.7292	.7300	.7308	.7316
5.4	.7324	.7332	.7340	.7348	.7356	.7364	.7372	.7380	.7388	.7396
N	0	1	2	3	4	5	6	7	8	9

TABLE 3 continued

N	0	1	2	3	4	5	6	7	8	9
5.5	.7404	.7412	.7419	.7427	.7435	.7443	.7451	.7459	.7466	.7474
5.6	.7482	.7490	.7497	.7505	.7513	.7520	.7528	.7536	.7543	.7551
5.7	.7559	.7566	.7574	.7582	.7589	.7597	.7604	.7612	.7619	.7627
5.8	.7634	.7642	.7649	.7657	.7664	.7672	.7679	.7686	.7694	.7701
5.9	.7709	.7716	.7723	.7731	.7738	.7745	.7752	.7760	.7767	.7774
6.0	.7782	.7789	.7796	.7803	.7810	.7818	.7825	.7832	.7839	.7846
6.1	.7853	.7860	.7868	.7875	.7882	.7889	.7896	.7903	.7910	.7917
6.2	.7924	.7931	.7938	.7945	.7952	.7959	.7966	.7973	.7980	.7987
6.3	.7993	.8000	.8007	.8014	.8021	.8028	.8035	.8041	.8048	.8055
6.4	.8062	.8069	.8075	.8082	.8089	.8096	.8102	.8109	.8116	.8122
6.5	.8129	.8136	.8142	.8149	.8156	.8162	.8169	.8176	.8182	.8189
6.6	.8195	.8202	.8209	.8215	.8222	.8228	.8235	.8241	.8248	.8254
6.7	.8261	.8267	.8274	.8280	.8287	.8293	.8299	.8306	.8312	.8319
6.8	.8325	.8331	.8338	.8344	.8351	.8357	.8363	.8370	.8376	.8382
6.9	.8388	.8395	.8401	.8407	.8414	.8420	.8426	.8432	.8439	.8445
7.0	.8451	.8457	.8463	.8470	.8476	.8482	.8488	.8494	.8500	.8506
7.1	.8513	.8519	.8525	.8531	.8537	.8543	.8549	.8555	.8561	.8567
7.2	.8573	.8579	.8585	.8591	.8597	.8603	.8609	.8615	.8621	.8627
7.3	.8633	.8639	.8645	.8651	.8657	.8663	.8669	.8675	.8681	.8686
7.4	.8692	.8698	.8704	.8710	.8716	.8722	.8727	.8733	.8739	.8745
7.5	.8751	.8756	.8762	.8768	.8774	.8779	.8785	.8791	.8797	.8802
7.6	.8808	.8814	.8820	.8825	.8831	.8837	.8842	.8848	.8854	.8859
7.7	.8865	.8871	.8876	.8882	.8887	.8893	.8899	.8904	.8910	.8915
7.8	.8921	.8927	.8932	.8938	.8943	.8949	.8954	.8960	.8965	.8971
7.9	.8976	.8982	.8987	.8993	.8998	.9004	.9009	.9015	.9020	.9025
8.0	.9031	.9036	.9042	.9047	.9053	.9058	.9063	.9069	.9074	.9079
8.1	.9085	.9090	.9096	.9101	.9106	.9112	.9117	.9122	.9128	.9133
8.2	.9138	.9143	.9149	.9154	.9159	.9165	.9170	.9175	.9180	.9186
8.3	.9191	.9196	.9201	.9206	.9212	.9217	.9222	.9227	.9232	.9238
8.4	.9243	.9248	.9253	.9258	.9263	.9269	.9274	.9279	.9284	.9289
8.5	.9294	.9299	.9304	.9309	.9315	.9320	.9325	.9330	.9335	.9340
8.6	.9345	.9350	.9355	.9360	.9365	.9370	.9375	.9380	.9385	.9390
8.7	.9395	.9400	.9405	.9410	.9415	.9420	.9425	.9430	.9435	.9440
8.8	.9445	.9450	.9455	.9460	.9465	.9469	.9474	.9479	.9484	.9489
8.9	.9494	.9499	.9504	.9509	.9513	.9518	.9523	.9528	.9533	.9538
9.0	.9542	.9547	.9552	.9557	.9562	.9566	.9571	.9576	.9581	.9586
9.1	.9590	.9595	.9600	.9605	.9609	.9614	.9619	.9624	.9628	.9633
9.2	.9638	.9643	.9647	.9652	.9657	.9661	.9666	.9671	.9675	.9680
9.3	.9685	.9689	.9694	.9699	.9703	.9708	.9713	.9717	.9722	.9727
9.4	.9731	.9736	.9741	.9745	.9750	.9754	.9759	.9763	.9768	.9773
9.5	.9777	.9782	.9786	.9791	.9795	.9800	.9805	.9809	.9814	.9818
9.6	.9823	.9827	.9832	.9836	.9841	.9845	.9850	.9854	.9859	.9863
9.7	.9868	.9872	.9877	.9881	.9886	.9890	.9894	.9899	.9903	.9908
9.8	.9912	.9917	.9921	.9926	.9930	.9934	.9939	.9943	.9948	.9952
9.9	.9956	.9961	.9965	.9969	.9974	.9978	.9983	.9987	.9991	.9996
N	0	1	2	3	4	5	6	7	8	9

* Adapted from *Handbook of Chemistry and Physics*, 35th ed. (Cleveland: Chemical Rubber Publishing Co., 1953), p. 14.

TABLE 4

AREAS OF THE NORMAL CURVE*

A fraction of the total area under the curve is given by the sum of a P value in the column at the left and another in the row across the top. This fraction is *outside* the interval $-x^*$ to $+x^*$, where x^* is $(x - \mu)/\sigma$. The entries in the table are values of x^*.

Since any given fractional area is equally divided between both tails of the curve, x^* corresponding to a particular area in one tail is found by entering the table at twice the desired value of P. Thus $P = 0.05$ in both tails at $x^* = 1.96$; but $P = 0.05$ in one tail when $P = 0.10$ in both tails, at $x^* = 1.64$. Likewise, $P = 0.01$ in both tails at $x^* = 2.58$, in one tail at $x^* = 2.33$.

P	0.00	0.01	0.02	0.03	0.04	0.05	0.06	0.07	0.08	0.09
0.00	∞	2.58	2.33	2.17	2.05	1.96	1.88	1.82	1.75	1.70
0.10	1.64	1.60	1.55	1.51	1.48	1.44	1.41	1.37	1.34	1.31
0.20	1.28	1.25	1.23	1.20	1.17	1.15	1.13	1.10	1.08	1.06
0.30	1.04	1.02	0.994	0.974	0.954	0.935	0.915	0.896	0.878	0.860
0.40	0.842	0.824	0.806	0.789	0.772	0.755	0.739	0.722	0.706	0.690
0.50	0.674	0.659	0.643	0.628	0.613	0.598	0.583	0.568	0.553	0.539
0.60	0.524	0.510	0.496	0.482	0.468	0.454	0.440	0.426	0.412	0.399
0.70	0.385	0.372	0.358	0.345	0.332	0.319	0.305	0.292	0.279	0.266
0.80	0.253	0.240	0.228	0.215	0.202	0.189	0.176	0.164	0.151	0.138
0.90	0.126	0.113	0.100	0.0878	0.0753	0.0627	0.0502	0.0376	0.0251	0.0125

* Table 4 is abridged from Table I of Fisher & Yates: *Statistical Tables for Biological, Agricultural and Medical Research* published by Oliver & Boyd Ltd., Edinburgh, and by permission of the authors and publishers.

TABLE 5

CRITICAL VALUES OF t*

Values of t equal to or greater than those tabulated occur by chance
less frequently than the indicated level of P.

DF	P = 0.05		P = 0.01	
	One Tail	Both Tails	One Tail	Both Tails
1	6.32	12.8	31.9	63.7
2	2.92	4.30	6.96	9.92
3	2.35	3.18	4.54	5.84
4	2.13	2.78	3.75	4.60
5	2.02	2.57	3.36	4.03
6	1.94	2.45	3.14	3.71
7	1.90	2.36	3.00	3.50
8	1.86	2.31	2.90	3.36
9	1.83	2.26	2.82	3.25
10	1.81	2.23	2.76	3.17
11	1.80	2.20	2.72	3.11
12	1.78	2.18	2.68	3.06
13	1.77	2.16	2.65	3.01
14	1.76	2.14	2.62	2.98
15	1.75	2.13	2.60	2.95
16	1.75	2.12	2.58	2.92
17	1.74	2.11	2.57	2.90
18	1.73	2.10	2.55	2.88
19	1.73	2.09	2.54	2.86
20	1.72	2.09	2.53	2.84
21	1.72	2.08	2.52	2.83
22	1.72	2.07	2.51	2.82
23	1.71	2.07	2.50	2.81
24	1.71	2.06	2.49	2.80
25	1.71	2.06	2.48	2.79
26	1.71	2.06	2.48	2.78
27	1.70	2.05	2.47	2.77
28	1.70	2.05	2.47	2.76
29	1.70	2.04	2.46	2.76
30	1.70	2.04	2.46	2.75
∞	1.64	1.96	2.33	2.58

* Table 5 is abridged from Table III of Fisher & Yates: *Statistical Tables for Biological, Agricultural and Medical Research* published by Oliver & Boyd Ltd., Edinburgh, and by permission of the authors and publishers.

TABLE 6

*FACTORS (K) FOR ONE-SIDED TOLERANCE LIMITS**

For a sample of size N, from which $\bar{x}$ and s are obtained, the table gives a factor K, which is used to compute an upper or lower tolerance limit, $\bar{x} + K(s)$ or $\bar{x} - K(s)$. A certain percent of the individual observations in the population represented by the sample may then be asserted to lie below (or above) the chosen limit. The columns of the table permit a choice of $P = 0.05$ or 0.01 that the assertion is wrong, and a further choice of the percent of observations (95% or 99%) that are bounded by the limit.

	$P = 0.05$		$P = 0.01$	
	Percent of observations that will be smaller than the upper tolerance limit *or* greater than the lower limit:			
N	95%	99%	95%	99%
3	7.66	10.6	—	—
4	5.14	7.04	—	—
5	4.20	5.74	—	—
6	3.71	5.06	5.41	7.33
7	3.40	4.64	4.73	6.41
8	3.19	4.35	4.29	5.81
9	3.03	4.14	3.97	5.39
10	2.91	3.98	3.74	5.08
11	2.82	3.85	3.56	4.83
12	2.74	3.75	3.41	4.63
13	2.67	3.66	3.29	4.47
14	2.61	3.58	3.19	4.34
15	2.57	3.52	3.10	4.22
16	2.52	3.46	3.03	4.12
17	2.49	3.42	2.96	4.04
18	2.45	3.37	2.91	3.96
19	2.42	3.33	2.86	3.89
20	2.40	3.30	2.81	3.83
21	2.37	3.26	2.77	3.78
22	2.35	3.23	2.73	3.73
23	2.33	3.21	2.69	3.68
24	2.31	3.18	2.66	3.64
25	2.29	3.16	2.63	3.60
30	2.22	3.06	2.52	3.45
35	2.17	2.99	2.43	3.33
40	2.13	2.94	2.36	3.25
45	2.09	2.90	2.31	3.18
50	2.06	2.86	2.30	3.12

* Extracted from A. H. Bowker and G. J. Lieberman, *Engineering Statistics* (Englewood Cliffs, N. J.: Prentice-Hall, Inc., 1959), Table 8.3.

TABLE 7

CRITICAL VALUES OF THE VARIANCE RATIO, F*

Values of F equal to or greater than those tabulated occur by chance less frequently than the indicated level of P. DF are degrees of freedom associated with the greater of the two variance estimates; DF' are degrees of freedom associated with the smaller of the two variance estimates.

$P = 0.05$

DF' \ DF	1	2	3	4	5	6	7	8	9	10	20	30	∞
1	161.4	199.5	215.7	224.6	230.2	234.0	236.8	238.9	240.5	241.9	248.0	250.1	254.3
2	18.51	19.00	19.16	19.25	19.30	19.33	19.35	19.37	19.38	19.40	19.45	19.46	19.50
3	10.13	9.55	9.28	9.12	9.01	8.94	8.89	8.85	8.81	8.79	8.66	8.62	8.53
4	7.71	6.94	6.59	6.39	6.26	6.16	6.09	6.04	6.00	5.96	5.80	5.75	5.63
5	6.61	5.79	5.41	5.19	5.05	4.95	4.88	4.82	4.77	4.74	4.56	4.50	4.36
6	5.99	5.14	4.76	4.53	4.39	4.28	4.21	4.15	4.10	4.06	3.87	3.81	3.67
7	5.59	4.74	4.35	4.12	3.97	3.87	3.79	3.73	3.68	3.64	3.44	3.38	3.23
8	5.32	4.46	4.07	3.84	3.69	3.58	3.50	3.44	3.39	3.35	3.15	3.08	2.93
9	5.12	4.26	3.86	3.63	3.48	3.37	3.29	3.23	3.18	3.14	2.94	2.86	2.71
10	4.96	4.10	3.71	3.48	3.33	3.22	3.14	3.07	3.02	2.98	2.77	2.70	2.54
11	4.84	3.98	3.59	3.36	3.20	3.09	3.01	2.95	2.90	2.85	2.65	2.57	2.40
12	4.75	3.89	3.49	3.26	3.11	3.00	2.91	2.85	2.80	2.75	2.54	2.47	2.30
13	4.67	3.81	3.41	3.18	3.03	2.92	2.83	2.77	2.71	2.67	2.46	2.38	2.21
14	4.60	3.74	3.34	3.11	2.96	2.85	2.76	2.70	2.65	2.60	2.39	2.31	2.13

15	4.54	3.68	3.29	3.06	2.90	2.79	2.71	2.64	2.59	2.54	2.33	2.25	2.07
16	4.49	3.63	3.24	3.01	2.85	2.74	2.66	2.59	2.54	2.49	2.28	2.19	2.01
17	4.45	3.59	3.20	2.96	2.81	2.70	2.61	2.55	2.49	2.45	2.23	2.15	1.96
18	4.41	3.55	3.16	2.93	2.77	2.66	2.58	2.51	2.46	2.41	2.19	2.11	1.92
19	4.38	3.52	3.13	2.90	2.74	2.63	2.54	2.48	2.42	2.38	2.16	2.07	1.88
20	4.35	3.49	3.10	2.87	2.71	2.60	2.51	2.45	2.39	2.35	2.12	2.04	1.84
21	4.32	3.47	3.07	2.84	2.68	2.57	2.49	2.42	2.37	2.32	2.10	2.01	1.81
22	4.30	3.44	3.05	2.82	2.66	2.55	2.46	2.40	2.34	2.30	2.07	1.98	1.78
23	4.28	3.42	3.03	2.80	2.64	2.53	2.44	2.37	2.32	2.27	2.05	1.96	1.76
24	4.26	3.40	3.01	2.78	2.62	2.51	2.42	2.36	2.30	2.25	2.03	1.94	1.73
25	4.24	3.39	2.99	2.76	2.60	2.49	2.40	2.34	2.28	2.24	2.01	1.92	1.71
26	4.23	3.37	2.98	2.74	2.59	2.47	2.39	2.32	2.27	2.22	1.99	1.90	1.69
27	4.21	3.35	2.96	2.73	2.57	2.46	2.37	2.31	2.25	2.20	1.97	1.88	1.67
28	4.20	3.34	2.95	2.71	2.56	2.45	2.36	2.29	2.24	2.19	1.96	1.87	1.65
29	4.18	3.33	2.93	2.70	2.55	2.43	2.35	2.28	2.22	2.18	1.94	1.85	1.64
30	4.17	3.32	2.92	2.69	2.53	2.42	2.33	2.27	2.21	2.16	1.93	1.84	1.62
40	4.08	3.23	2.84	2.61	2.45	2.34	2.25	2.18	2.12	2.08	1.84	1.74	1.51
60	4.00	3.15	2.76	2.53	2.37	2.25	2.17	2.10	2.04	1.99	1.75	1.65	1.39
120	3.92	3.07	2.68	2.45	2.29	2.17	2.09	2.02	1.96	1.91	1.66	1.55	1.25
∞	3.84	3.00	2.60	2.37	2.21	2.10	2.01	1.94	1.88	1.83	1.57	1.46	1.00

TABLE 7—continued

$P = 0.01$

DF'＼DF	1	2	3	4	5	6	7	8	9	10	20	30	∞
1	4052	5000	5403	5625	5764	5859	5928	5982	6022	6056	6209	6261	6366
2	98.50	99.00	99.17	99.25	99.30	99.33	99.36	99.37	99.39	99.40	99.45	99.47	99.50
3	34.12	30.82	29.46	28.71	28.24	27.91	27.67	27.49	27.35	27.23	26.69	26.50	26.13
4	21.20	18.00	16.69	15.98	15.52	15.21	14.98	14.80	14.66	14.55	14.02	13.84	13.46
5	16.26	13.27	12.06	11.39	10.97	10.67	10.46	10.29	10.16	10.05	9.55	9.38	9.02
6	13.75	10.92	9.78	9.15	8.75	8.47	8.26	8.10	7.98	7.87	7.40	7.23	6.88
7	12.25	9.55	8.45	7.85	7.46	7.19	6.99	6.84	6.72	6.62	6.16	5.99	5.65
8	11.26	8.65	7.59	7.01	6.63	6.37	6.18	6.03	5.91	5.81	5.36	5.20	4.86
9	10.56	8.02	6.99	6.42	6.06	5.80	5.61	5.47	5.35	5.26	4.81	4.65	4.31
10	10.04	7.56	6.55	5.99	5.64	5.39	5.20	5.06	4.94	4.85	4.41	4.25	3.91
11	9.65	7.21	6.22	5.67	5.32	5.07	4.89	4.74	4.63	4.54	4.10	3.94	3.60
12	9.33	6.93	5.95	5.41	5.06	4.82	4.64	4.50	4.39	4.30	3.86	3.70	3.36
13	9.07	6.70	5.74	5.21	4.86	4.62	4.44	4.30	4.19	4.10	3.66	3.51	3.17
14	8.86	6.51	5.56	5.04	4.69	4.46	4.28	4.14	4.03	3.94	3.51	3.35	3.00

15	8.68	6.36	5.42	4.89	4.56	4.32	4.14	4.00	3.89	3.80	3.37	3.21	2.87
16	8.53	6.23	5.29	4.77	4.44	4.20	4.03	3.89	3.78	3.69	3.26	3.10	2.75
17	8.40	6.11	5.18	4.67	4.34	4.10	3.93	3.79	3.68	3.59	3.16	3.00	2.65
18	8.29	6.01	5.09	4.58	4.25	4.01	3.84	3.71	3.60	3.51	3.08	2.92	2.57
19	8.18	5.93	5.01	4.50	4.17	3.94	3.77	3.63	3.52	3.43	3.00	2.84	2.49
20	8.10	5.85	4.94	4.43	4.10	3.87	3.70	3.56	3.46	3.37	2.94	2.78	2.42
21	8.02	5.78	4.87	4.37	4.04	3.81	3.64	3.51	3.40	3.31	2.88	2.72	2.36
22	7.95	5.72	4.82	4.31	3.99	3.76	3.59	3.45	3.35	3.26	2.83	2.67	2.31
23	7.88	5.66	4.76	4.26	3.94	3.71	3.54	3.41	3.30	3.21	2.78	2.62	2.26
24	7.82	5.61	4.72	4.22	3.90	3.67	3.50	3.36	3.26	3.17	2.74	2.58	2.21
25	7.77	5.57	4.68	4.18	3.85	3.63	3.46	3.32	3.22	3.13	2.70	2.54	2.17
26	7.72	5.53	4.64	4.14	3.82	3.59	3.42	3.29	3.18	3.09	2.66	2.50	2.13
27	7.68	5.49	4.60	4.11	3.78	3.56	3.39	3.26	3.15	3.06	2.63	2.47	2.10
28	7.64	5.45	4.57	4.07	3.75	3.53	3.36	3.23	3.12	3.03	2.60	2.44	2.06
29	7.60	5.42	4.54	4.04	3.73	3.50	3.33	3.20	3.09	3.00	2.57	2.41	2.03
30	7.56	5.39	4.51	4.02	3.70	3.47	3.30	3.17	3.07	2.98	2.55	2.39	2.01
40	7.31	5.18	4.31	3.83	3.51	3.29	3.12	2.99	2.89	2.80	2.37	2.20	1.80
60	7.08	4.98	4.13	3.65	3.34	3.12	2.95	2.82	2.72	2.63	2.20	2.03	1.60
120	6.85	4.79	3.95	3.48	3.17	2.96	2.79	2.66	2.56	2.47	2.03	1.86	1.38
∞	6.63	4.61	3.78	3.32	3.02	2.80	2.64	2.51	2.41	2.32	1.88	1.70	1.00

* Adapted from E. S. Pearson and H. O. Hartley, *Biometrika Tables for Statisticians*, Vol. 1 (London: Cambridge University Press, 1954), Table 18.

TABLE 8

FACTORS (k*) FOR THE STUDENTIZED RANGE†

For a given number of samples (n) and within-samples degrees of freedom (DF), the table gives the factor (k^*) by which $\sqrt{V_e/N_m}$ must be multiplied to obtain the minimum significant range, where V_e is the error variance estimate and N_m is the number of observations per sample. DF is that for the error variance in the analysis of variance table; it is $n(N_m - 1)$.

$$P = 0.05$$

DF \ n	2	3	4	5	6	7	8	9	10	11	12	13	14	15	16	17	18	19	20
1	18.0	27.0	32.8	37.1	40.4	43.1	45.4	47.4	49.1	50.6	52.0	53.2	54.3	55.4	56.3	57.2	58.0	58.8	59.6
2	6.08	8.33	9.80	10.9	11.7	12.4	13.0	13.5	14.0	14.4	14.7	15.1	15.4	15.7	15.9	16.1	16.4	16.6	16.8
3	4.50	5.91	6.82	7.50	8.04	8.48	8.85	9.18	9.46	9.72	9.95	10.2	10.3	10.5	10.7	10.8	11.0	11.1	11.2
4	3.93	5.04	5.76	6.29	6.71	7.05	7.35	7.60	7.83	8.03	8.21	8.37	8.52	8.66	8.79	8.91	9.03	9.13	9.23
5	3.64	4.60	5.22	5.67	6.03	6.33	6.58	6.80	6.99	7.17	7.32	7.47	7.60	7.72	7.83	7.93	8.03	8.12	8.21
6	3.46	4.34	4.90	5.30	5.63	5.90	6.12	6.32	6.49	6.65	6.79	6.92	7.03	7.14	7.24	7.34	7.43	7.51	7.59
7	3.34	4.16	4.68	5.06	5.36	5.61	5.82	6.00	6.16	6.30	6.43	6.55	6.66	6.76	6.85	6.94	7.02	7.10	7.17
8	3.26	4.04	4.53	4.89	5.17	5.40	5.60	5.77	5.92	6.05	6.18	6.29	6.39	6.48	6.57	6.65	6.73	6.80	6.87
9	3.20	3.95	4.41	4.76	5.02	5.24	5.43	5.59	5.74	5.87	5.98	6.09	6.19	6.28	6.36	6.44	6.51	6.58	6.64
10	3.15	3.88	4.33	4.65	4.91	5.12	5.30	5.46	5.60	5.72	5.83	5.93	6.03	6.11	6.19	6.27	6.34	6.40	6.47
11	3.11	3.82	4.26	4.57	4.82	5.03	5.20	5.35	5.49	5.61	5.71	5.81	5.90	5.98	6.06	6.13	6.20	6.27	6.33
12	3.08	3.77	4.20	4.51	4.75	4.95	5.12	5.27	5.39	5.51	5.61	5.71	5.80	5.88	5.95	6.02	6.09	6.15	6.21
13	3.06	3.73	4.15	4.45	4.69	4.88	5.05	5.19	5.32	5.43	5.53	5.63	5.71	5.79	5.86	5.93	5.99	6.05	6.11
14	3.03	3.70	4.11	4.41	4.64	4.83	4.99	5.13	5.25	5.36	5.46	5.55	5.64	5.71	5.79	5.85	5.91	5.97	6.03
15	3.01	3.67	4.08	4.37	4.59	4.78	4.94	5.08	5.20	5.31	5.40	5.49	5.57	5.65	5.72	5.78	5.85	5.90	5.96
16	3.00	3.65	4.05	4.33	4.56	4.74	4.90	5.03	5.15	5.26	5.35	5.44	5.52	5.59	5.66	5.73	5.79	5.84	5.90
17	2.98	3.63	4.02	4.30	4.52	4.70	4.86	4.99	5.11	5.21	5.31	5.39	5.47	5.54	5.61	5.67	5.73	5.79	5.84
18	2.97	3.61	4.00	4.28	4.49	4.67	4.82	4.96	5.07	5.17	5.27	5.35	5.43	5.50	5.57	5.63	5.69	5.74	5.79
19	2.96	3.59	3.98	4.25	4.47	4.65	4.79	4.92	5.04	5.14	5.23	5.31	5.39	5.46	5.53	5.59	5.65	5.70	5.75
20	2.95	3.58	3.96	4.23	4.45	4.62	4.77	4.90	5.01	5.11	5.20	5.28	5.36	5.43	5.49	5.55	5.61	5.66	5.71
24	2.92	3.53	3.90	4.17	4.37	4.54	4.68	4.81	4.92	5.01	5.10	5.18	5.25	5.32	5.38	5.44	5.49	5.55	5.59
30	2.89	3.49	3.85	4.10	4.30	4.46	4.60	4.72	4.82	4.92	5.00	5.08	5.15	5.21	5.27	5.33	5.38	5.43	5.47
40	2.86	3.44	3.79	4.04	4.23	4.39	4.52	4.63	4.73	4.82	4.90	4.98	5.04	5.11	5.16	5.22	5.27	5.31	5.36
60	2.83	3.40	3.74	3.98	4.16	4.31	4.44	4.55	4.65	4.73	4.81	4.88	4.94	5.00	5.06	5.11	5.15	5.20	5.24
120	2.80	3.36	3.68	3.92	4.10	4.24	4.36	4.47	4.56	4.64	4.71	4.78	4.84	4.90	4.95	5.00	5.04	5.09	5.13
∞	2.77	3.31	3.63	3.86	4.03	4.17	4.29	4.39	4.47	4.55	4.62	4.68	4.74	4.80	4.85	4.89	4.93	4.97	5.01

$P = 0.01$

DF \ n	2	3	4	5	6	7	8	9	10	11	12	13	14	15	16	17	18	19	20
1	90.0	135	164	186	202	216	227	237	246	253	260	266	272	277	282	286	290	294	298
2	14.0	19.0	22.3	24.7	26.6	28.2	29.5	30.7	31.7	32.6	33.4	34.1	34.8	35.4	36.0	36.5	37.0	37.5	37.9
3	8.26	10.6	12.2	13.3	14.2	15.0	15.6	16.2	16.7	17.1	17.5	17.9	18.2	18.5	18.8	19.1	19.3	19.5	19.8
4	6.51	8.12	9.17	9.96	10.6	11.1	11.5	11.9	12.3	12.6	12.8	13.1	13.3	13.5	13.7	13.9	14.1	14.2	14.4
5	5.70	6.97	7.80	8.42	8.91	9.32	9.67	9.97	10.2	10.5	10.7	10.9	11.1	11.2	11.4	11.6	11.7	11.8	11.9
6	5.24	6.33	7.03	7.56	7.97	8.32	8.61	8.87	9.10	9.30	9.49	9.65	9.81	9.95	10.1	10.2	10.3	10.4	10.5
7	4.95	5.92	6.54	7.01	7.37	7.68	7.94	8.17	8.37	8.55	8.71	8.86	9.00	9.12	9.24	9.35	9.46	9.55	9.65
8	4.74	5.63	6.20	6.63	6.96	7.24	7.47	7.68	7.87	8.03	8.18	8.31	8.44	8.55	8.66	8.76	8.85	8.94	9.03
9	4.60	5.43	5.96	6.35	6.66	6.91	7.13	7.32	7.49	7.65	7.78	7.91	8.03	8.13	8.23	8.32	8.41	8.49	8.57
10	4.48	5.27	5.77	6.14	6.43	6.67	6.87	7.05	7.21	7.36	7.48	7.60	7.71	7.81	7.91	7.99	8.07	8.15	8.22
11	4.39	5.14	5.62	5.97	6.25	6.48	6.67	6.84	6.99	7.13	7.25	7.36	7.46	7.56	7.65	7.73	7.81	7.88	7.95
12	4.32	5.04	5.50	5.84	6.10	6.32	6.51	6.67	6.81	6.94	7.06	7.17	7.26	7.36	7.44	7.52	7.59	7.66	7.73
13	4.26	4.96	5.40	5.73	5.98	6.19	6.37	6.53	6.67	6.79	6.90	7.01	7.10	7.19	7.27	7.34	7.42	7.48	7.55
14	4.21	4.89	5.32	5.63	5.88	6.08	6.26	6.41	6.54	6.66	6.77	6.87	6.96	7.05	7.12	7.20	7.27	7.33	7.39
15	4.17	4.83	5.25	5.56	5.80	5.99	6.16	6.31	6.44	6.55	6.66	6.76	6.84	6.93	7.00	7.07	7.14	7.20	7.26
16	4.13	4.78	5.19	5.49	5.72	5.92	6.08	6.22	6.35	6.46	6.56	6.66	6.74	6.82	6.90	6.97	7.03	7.09	7.15
17	4.10	4.74	5.14	5.43	5.66	5.85	6.01	6.15	6.27	6.38	6.48	6.57	6.66	6.73	6.80	6.87	6.94	7.00	7.05
18	4.07	4.70	5.09	5.38	5.60	5.79	5.94	6.08	6.20	6.31	6.41	6.50	6.58	6.65	6.72	6.79	6.85	6.91	6.96
19	4.05	4.67	5.05	5.33	5.55	5.73	5.89	6.02	6.14	6.25	6.34	6.43	6.51	6.58	6.65	6.72	6.78	6.84	6.89
20	4.02	4.64	5.02	5.29	5.51	5.69	5.84	5.97	6.09	6.19	6.29	6.37	6.45	6.52	6.59	6.65	6.71	6.76	6.82
24	3.96	4.54	4.91	5.17	5.37	5.54	5.69	5.81	5.92	6.02	6.11	6.19	6.26	6.33	6.39	6.45	6.51	6.56	6.61
30	3.89	4.45	4.80	5.05	5.24	5.40	5.54	5.65	5.76	5.85	5.93	6.01	6.08	6.14	6.20	6.26	6.31	6.36	6.41
40	3.82	4.37	4.70	4.93	5.11	5.27	5.39	5.50	5.60	5.69	5.77	5.84	5.90	5.96	6.02	6.07	6.12	6.17	6.21
60	3.76	4.28	4.60	4.82	4.99	5.13	5.25	5.36	5.45	5.53	5.60	5.67	5.73	5.79	5.84	5.89	5.93	5.98	6.02
120	3.70	4.20	4.50	4.71	4.87	5.01	5.12	5.21	5.30	5.38	5.44	5.51	5.56	5.61	5.66	5.71	5.75	5.79	5.83
∞	3.64	4.12	4.40	4.60	4.76	4.88	4.99	5.08	5.16	5.23	5.29	5.35	5.40	5.45	5.49	5.54	5.57	5.61	5.65

† Adapted from H. Scheffé. *The Analysis of Variance* (New York: John Wiley & Sons, Inc., 1959) pp. 435–436.

TABLE 9

CRITICAL VALUES OF χ^{2*}

Values of χ^2 equal to or greater than those tabulated occur by chance less frequently than the indicated level of P.

	P = 0.05		P = 0.01	
DF	*One Tail*	*Both Tails*	*One Tail*	*Both Tails*
1	2.71	3.84	5.41	6.64
2	4.60	5.99	7.82	9.21
3	6.25	7.82	9.84	11.3
4	7.78	9.49	11.7	13.3
5	9.24	11.1	13.4	15.1
6	10.6	12.6	15.0	16.8
7	12.0	14.1	16.6	18.5
8	13.4	15.5	18.2	20.1
9	14.7	16.9	19.7	21.7
10	16.0	18.3	21.2	23.2
15	22.3	25.0	28.3	30.6
20	28.4	31.4	35.0	37.6
25	34.4	37.7	41.6	44.3
30	40.3	43.8	48.0	50.9

* Table 9 is abridged from Table IV of Fisher & Yates: *Statistical Tables for Biological, Agricultural and Medical Research* published by Oliver & Boyd Ltd., Edinburgh, and by permission of the authors and publishers.

TABLE 10

CRITICAL NUMBERS OF ITEMS IN THE SMALLER BINOMIAL CATEGORY*

Numbers of items equal to or smaller than those tabulated occur by chance less frequently than the indicated level of *P*. The tabulation is for the case of equal probabilities in the two binomial categories ($\pi = \frac{1}{2}$).

	One Tail	
N	P = 0.05	P = 0.01
5	0	–
6	0	–
7	0	0
8	1	0
9	1	0
10	1	0
11	2	1
12	2	1
13	3	1
14	3	2
15	3	2
16	4	2
17	4	3
18	5	3
19	5	4
20	5	4
21	6	4
22	6	5
23	7	5
24	7	5
25	7	6

* Adapted from H. Walker and J. Lev, *Statistical Inference* (New York: Holt, Rinehart and Winston, Inc., 1953), Table IVB.

TABLE 11

BINOMIAL CONFIDENCE LIMITS*

The table is entered at the observed value of p, along the bottom or top horizontal axis. Moving vertically up or down, find (or interpolate) the two curves corresponding to the sample size. Then move horizontally left or right and read the confidence limits for π. The bottom and left scales are used together, as are the top and right scales.

95% Confidence limits

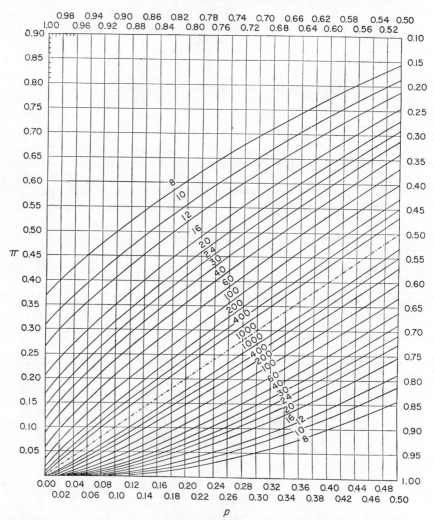

* Adapted from E. S. Pearson and H. O. Hartley, *Biometrika Tables for Statisticians*, Vol. 1 (London: Cambridge University Press, 1954), Table 41.

TABLE 11—continued
99% *Confidence limits*

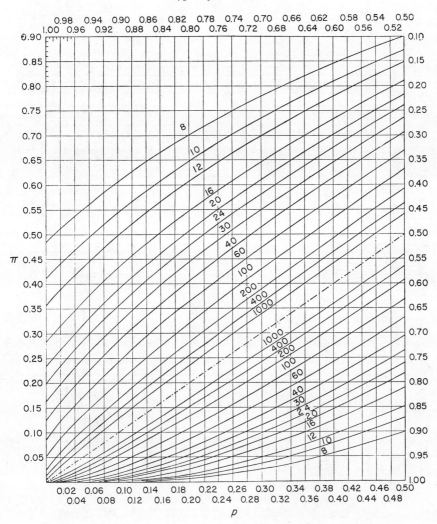

TABLE 12
VALUES OF THE EXPONENTIAL FUNCTION, $e^{-\lambda}$*

For each value of λ is found, at the appropriate intersection, the corresponding value of $e^{-\lambda}$.

λ	0.00	0.01	0.02	0.03	0.04	0.05	0.06	0.07	0.08	0.09
0.00	1.000	0.990	0.980	0.970	0.961	0.951	0.942	0.932	0.923	0.914
0.10	0.905	0.896	0.887	0.878	0.869	0.861	0.852	0.844	0.835	0.827
0.20	0.819	0.811	0.803	0.795	0.787	0.779	0.771	0.763	0.756	0.748
0.30	0.741	0.733	0.726	0.719	0.712	0.705	0.698	0.691	0.684	0.677
0.40	0.670	0.664	0.657	0.651	0.644	0.638	0.631	0.625	0.619	0.613
0.50	0.607	0.600	0.595	0.589	0.583	0.577	0.571	0.566	0.560	0.554
0.60	0.549	0.543	0.538	0.533	0.527	0.522	0.517	0.512	0.507	0.502
0.70	0.497	0.492	0.487	0.482	0.477	0.472	0.468	0.463	0.458	0.454
0.80	0.449	0.445	0.440	0.436	0.432	0.427	0.423	0.419	0.415	0.411
0.90	0.407	0.403	0.399	0.395	0.391	0.387	0.383	0.379	0.375	0.372
1.00	0.368	0.364	0.361	0.357	0.353	0.350	0.346	0.343	0.340	0.336
1.10	0.333	0.330	0.326	0.323	0.320	0.317	0.313	0.310	0.307	0.304
1.20	0.301	0.298	0.295	0.292	0.289	0.287	0.284	0.281	0.278	0.275
1.30	0.273	0.270	0.267	0.264	0.262	0.259	0.257	0.254	0.252	0.249
1.40	0.247	0.244	0.242	0.239	0.237	0.235	0.232	0.230	0.228	0.225
1.50	0.223	0.221	0.219	0.217	0.214	0.212	0.210	0.208	0.206	0.204
1.60	0.202	0.200	0.198	0.196	0.194	0.192	0.190	0.188	0.186	0.185
1.70	0.183	0.181	0.179	0.177	0.176	0.174	0.172	0.170	0.169	0.167
1.80	0.165	0.164	0.162	0.160	0.159	0.157	0.156	0.154	0.153	0.151
1.90	0.150	0.148	0.147	0.145	0.144	0.142	0.141	0.139	0.138	0.137
2.00	0.135	0.134	0.133	0.131	0.130	0.129	0.127	0.126	0.125	0.124
2.10	0.122	0.121	0.120	0.119	0.118	0.116	0.115	0.114	0.113	0.112
2.20	0.111	0.110	0.109	0.108	0.106	0.105	0.104	0.103	0.102	0.101
2.30	0.100	0.0992	0.0983	0.0973	0.0963	0.0953	0.0944	0.0935	0.0926	0.0916
2.40	0.0907	0.0898	0.0889	0.0880	0.0872	0.0863	0.0854	0.0846	0.0837	0.0829
2.50	0.0821	0.0813	0.0805	0.0797	0.0789	0.0781	0.0773	0.0765	0.0758	0.0750
2.60	0.0743	0.0735	0.0728	0.0721	0.0714	0.0707	0.0699	0.0693	0.0686	0.0679
2.70	0.0672	0.0665	0.0659	0.0652	0.0646	0.0639	0.0633	0.0627	0.0620	0.0614
2.80	0.0608	0.0602	0.0596	0.0590	0.0584	0.0578	0.0573	0.0567	0.0561	0.0556
2.90	0.0550	0.0545	0.0539	0.0534	0.0529	0.0523	0.0518	0.0513	0.0508	0.0503

TABLE 12—continued

λ \	0.00	0.01	0.02	0.03	0.04	0.05	0.06	0.07	0.08	0.09
3.00	0.0498	0.0493	0.0488	0.0483	0.0478	0.0474	0.0469	0.0464	0.0460	0.0455
3.10	0.0450	0.0446	0.0442	0.0437	0.0433	0.0429	0.0424	0.0420	0.0416	0.0412
3.20	0.0408	0.0404	0.0400	0.0396	0.0392	0.0388	0.0384	0.0380	0.0376	0.0373
3.30	0.0369	0.0365	0.0362	0.0358	0.0354	0.0351	0.0347	0.0344	0.0340	0.0337
3.40	0.0334	0.0330	0.0327	0.0324	0.0321	0.0317	0.0314	0.0311	0.0308	0.0305
3.50	0.0302	0.0299	0.0296	0.0293	0.0290	0.0287	0.0284	0.0282	0.0279	0.0276
3.60	0.0273	0.0271	0.0268	0.0265	0.0263	0.0260	0.0257	0.0255	0.0252	0.0250
3.70	0.0247	0.0245	0.0242	0.0240	0.0238	0.0235	0.0233	0.0231	0.0228	0.0226
3.80	0.0224	0.0221	0.0219	0.0217	0.0215	0.0213	0.0211	0.0209	0.0207	0.0204
3.90	0.0202	0.0200	0.0198	0.0196	0.0194	0.0193	0.0191	0.0189	0.0187	0.0185
4.00	0.0183	0.0181	0.0180	0.0178	0.0176	0.0174	0.0172	0.0171	0.0169	0.0167
4.10	0.0166	0.0164	0.0162	0.0161	0.0159	0.0158	0.0156	0.0155	0.0153	0.0151
4.20	0.0150	0.0148	0.0147	0.0146	0.0144	0.0143	0.0141	0.0140	0.0138	0.0137
4.30	0.0136	0.0134	0.0133	0.0132	0.0130	0.0129	0.0128	0.0127	0.0125	0.0124
4.40	0.0123	0.0122	0.0120	0.0119	0.0118	0.0117	0.0116	0.0114	0.0113	0.0112
4.50	0.0111	0.0110	0.0109	0.0108	0.0107	0.0106	0.0105	0.0104	0.0103	0.0102
4.60	0.0101	0.00995	0.00985	0.00976	0.00966	0.00956	0.00947	0.00937	0.00928	0.00919
4.70	0.00910	0.00901	0.00892	0.00883	0.00874	0.00865	0.00857	0.00848	0.00840	0.00831
4.80	0.00823	0.00815	0.00807	0.00799	0.00791	0.00783	0.00775	0.00767	0.00760	0.00752
4.90	0.00745	0.00737	0.00730	0.00723	0.00716	0.00708	0.00701	0.00694	0.00687	0.00681

λ \	0.0	0.1	0.2	0.3	0.4	0.5	0.6	0.7	0.8	0.9
5.0	0.00674	0.00610	0.00552	0.00499	0.00452	0.00409	0.00370	0.00335	0.00303	0.00274
6.0	0.00248	0.00224	0.00203	0.00184	0.00166	0.00150	0.00136	0.00123	0.00111	0.00101
7.0	0.000912	0.000825	0.000747	0.000676	0.000611	0.000553	0.000500	0.000453	0.000410	0.000371
8.0	0.000335	0.000304	0.000275	0.000249	0.000225	0.000203	0.000184	0.000167	0.000151	0.000136
9.0	0.000123	0.000112	0.000101	0.000091	0.000083	0.000075	0.000068	0.000061	0.000055	0.000050

* Adapted from *Handbook of Chemistry and Physics*, 35th ed. (Cleveland: Chemical Rubber Publishing Co., 1953), p. 174.

TABLE 13

CONFIDENCE LIMITS FOR THE POISSON EXPECTATION*

For each observed frequency or count (L) are given the corresponding lower and upper 95% and 99% confidence limits of the expectation (λ).

L	95% Limits		99% Limits	
	Lower	Upper	Lower	Upper
0	0.0000	3.69	0.00000	5.30
1	.0253	5.57	.00501	7.43
2	.242	7.22	.103	9.27
3	.619	8.77	.338	10.98
4	1.09	10.24	.672	12.59
5	1.62	11.67	1.08	14.15
6	2.20	13.06	1.54	15.66
7	2.81	14.42	2.04	17.13
8	3.45	15.76	2.57	18.58
9	4.12	17.08	3.13	20.00
10	4.80	18.39	3.72	21.40
11	5.49	19.68	4.32	22.78
12	6.20	20.96	4.94	24.14
13	6.92	22.23	5.58	25.50
14	7.65	23.49	6.23	26.84
15	8.40	24.74	6.89	28.16
16	9.15	25.98	7.57	29.48
17	9.90	27.22	8.25	30.79
18	10.67	28.45	8.94	32.09
19	11.44	29.67	9.64	33.38
20	12.22	30.89	10.35	34.67
21	13.00	32.10	11.07	35.95
22	13.79	33.31	11.79	37.22
23	14.58	34.51	12.52	38.48
24	15.38	35.71	13.25	39.74
25	16.18	36.90	14.00	41.00
26	16.98	38.10	14.74	42.25
27	17.79	39.28	15.49	43.50
28	18.61	40.47	16.24	44.74
29	19.42	41.65	17.00	45.98
30	20.24	42.83	17.77	47.21
35	24.38	48.68	21.64	53.32
40	28.58	54.47	25.59	59.36
45	32.82	60.21	29.60	65.34
50	37.11	65.92	33.66	71.27

* Adapted from E. S. Pearson and H. O. Hartley, *Biometrika Tables for Statisticians*, Vol. 1 (London: Cambridge University Press, 1954), Table 40.

TABLE 14   Tables **257**

SIGNIFICANCE OF AN OBSERVED DIFFERENCE
BETWEEN TWO POISSON VARIABLES*

For a given sum of the observed counts $(L + L')$ the table gives the greatest permissible value of the smaller count, for the indicated P in a one-tail test.

$L + L'$	0.05	0.01	$L + L'$	0.05	0.01
1			41	14	12
2			42	15	13
3			43	15	13
4			44	16	13
5	0		45	16	14
6	0		46	16	14
7	0	0	47	17	15
8	1	0	48	17	15
9	1	0	49	18	15
10	1	0	50	18	16
11	2	1	51	19	16
12	2	1	52	19	17
13	3	1	53	20	17
14	3	2	54	20	18
15	3	2	55	20	18
16	4	2	56	21	18
17	4	3	57	21	19
18	5	3	58	22	19
19	5	4	59	22	20
20	5	4	60	23	20
21	6	4	61	23	20
22	6	5	62	24	21
23	7	5	63	24	21
24	7	5	64	24	22
25	7	6	65	25	22
26	8	6	66	25	23
27	8	7	67	26	23
28	9	7	68	26	23
29	9	7	69	27	24
30	10	8	70	27	24
31	10	8	71	28	25
32	10	8	72	28	25
33	11	9	73	28	26
34	11	9	74	29	26
35	12	10	75	29	26
36	12	10	76	30	27
37	13	10	77	30	27
38	13	11	78	31	28
39	13	11	79	31	28
40	14	12	80	32	29

* Adapted from E. S. Pearson and H. O. Hartley, *Biometrika Tables for Statisticians*, Vol. 1 London: Cambridge University Press, 1954), Table 36.

TABLE 15(A)

CRITICAL VALUES OF U IN THE TWO-SAMPLE RANK TEST*

Values of U equal to or smaller than those tabulated occur by chance less frequently than the indicated level of P.

$P = 0.05$ (One tail) or 0.10 (Both tails)

N＼N'	3	4	5	6	7	8	9	10	11	12	13	14	15	16	17	18	19	20
1	—	—	—	—	—	—	—	—	—	—	—	—	—	—	—	—	0	0
2	—	0	0	0	0	1	1	1	1	2	2	2	3	3	3	4	4	4
3	0	1	1	2	2	3	3	4	5	5	6	7	7	8	9	9	10	11
4			2	3	4	5	6	7	8	9	10	11	12	14	15	16	17	18
5			4	5	6	8	9	11	12	13	15	16	18	19	20	22	23	25
6				7	8	10	12	14	16	17	19	21	23	25	26	28	30	32
7					11	13	15	17	19	21	24	26	28	30	33	35	37	39
8						15	18	20	23	26	28	31	33	36	39	41	44	47
9							21	24	27	30	33	36	39	42	45	48	51	54
10								27	31	34	37	41	44	48	51	55	58	62
11									34	38	42	46	50	54	57	61	65	69
12										42	47	51	55	60	64	68	72	77
13											51	56	61	65	70	75	80	84
14												61	66	71	77	82	87	92
15													72	77	83	88	94	100
16														83	89	95	101	107
17															96	102	109	115
18																109	116	123
19																	123	130
20																		138

TABLE 15—Continued (B)

P = 0.025 (One tail) or 0.05 (Both tails)

N' \ N	3	4	5	6	7	8	9	10	11	12	13	14	15	16	17	18	19	20
1	—	—	—	—	—	—	—	—	—	—	—	—	—	—	—	—	—	—
2	—	—	—	—	—	0	0	0	0	1	1	1	1	1	2	2	2	2
3	—	—	0	1	1	2	2	3	3	4	4	5	5	6	6	7	7	8
4		0	1	2	3	4	4	5	6	7	8	9	10	11	11	12	13	13
5			2	3	5	6	7	8	9	11	12	13	14	15	17	18	19	20
6				5	6	8	10	11	13	14	16	17	19	21	22	24	25	27
7					8	10	12	14	16	18	20	22	24	26	28	30	32	34
8						13	15	17	19	22	24	26	29	31	34	36	38	41
9							17	20	23	26	28	31	34	37	39	42	45	48
10								23	26	29	33	36	39	42	45	48	52	55
11									30	33	37	40	44	47	51	55	58	62
12										37	41	45	49	53	57	61	65	69
13											45	50	54	59	63	67	72	76
14												55	59	64	67	74	78	83
15													64	70	75	80	85	90
16														75	81	86	92	98
17															87	93	99	105
18																99	106	112
19																	113	119
20																		127

TABLE 15—Continued (c)

P = 0.01 (One tail) or 0.02 (Both tails)

n \ N'	3	4	5	6	7	8	9	10	11	12	13	14	15	16	17	18	19	20
1	—	—	—	—	—	—	—	—	—	—	—	—	—	—	—	—	—	—
2	—	—	—	—	—	—	—	—	—	—	0	0	0	0	0	0	1	1
3	—	—	—	—	0	0	1	1	1	2	2	2	3	3	4	4	4	5
4		—	0	1	1	2	3	3	4	5	5	6	7	7	8	9	9	10
5			1	2	3	4	5	6	7	8	9	10	11	12	13	14	15	16
6				3	4	6	7	8	9	11	12	13	15	16	18	19	20	22
7					6	7	9	11	12	14	16	17	19	21	23	24	26	28
8						9	11	13	15	17	20	22	24	26	28	30	32	34
9							14	16	18	21	23	26	28	31	33	36	38	40
10								19	22	24	27	30	33	36	38	41	44	47
11									25	28	31	34	37	41	44	47	50	53
12										31	35	38	42	46	49	53	56	60
13											39	43	47	51	55	59	63	67
14												47	51	56	60	65	69	73
15													56	61	66	70	75	80
16														66	71	76	82	87
17															77	82	88	93
18																88	94	100
19																	101	107
20																		114

TABLE 15—Continued (D)

P = 0.005 (One tail) or 0.01 (Both tails)

N'＼N	3	4	5	6	7	8	9	10	11	12	13	14	15	16	17	18	19	20
1	—	—	—	—	—	—	—	—	—	—	—	—	—	—	—	—	—	—
2	—	—	—	—	—	—	—	—	—	—	—	—	—	—	—	—	0	0
3	—	—	—	—	—	—	0	0	0	1	1	1	2	2	2	2	3	3
4		—	—	0	0	1	1	2	2	3	3	4	5	5	6	6	7	8
5			0	1	1	2	3	4	5	6	7	7	8	9	10	11	12	13
6				2	3	4	5	6	7	9	10	11	12	13	15	16	17	18
7					4	6	7	9	10	12	13	15	16	18	19	21	22	24
8						7	9	11	13	15	17	18	20	22	24	26	28	30
9							11	13	16	18	20	22	24	27	29	31	33	36
10								16	18	21	24	26	29	31	34	37	39	42
11									21	24	27	30	33	36	39	42	45	48
12										27	31	34	37	41	44	47	51	54
13											34	38	42	45	49	53	56	60
14												42	46	50	54	58	63	67
15													51	55	60	64	69	73
16														60	65	70	74	79
17															70	75	81	86
18																81	87	92
19																	93	99
20																		105

* Adapted from D. Auble, *Bulletin of the Institute of Educational Research, Indiana University*, vol. 1, no. 2, 1953.

TABLE 16

CRITICAL VALUES OF THE SMALLER SUM (T) IN THE SIGNED-RANKS TEST*

T is the smaller sum of signed ranks. Values of T smaller than those tabulated occur by chance with the indicated probability. Nonintegral values may arise as a result of tied ranks. N is the number of pairs.

N	P = 0.05		P = 0.01	
	One Tail	Both Tails	One Tail	Both Tails
5	0.6	—	—	—
6	2.1	0.6	—	—
7	3.7	2.1	0.3	—
8	5.8	3.7	1.6	0.3
9	8.1	5.7	3.1	1.6
10	10.8	8.1	5.1	3.1
11	13.9	10.8	7.2	5.1
12	17.5	13.8	9.8	7.2
13	21.4	17.2	12.7	9.8
14	25.7	21.1	15.9	12.7
15	30.4	25.3	19.6	15.9
16	35.6	29.9	23.6	19.5
17	41.2	34.9	28.0	23.4
18	47.2	40.3	32.7	27.7
19	53.6	46.1	37.8	32.4
20	60.4	52.3	43.4	37.5
21	67.6	58.9	49.3	42.9
22	75.3	66.0	55.6	48.7
23	83.9	73.4	62.3	54.9
24	91.9	81.3	69.4	61.5
25	100.9	89.5	76.9	68.5

* Extracted from C. A. Bennett and N. L. Franklin, *Statistical Analysis in Chemistry and the Chemical Industry* (New York: John Wiley & Sons, Inc., 1954), p. 183. Data were originally given by J. W. Tukey in Memorandum Report 17, "The Simplest Signed Rank Test," Statistical Research Group, Princeton University, 1949.

TABLE 17

CONVERSIONS OF PERCENTS TO PROBITS*

%	0	1	2	3	4	5	6	7	8	9
0	—	2.67	2.95	3.12	3.25	3.36	3.45	3.52	3.59	3.66
10	3.72	3.77	3.82	3.87	3.92	3.96	4.01	4.05	4.08	4.12
20	4.16	4.19	4.23	4.26	4.29	4.33	4.36	4.39	4.42	4.45
30	4.48	4.50	4.53	4.56	4.59	4.61	4.64	4.67	4.69	4.72
40	4.75	4.77	4.80	4.82	4.85	4.87	4.90	4.92	4.95	4.97
50	5.00	5.03	5.05	5.08	5.10	5.13	5.15	5.18	5.20	5.23
60	5.25	5.28	5.31	5.33	5.36	5.39	5.41	5.44	5.47	5.50
70	5.52	5.55	5.58	5.61	5.64	5.67	5.71	5.74	5.77	5.81
80	5.84	5.88	5.92	5.95	5.99	6.04	6.08	6.13	6.18	6.23
90	6.28	6.34	6.41	6.48	6.55	6.64	6.75	6.88	7.05	7.33

* Adapted from D. J. Finney, *Probit Analysis*, 2d ed. (London: Cambridge University Press, 1952), Table I.

TABLE 18

WORKING PROBITS AND WEIGHTING COEFFICIENTS*

To obtain a working probit (y), enter the table with the expected probit (Y) read from the provisional regression line. Multiply the corresponding value of y_{max} by the observed proportion (p) and y_{min} by ($1 - p$). The working probit is the sum of these two products.

The weighting coefficient corresponding to each Y is tabulated directly.

Expected Probit, Y	y_{max}	y_{min}	Weighting Coefficient, w
1.1	5030.	0.85	0.00082
1.2	3430.	0.95	0.00118
1.3	2360.	1.05	0.00167
1.4	1640.	1.14	0.00235
1.5	1150.	1.23	0.00327
1.6	813.	1.33	0.00451
1.7	582.	1.42	0.00614
1.8	421.	1.51	0.00828
1.9	308.	1.60	0.0110
2.0	227.	1.69	0.0146
2.1	170.	1.79	0.0190
2.2	128.	1.88	0.0246
2.3	97.9	1.97	0.0314
2.4	75.7	2.06	0.0398
2.5	59.2	2.15	0.0498

TABLE 18—continued

Expected Probit, Y	y_{max}	y_{min}	Weighting Coefficient, w
2.6	46.9	2.23	0.0617
2.7	37.6	2.32	0.0756
2.8	30.6	2.41	0.0918
2.9	25.2	2.49	0.110
3.0	21.1	2.58	0.131
3.1	17.9	2.66	0.154
3.2	15.4	2.74	0.180
3.3	13.5	2.83	0.208
3.4	11.9	2.91	0.237
3.5	10.7	2.98	0.269
3.6	9.74	3.06	0.302
3.7	8.97	3.14	0.336
3.8	8.36	3.21	0.370
3.9	7.87	3.28	0.405
4.0	7.48	3.34	0.439
4.1	7.17	3.41	0.471
4.2	6.92	3.47	0.503
4.3	6.73	3.53	0.532
4.4	6.58	3.58	0.558
4.5	6.46	3.62	0.581
4.6	6.38	3.66	0.601
4.7	6.32	3.70	0.616
4.8	6.28	3.72	0.627
4.9	6.26	3.74	0.634
5.0	6.25	3.75	0.637
5.1	6.26	3.74	0.634
5.2	6.28	3.72	0.627
5.3	6.30	3.68	0.616
5.4	6.34	3.62	0.601
5.5	6.38	3.54	0.581
5.6	6.42	3.42	0.558
5.7	6.47	3.27	0.532
5.8	6.53	3.08	0.503
5.9	6.59	2.83	0.471
6.0	6.66	2.52	0.439
6.1	6.72	2.13	0.405
6.2	6.79	1.64	0.370
6.3	6.86	1.03	0.336
6.4	6.94	0.261	0.302
6.5	7.02	−0.705	0.269

TABLE 18—continued

Expected Probit, Y	y_{max}	y_{min}	Weighting Coefficient, w
6.6	7.09	−1.92	0.238
6.7	7.17	−3.46	0.208
6.8	7.26	−5.41	0.180
6.9	7.34	−7.90	0.154
7.0	7.42	−11.1	0.131
7.1	7.51	−15.2	0.110
7.2	7.59	−20.6	0.0918
7.3	7.68	−27.6	0.0756
7.4	7.77	−36.9	0.0617
7.5	7.85	−49.2	0.0498
7.6	7.94	−65.7	0.0398
7.7	8.03	−87.9	0.0314
7.8	8.12	−118.	0.0246
7.9	8.21	−160.	0.0190
8.0	8.30	−217.	0.0146
8.1	8.40	−298.	0.0110
8.2	8.49	−411.	0.00828
8.3	8.58	−572.	0.00614
8.4	8.67	−803.	0.00451
8.5	8.77	−1140.	0.00327
8.6	8.86	−1620.	0.00235
8.7	8.95	−2340.	0.00167
8.8	9.05	−3420.	0.00118
8.9	9.14	−5020.	0.00082

* Table 18 is abridged from Table XI of Fisher & Yates: *Statistical Tables for Biological, Agricultural and Medical Research* published by Oliver & Boyd Ltd., Edinburgh, and by permission of the authors and publishers.

Index and Glossary

of Symbols

α

Probability of a type I error. *See* Error, type I.

β

Probability of a type II error. *See* Error, type II.
True slope of a regression line. *See* Slope.

λ

True count. *See* Counts.

μ

True mean. *See* Mean.

π

True proportion. *See* Proportion.

σ

True standard deviation. *See* Standard deviation.

σ^2

True variance. *See* Variance.

χ^2

Chi-square. *See* Chi-square.
Analysis of variance.
See Variance, analysis of.
Average.
See Mean, Mode, Median.

b

Sample slope of a regression line. *See* Slope.
Balanced design, 10
Binomial distribution, 93 ff.

table of critical number of items in, *250*
table of binomial confidence limits, *251–252*
Binomial expansion, 95
Bioassay,
definition, 161
parallel-line procedures, 162 ff., 166 (Ex. 4–11), 178 ff., 179 (4–13).
Blind design, 9–10
CD_{50}
See Median curative dose.
C.V.
See Coefficient of variation.
Central limit theorem, 39
Chi-square (χ^2), 102 ff.
difference between observed and expected proportion, 104 (Ex. 3–7).
difference between observed and hypothetical outcome, 106 (Ex. 3–9).
in contingency tables, 107 ff.
test of conformity to Poisson distribution, 118 (Ex. 3–14).
test of fit in quantal log dose-response data, 177, 182.
test of randomness of counts, 124 (Ex. 3–21).
table of, *250*
Class intervals, computation by, 48 (Ex. 2–5).

267